MECHANICS OF MATERIALS

Textbook for a Fundamental  se

Ganesh Thiagarajan, Ph.D., P.E.
Kavita Deskmukh, M.S.

ISBN: 978-1-58503-154-2

PUBLICATIONS

Schroff Development Corporation

www.schroff.com

Schroff Development Corporation
P.O. Box 1334
Mission KS 66222
(913) 262-2664
www.schroff.com

Publisher: Stephen Schroff

Examination Copies:

Books received as examination copies are for review purposes only and may not be made available for student use. Resale of examination copies is prohibited.

Electronic Files:

Any electronic files associated with this book are licensed to the original user only. These files may not be transferred to any other party.

Mechanics of Materials, 1st Edition

Authors

Ganesh Thiagarajan, University of Missouri Kansas City

Kavita P Deshmukh, Structural Engineer

OBJECTIVES

The primary objective of this fundamental book on Mechanics of Materials by the authors is to expose and educate the engineering student, who has already taken the basic course in Statics, on the principles governing the behavior of structures – in any branch of engineering – and help him or her develop the ability to perform simple designs. The principles presented in this book should help the student become skillful in the three S's adopted in any design, namely; Strength, Stiffness and Stability.

ADOPTED APPROACH TO THIS BOOK and PEDAGOGY

The first author has several years of experience in teaching this course, and the main goal in developing this book was to give the student and the instructor the basic material that can be reasonably covered in one semester. The author has typically covered about eighty percent of the material presented in this book during the course of a semester. The material presented in the book should be useful to the student for several years beyond the year in which the course was first taken. The book should be helpful in preparation for different licensure related exams that an engineer is expected to take during her or his career.

In developing this book, the authors have attempted to focus on the following salient pedagogical features:

a) Developing the topics in a sequential and logical manner such that the knowledge of one topic is useful in subsequent chapters. The instructor should not have to jump back and forth in teaching the material.

b) For each topic a detailed description of the theoretical material, wherever applicable, is presented in the narrative. Applicable sign conventions are suitably explained.

c) The applicable equations are also summarized in each chapter, for ready reference, when the student is attempting the problems.

d) Problems have been presented with a dual purpose to help the student understand how to correctly apply the equations and later on to illustrate how the equations are applied in a design context.

e) Exposing the student to the two systems of units that are commonly used, namely the SI (*Systems International)* and the U.S customary units. Derived units, such as stress, that are commonly used in both systems are also outlined in the text and the problems.

g) All the examples have been presented in complete detail without skipping any steps or calculations. A logical order to steps is presented for each example, in which the purpose of the step is outlined first. The student can expect to solve most of the problems using a similar step-by-step approach of breaking down the problem.

h) The authors believe that a new subject can be learnt by clearly exposing the student to keywords commonly used. The authors have included a set of keywords and their meanings in the summary section of each chapter.

i) The summary section of each chapter also contains a set of commonly used equations for that chapter.

FLOW OF THE BOOK

1) The first chapter is a review chapter on Statics and concepts that will be useful in the concepts presented in subsequent chapters.

2) The second chapter introduces the concept of stress produced by an axial load. The dependence of stress on the orientation of the surface in which it acts is also introduced in chapter 2.

3) Chapter 3 is devoted purely to the basic form of stress, namely the axial stress in one direction.

4) Chapter 4 extends the concept of the axial stress acting simultaneously in three different directions.

5) Chapter 5 then takes up the topic of shear stress in the context of torsion acting on bodies.

6) Chapter 6 introduces the topic of shear force diagrams and bending moment diagrams.

7) Chapter 7 uses the bending moment concept and discusses the stresses caused by the bending moment.

8) Chapter 8 discusses the stresses caused by the shear force acting on beams.

9) Chapter 9 elaborates the treatment of elements in which combined bending and shear stresses act and introduces the concept of transformation of stresses and Mohr's circle.

10) Chapter 10 talks about the behavior of beams from a stiffness perspective and outlines the computation of deflection in beams due to applied loads.

11) Chapter 11 introduces the concept of stability as applied to axial members in compression.

ACKNOWLEDGEMENTS

The authors would like to deeply acknowledge the whole-hearted encouragement and support of their parents and family members, who have been very patient and gracious in allowing the authors to devote time to the development of this book. Without their support, the book would not have seen the light of the day.

Contents

Chapter 1

Introduction and Review

Goal: The learning objectives in this chapter are as follows:

1. Establishing the need and significance of the subject
2. Introduce Strength, Stiffness and Stability concepts
3. Review of the relevant material learnt in Statics

1 Introduction and Review

The course on strength of materials or mechanics of materials is a very fundamental course in understanding the basic concepts involved in any design process in engineering. Figure 1.1 and Figure 1.2 shows two examples in the field of civil and mechanical engineering, wherein the principles of strength of materials are required for the design process.

Figure 1.1: Foundation of a building is required to resist pressure due to gravity and wind forces

Figure 1.2:Automotive vehicles components experience complex states of stress

Figure 1.1 shows a building subjected to gravity and wind loads. The design of the size of the footing is based on calculations of the soil pressures at the two ends of the footing, to ensure that these pressures do not exceed the allowable bearing capacity of the building. Basic mechanics of materials' principles are used to calculate these values. Many components of the automotive car, shown in Figure 1.2, such as the frame, transmission system etc. are designed based on fundamental principles of mechanics of materials.

Need and Significance of Mechanics of Materials:

In addition to the two examples described above, the subject of mechanics of materials can be viewed as a *gateway* to any stream of engineering that involves any semblance of analysis or design. These are briefly listed below:

1. **Aeronautical Engineering:** The design of all structural components of any aircraft, helicopters, rockets, space shuttles, satellites etc. is based on many principles taught in this course.

Figure 1.3: Aircraft

2. **Agricultural Engineering:** The design of many equipment used in the farms such as, tractors, auger, belt conveyor, box scraper etc, all involve many basic principles of mechanics of materials

Figure 1.4: Tractor

Figure 1.5: Auger

3. **Biological Engineering and Biomechanics:** This is one of the hottest areas of research in modern times. The response of the body to various forces and the biological mechanisms it triggers, such as the behavior of bone (bone mechanics), tissues (tissue mechanics), spine (spinal mechanics), teeth (dental mechanics) to name just a few, are exciting areas of research that start with a comprehensive understanding of the subject that you are about to learn – *Mechanics of Materials.*

4. **Civil Engineering:** The design of almost all civil engineering structures such as, concrete and steel buildings, bridge structures, industrial buildings, commercial buildings, trusses, dams, retaining walls, towers etc. all involve the principles of 'mechanics of materials'.

Figure 1.6: Millennium Bridge

Figure 1.7: Steel Truss

5. **Mechanical Engineering:** Mechanical engineering is a very broad field of engineering that involves the application of 'mechanics of materials' principles for analysis, design, manufacturing and maintenance of mechanical systems.

Figure 1.8: Engine

Fundamental Principles of Mechanics of Materials:

Mechanics of materials is primarily concerned with the study of three *S*'s, namely
➢ Strength
➢ Stiffness
➢ Stability

Strength: The goal here is to study the behavior of a structure subjected to external forces and moments, by computing the various internal forces and moments. These internal forces and moments are used to compute two basic stress quantities; namely the normal and shear stress in the material. The structure is said to be safe in its strength behavior if the computed internal stresses are lesser than the allowable values.

Stiffness: The second objective in the design of any structure is to ensure that the deformations in it are within acceptable limits. Quantities used to calculate the deformations and displacements include the applied forces and moments along with the structure geometric properties such as the area, inertia etc. Acceptable limits to deflection are often based on personal experiences and can be subjective.

Stability: The third important objective in this study is to ensure that certain type of members, known as compression members, do not fail by buckling. Buckling is an instability phenomenon. This type of failure often occurs before the actual strength of the material is reached and should be avoided. Failure by buckling is often catastrophic with relatively no warning period.

1.1 Determinate and Indeterminate Structures

An important reason for studying mechanics of materials is to be able to compute reactions for any type of structure. In statics, it was seen that a structure can be classified as either a determinate or an indeterminate structure. A determinate structure is one in which all the unknown reactions can be computed from equations of static equilibrium alone. Figure 1.9 shows an example of a determinate structure, where there are three unknown reactions which can be computed from the three equations of static equilibrium.

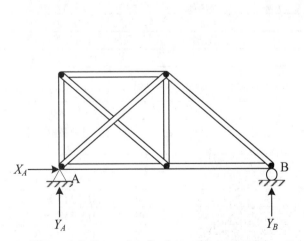

Figure 1.9: Example of a determinate structure

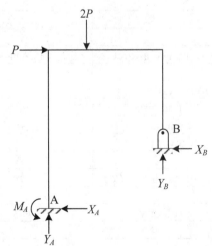

Figure 1.10: Example of an indeterminate structure

Figure 1.10 shows the structure with applied forces and reactions, where it can be seen that there are five reaction unknowns, while only three equations of equilibrium are available. The principles that you will learn in this course, such as deformation compatibility, will help you develop additional equations needed to determine all the reactions.

1.2 Units and Conversions

Probably the most important aspect that a good designer has to pay attention to is the units that he or she is using and be consistent with them. There are two systems of units being used in practice in the United States. They are:

➢ International System of Units (*Systeme Internationale or SI*)
➢ U.S. Customary Units

Table 1.1 gives the base units and the derived units for the two systems. The derived units are shown in the table in the form of the expanded base units. Thus, in the SI system, Force is the derived unit, while in the U.S. Customary system, the mass (slug) is the derived unit.

Quantity	SI Customary Units	U.S. Customary Units	SI Equivalent
Acceleration	m/s^2	ft/s^2	$0.3048\ m/s^2$
		in/s^2	$0.0254\ m/s^2$
Area	m^2	ft^2	$0.0929\ m^2$
		in^2	$645.2\ mm^2$
Energy (*J*)	*N-m*	*ft-lb*	$1.356\ J$
* Force (*N*)	$kg.\ m/s^2$	*kip*	$4.448\ kN$
		lb	$4.448\ N$
		oz	$0.2780\ N$
Length	*m*	*ft*	$0.3048\ m$
		in	$25.40\ mm$
		mi	$1.609\ km$
* Mass	*kg*	*oz mass*	$28.35\ g$
		lb mass	$0.4536\ kg$
		* *slug*	$14.59\ kg$
		ton	$907.2\ kg$
Moment of a force	*N-m*	*lb-ft*	$1.356\ N.m$
		lb-in	$0.1130\ N.m$
Moment of inertia:			
Of an area	m^4	in^4	$0.4162 \times 10^6\ mm^4$
Of a mass	$kg\text{-}m^2$	$lb\text{-}ft\text{-}s^2$	$1.356\ kg.\ m^2$
Power (*W*)	*J/s*	*ft-lb/s*	$1.356\ W$
		hp	$745.7\ W$
Pressure / stress (*Pa*)	N/m^2	lb/ft^2	$47.88\ Pa$
		lb/in^2 (*psi*)	$6.895\ kPa$
Velocity	*m/s*	*ft/s*	$0.3048\ m/s$
		in/s	$0.0254\ m/s$
		mi/h (*mph*)	$0.4470\ m/s$
Volume:			
Solids	m^3	ft^3	$0.02832\ m^3$
		in^3	$16.39\ cm^3$

Liquids (L)	$10^{-3}\ m^3$	gal	3.785 L
		qt	0.9464 L
Work (J)	N.m	ft.lb	1.356 J

Table 1.1: Base and derived units in the two systems [* Derived unit]

While, the basic units are defined as shown in Table 1.1, it is practical to use appropriate conversions to express quantities used in design. For example, one Newton (N) is a very small force (four *Fignewtons* approximately weigh a *Newton*). Hence, a pressure defined as N/m^2, also known as *Pascal* (Pa) is a very small number. Practical values of pressures in SI system are of the order of $10^6\ Pa$ or a *Mega Pascal* (MPa). Table 1.2 gives some of the commonly used conversions.

Prefix	Multiple	Abbreviation
atto	10^{-18}	a
femto	10^{-15}	f
pico	10^{-12}	p
nano	10^{-9}	n
micro	10^{-6}	μ
milli	10^{-3}	m
centi	10^{-2}	c
deci	10^{-1}	d
Deca	10^{1}	da
Hecto	10^{2}	h
Kilo	10^{3}	k
Mega	10^{6}	M
Giga	10^{9}	G
Tera	10^{12}	T

Table 1.2: Conversion prefixes

1.3 Review of Statics

1.3.1 Equilibrium and Free Body Diagrams

A fundamental concept which was introduced in Statics with applications in almost every aspect of everyday engineering life is the concept of equilibrium and free body diagrams (FBD). Any body in static equilibrium has a set of applied forces acting anywhere on the body and a set of reaction forces at the supports as shown in Figure 1.11.

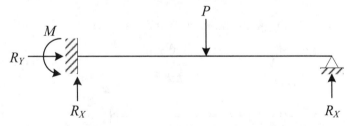

Figure 1.11: Applied and Reaction forces acting on a body

The concept of equilibrium implies *no motion*. There are three basic motions that must be prevented for any object to be in equilibrium. The motions and the mathematical equations (also known as equilibrium equations) to represent them, in a two dimensional problem, are shown below

1. Prevent x-motion : $\sum F_x = 0$

2. Prevent y-motion : $\sum F_y = 0$

3. Prevent z-rotation : $\sum M_z = 0$

There are other combinations of equations, using 1 force and 2 moment equations, that are equally applicable, but have preconditions attached to their usage. The above set of equations give three independent equations under any set of circumstances.

Central to the determination of the reactions, is the idea of drawing a *free body diagram*. The expanded version of the free body diagram may be described as follows: *Free* the *Body* from its supports and draw a *Diagram* showing clearly the applied (known) and the reaction (unknown) forces. The steps involved in drawing a FBD can be summarized as follows

Step 1: Isolate the entire object from the supports (free the body)

Step 2: Identify the type of supports and replace the supports by unknown reaction forces and moments. Assume +ve directions for these unknown forces

Step 3: Show the unknown and known forces and moments clearly on the free body diagram.

Step 4: Clearly mark all the dimensions required (in *x* and *y* directions)

An excellent test of drawing a correct FBD is that another person should be able to find the unknown reactions from the FBD without having to look at the original problem description. It is absolutely certain that if a FBD is drawn incorrectly, the reactions determined will also be wrong.

Example 1-1 shows the steps involved in drawing the FBD and the determination of reactions of a simple two-dimensional structure.

Example 1-1: Two-Dimensional Equilibrium Problem

Problem Statement: The structure shown in the figure is built into the wall at A. Given the loads as shown, determine the reactions at A.

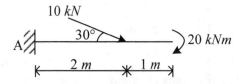

Required: A_x, A_y and M_A

Solution:

Step 1: Draw the Free Body Diagram and identify the unknowns

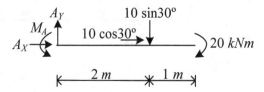

Step 2: Write Equilibrium Equations

$$\sum F_x = A_x + 10 \times \cos 30° = 0$$

$$\sum F_y = A_y - 10 \times \sin 30° = 0$$

$$\sum M_A = M_A - (10 \times \sin 30°) \times 2 - 20 = 0$$

Step 3: Solve the equations to find the unknowns, Interpretation of results (direction and magnitude of reactions)

$$A_x = -8.67 \ kN = 8.67 \ kN \leftarrow$$

$$A_y = +5 kN \uparrow$$

$$M_A = +30 \ kNm \quad CCW$$

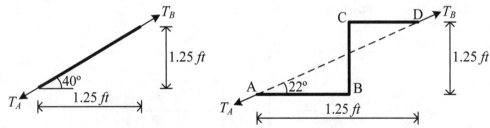

A negative sign implies that the actual direction of the force is opposite to what we had assigned.

1.3.2   Two Force and Multiforce Body Equilibrium

Structures are composed of members, straight and bent, interconnected together to carry loads applied to them. In the analysis of structures, an important visual recognition, namely whether it is a two force or a multiforce body needs to be made in order to ease the analysis of forces in the members. In general, structures are composed of two types of members

➢   Two force members (2F)
➢   Multi force members (MF)

A *two force* member is one in which a member is acted upon by forces at *only two points* (this is different from just two forces acting on the member). Figure 1.12 shows an example of both a straight and a bent two force member. This member is in equilibrium, if it has no resultant force (equal and opposite forces at the two points) and no resultant moment (the line of action of the two forces passes through the line joining the two points.

Figure 1.12: Example of two force members

For equilibrium: Join the two points where the forces act by a straight line and get the angle of the line. The resultant force acts along this angle as seen in Figure 1.12

A *multi force member* is one where forces act at more than two points. Equilibrium of these members can readily be handled by usual procedure of drawing a free body diagram and using the three equations of equilibrium to solve for the unknowns.

1.3.3   Analysis of Trusses

A truss is a structure which is composed of only straight two force members. It is more appropriate to term the structure as having a truss like action. It is important to note that truss members therefore carry only axial force.

Figure 1.13: Old Little Belt Bridge, Denmark - A Truss Bridge Structure

Bridge structures as shown in Figure 1.13 are very good examples of a truss type behavior. There are two methods to analyze trusses, namely
➤ Method of Joints
➤ Method of Sections
Example 1-2 presented below shows the analysis of the truss member forces which are analyzed using a combination of the two methods

---

Example 1-2 Truss Analysis using Method of Joints and Sections

---

Problem Statement: Analyze the truss shown in the figure and determine the member forces. Indicate whether they are in tension or compression.

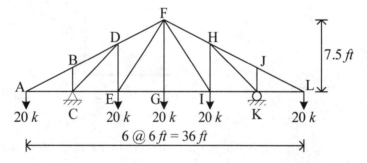

Required: Magnitude and type of force in the members AB, AC, EF and EG.

Solution:

Step 1: Draw the overall FBD and determine the reactions.

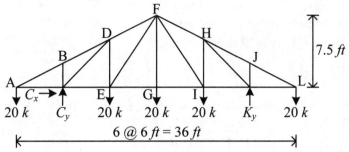

$$\sum F_x = C_x = 0$$

$$\sum F_y = -20 - 20 - 20 - 20 - 20 + C_y + K_y = 0$$

$$\sum M_C = 20 \times 6 - 20 \times 6 - 20 \times 12 - 20 \times 18 - 20 \times 30 + K_y \times 24 = 0$$

From the above equations we get,

$$C_y = +50 = 50 \; k \uparrow$$

$$C_x = 0$$

$$K_y = +50 = 50 \; k \uparrow$$

Step 2: Use method of joints to analyze forces in members at joint A. The member forces are treated as tension (indicated by arrows away from the joint). Write two force equations of equilibrium per joint.

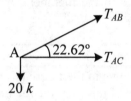

$$\sum F_x = T_{AB} \cos 22.62° + T_{AC} = 0$$

$$\sum F_y = -20 + T_{AB} \sin 22.62° = 0$$

$$\therefore T_{AB} = 52 \; k \; (\text{Tension})$$

$$T_{AC} = -48 \; k \; (\text{Compression})$$

Step 3: Analyze forces in DF and EF by method of sections.

- Take a section (A-A) through DF and two other members (EF and EG)
- Consider the FBD of the left hand side of section A-A
- This section contains a support. The support *must* be replaced by reaction force.
- Replace the members cut by tension forces (arrows away from the joint). We have three unknown forces here: T_{DF}, T_{EF}, T_{EG}

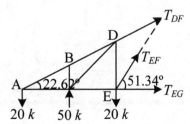

To determine T_{DF} we have to eliminate the other two forces. This can be done by considering a moment equation through a point through with these two forces pass. Here it is point E.

$$\sum M_E = 20 \times 12 - 50 \times 6 - (T_{DF} \cos 22.62°) \times 5 = 0$$

$$T_{DF} = -13 \, k \, (\text{Compression})$$

To determine the force in T_{EF} take moments through the point where the lines of action of members DF and EG intersect. Here it is point A.

$$\sum M_A = 50 \times 6 - 20 \times 12 - (T_{EF} \sin 51.34°) \times 12 = 0$$

$$T_{EF} = 6.4 \, k \, (\text{Tension})$$

Note: Here negative sign implies a compression member. Throughout this textbook all truss members will be initially assumed to be in tension (arrow away from the joint).

1.3.4   Analysis of Frames

A frame is defined as a structure consisting of both two force and multi force members. All the members of the frame need not be straight members. Frames can be loaded both at joints and in between members. This is the main point that differentiates them from trusses.

Example 1-3 illustrates the important steps in any frame analysis. Of particular importance is the last step which shows the final forces in the members, which would the starting point for any subsequent design calculations.

Example 1-3: Frame analysis problem

Problem Statement: The structure shown in the figure is subjected to two forces on 10 kN at C and F. Find the reactions and the internal forces in the members.

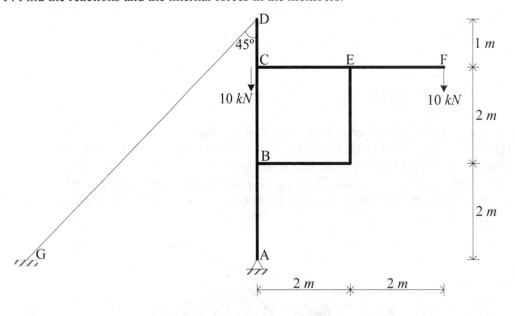

Required: Reactions and Member forces

Solution:

Step 1: Determine the reactions at support A and cable DG. Here the cable acts as a support. (Force in a cable is always in tension, hence is shown as an arrow away from point D). The overall FBD is used in this step.

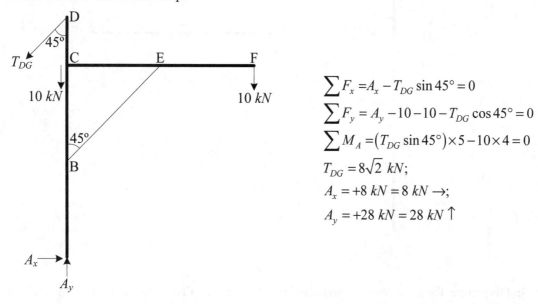

$$\sum F_x = A_x - T_{DG} \sin 45° = 0$$

$$\sum F_y = A_y - 10 - 10 - T_{DG} \cos 45° = 0$$

$$\sum M_A = (T_{DG} \sin 45°) \times 5 - 10 \times 4 = 0$$

$$T_{DG} = 8\sqrt{2} \ kN;$$

$$A_x = +8 \ kN = 8 \ kN \rightarrow;$$

$$A_y = +28 \ kN = 28 \ kN \uparrow$$

Step 2: Identify two force (2F) and multi force (MF) members. If the frame is dismembered, each full piece is defined as a member.

- ABCD – this member had support at A (force point), internal bolts at B and C (force points) and cable force at D. (MF member)
- CEF – forces at C, E and F – MF member
- BE – forces at B and E – 2F member

Step 3: 2F member equilibrium – get the angle of the resultant force in the member. The resultant forces at B and E act *along the line joining B and E.* The angle of the line BE is the required angle.

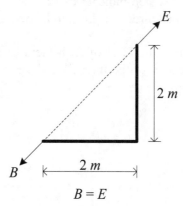

$B = E$

Step 4: Draw the FBD of all MF members and *identify the unknowns*

- At joints connecting two MF members (joint C), draw two equal and opposite forces in the two members at C.
- At joints connecting a MF and a 2F member, draw one resultant force at an angle determined from 2F member equilibrium (Step 3).

- For loads at joints – attach the force to either member (*not both*).
- Identify the unknowns; here they are C_x, C_y and B

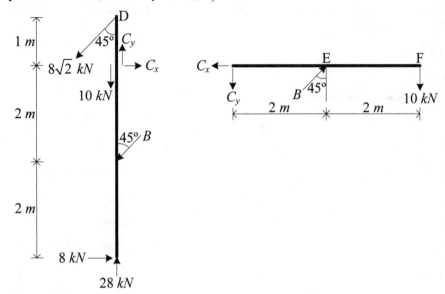

Step 5: Determine the unknown internal forces. Here either FBD can be used. The FBD of member ABCD is used for simplicity.

$$\sum F_x = C_x - 8\sqrt{2}\sin 45° - B\sin 45° + 8 = 0$$

$$\sum F_y = C_y - 8\sqrt{2}\cos 45 - 10 + 28 = 0$$

$$\sum M_B = \left(8\sqrt{2}\sin 45°\right)\times 3 - C_x \times 2 + 8\times 2 = 0$$

$C_x = +20\ kN = 20\ kN \leftarrow;$

$C_y = -10\ kN = 10\ kN \downarrow;$

$B = +20\sqrt{2}\ kN;$

Note: Positive sign of forces in this step indicate that the assumed directions are correct and a negative sign indicates that the actual directions have to be reversed.

Step 6: *Most Important Step:* Draw the FBD of each member showing the final forces in each member. The final forces are the sum of the internal and the external forces at any point in the member.

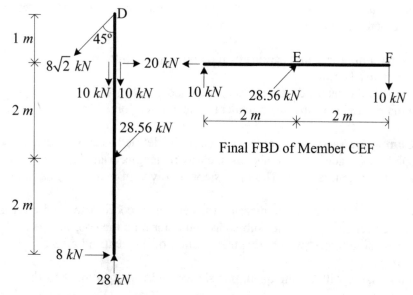

Final FBD of Member CEF

Final FBD of Member ABCD

1.3.5 Centroid and Applications

The concept of centroid of an area is applied frequently in many applications. The axis passing through the centroid is called the *Centroidal axis*. Figure 1.14 shows an arbitrary area and the Centroidal axis passing through C.

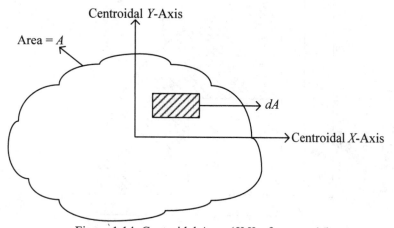

Figure 1.14: Centroidal Axes (*X-Y*) of an area (*A*)

The location of the Centroidal axis (*X-Y*) is defined using the *Moment of Area* (*Q*) concept. Mathematically it can be stated as follows

$$Q_y = \bar{x}A = \int x\,dA = \sum x_i A_i$$
$$Q_x = \bar{y}A = \int y\,dA = \sum y_i A_i$$

Eqn (1.1)

Here Q_y is the moment of area about the *y*-axis; *x* is the distance of the infinitesimal area *dA* from the *y*-axis. Physically, this represents the concept of a moment (which is a product of a quantity and a distance). Equation 1.1 shows both the integral and the summation representation of the equations used to determine the centroid of an area.

Applications: Two important applications of the concept of centroid of an area are illustrated in the following sections. They are
1. Determination of the centroid of the area of a composite section
2. Replacing distributed loads by an equivalent concentrated force

Centroid of Composite Section: A composite section is defined as an area that can be broken up into smaller sub areas made of basic shapes such as rectangle, triangle, circle etc. Holes in the section are treated as negative areas. The main steps involved in the determination of the centroid are as follows:

Step 1: Choose an axis of reference to measure the centroidal coordinates of the areas.

Step 2: Divide the section into simpler sub areas and determine the coordinates of the centroid of each area, using tables (which give the location of the centroid of each area) and the axis of reference.

Step 3: Setup up a table with all the quantities shown and use equation 1 to find the centroid of the composite area.

Example 1-4 illustrates the steps shown above.

Example 1-4: Centroid of an Area

Problem Statement: Determine the x and y centroid of the area with a hole as shown in the figure.

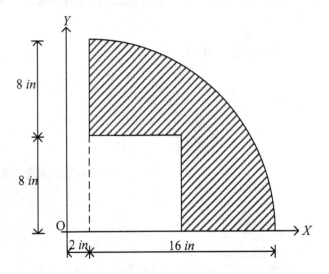

Required: $\overline{x}$ and $\overline{y}$ from the reference axis shown

---

Solution:

Step 1: Divide the area into well defined sub areas (such as triangles, rectangles, circles, semi-circles etc.). Draw these areas with respect to common axes *of reference.*

Step 2: Determine the coordinates $\overline{x}_i$ and $\overline{y}_i$ of each sub area and apply the centroid equation as shown in the following table. When determining these coordinates, it is important to read the standard table of areas with their respective centroidal values and translate them to actual problem coordinate values (with respect to the problem reference axis)

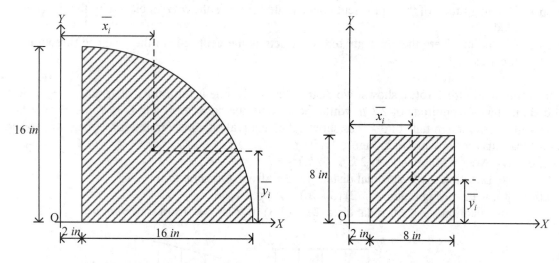

Shape	$A\ (in^2)$	$\overline{x}_i\ (in)$	$\overline{y}_i\ (in)$	$A\,\overline{x}_i\ (in^3)$	$A\,\overline{y}_i\ (in^3)$
Quarter Circle	201.06	$\dfrac{4\times16}{3\times\pi}+2=8.8$	$\dfrac{4\times16}{3\times\pi}=6.8$	1774.08	1367.21
Rectangle	-64	4+2=6	4	-384	-256

$$\sum A_i = 137.06 \qquad\qquad \sum \overline{x}_i A_i = 1390.08 \qquad \sum \overline{y}_i A_i = 1111.21$$

$$\overline{x} = \frac{\sum \overline{x}_i A_i}{\sum A_i} = \frac{1390.08}{137.06} = 10.14\ in$$

$$\overline{y} = \frac{\sum \overline{y}_i A_i}{\sum A_i} = \frac{1111.21}{137.06} = 8.11\ in$$

Step 3: Physical interpretation of results
The coordinates of the centroid are 10.14 *in* and 8.11 *in* in the *x* and *y* directions from the reference axis shown.

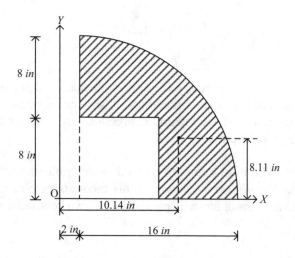

Distributed Load: The concept of centroid is used to replace distributed loads on beam by equivalent concentrated forces. Two steps are involved in this process, namely

Step 1: The magnitude of the equivalent concentrated force is the *area* enclosed by the distributed load.

Step 2: The point where the concentrated force acts is the centroid (in the distance direction) of the area.

For example, Figure 1.15(a), shows two distributed loads, one is uniformly distributed between A and B and has a magnitude of 2 *k/ft.* while the second one between B and C is a linearly varying load with a peak magnitude of 3 *k/ft* as shown. The equivalent concentrated force magnitudes and their locations are shown also in Figure 1.15(b).

Section AB: Area = Magnitude = (2 *k/ft*) (4 *ft.*) = 8 *k*

Location = *x*-Centroidal distance = 2 *ft.* from A (*rectangle*)

Section BC: Area = Magnitude = (1/2) (3 *k/ft.*)(6 *ft.*) = 9 *k*

Location = *x*-Centroidal distance = (2/3) (6 *ft.*) = 4 *ft.* from B. (*triangle*)

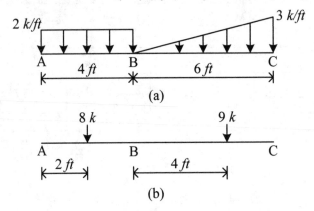

Figure 1.15: Application of centroid concepts to distributed loads.

1.3.6 Moments of Inertia

A concept that is used very frequently in chapters related to bending of beams is *moment of inertia* of the cross section of the beam. The moment of inertia in physical terms represents the resistance (inertia) to a moment (bending). From a purely mathematical perspective, the moment of inertia is defined as the second moment of an area and can be represented mathematically as follows.

$$I_y = \int x^2 dA$$

$$I_x = \int y^2 dA$$

Eqn (1.2)

Where *x, y* and *dA* are as shown in Figure 1.16. This mathematical equation can be visualized as a measure of the resistance of the area to bending; it will be seen as a byproduct of bending equations in a later chapter. The above integral expressions are used primarily to derive moment of inertia of some basic geometric shapes.

Parallel Axis Theorem: The most common method of determination of moments of inertia of composite shapes is the *Parallel Axis Theorem*. This theorem enables the determination of the moment of inertia of the area about any axis parallel to its own centroidal axis.

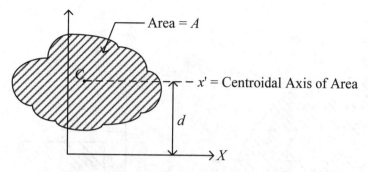

Figure 1.16: Parallel axis theorem representation

As seen in Figure 1.16, x' represents the centroidal axis of the area, while X represents an axis parallel to x' and d is the distance between these two axes. The parallel axis theorem can be given as

$$I_x = I_{x'} + Ad^2$$

where,

I_X = Moment of Inertia about X axis (resistance to bend about the x axis)
$I_{x'}$ = Moment of Inertia about x' axis

An example of the usage of the parallel axis theorem is shown below.

Example 1-5: Parallel Axis Theorem

Problem Statement: Using the Parallel Axis Theorem, determine the moment of inertia about the given X and Y axis of the shape shown.

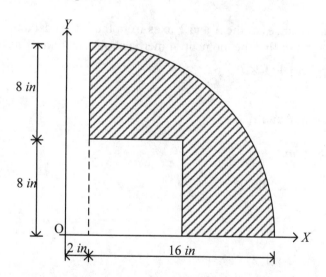

Required: I_x and I_y

Solution: The composite area is broken up into basic shapes. Here the composite shape can be considered as a quarter circle minus a square as shown below.

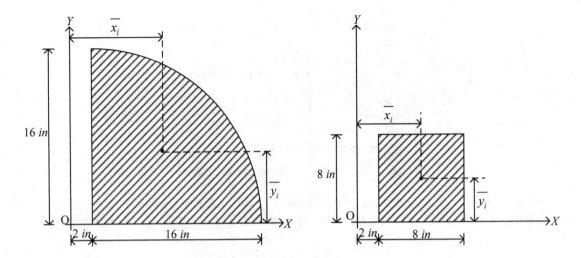

Step 1: Determine the centroidal moments of inertia of each shape. This is the moment of inertia about the axis passing through the centroid of each area.

$$\overline{I}_{x1} = 0.0549r^4 = 0.0549 \times 16^4 = 3597.92 \ in^4$$

$$\overline{I}_{x2} = \frac{1}{12}bh^3 = \frac{1}{12}8 \times 8^3 = 341.33 \ in^4$$

$$\overline{I}_{y1} = 0.0549r^4 = 0.0549 \times 16^4 = 3597.92 \ in^4$$

$$\overline{I}_{y2} = \frac{1}{12}bh^3 = \frac{1}{12}8 \times 8^3 = 341.33 \ in^4$$

Step 2: Determine the distances of the X and Y axes from the centroidal axis of each area and use the Parallel Axis Theorem to find the moment of inertia about the X and Y axes.

$$I_X = \left(\overline{I}_{x1} + A_1 \times d_{1y}^2\right) + \left(\overline{I}_{x2} + A_2 \times d_{2y}^2\right)$$

where

$$d_{1y} = y \text{ distance between } X \text{ and } x'$$

$$= \frac{4r}{3\pi} = \frac{4 \times 16}{3 \times \pi} = 6.79 \ in.$$

$$A_1 = \pi r^2 / 4 = \pi \times 16^2 / 4 = 201.06 \ in^2$$

$$d_{2y} = 4 \ in.$$

$$A_2 = 8 \times 8 = 64 \ in^2$$

giving

$$I_X = (3597.92 + 201.06 \times 6.79^2) - (341.33 + 64 \times 4^2)$$

$$= 12,867.61 - 1365.33 = 11,502.28 \ in^4$$

$$I_Y = \left(\overline{I}_{y1} + A_1 \times d_{1x}^{\,2}\right) + \left(\overline{I}_{y2} + A_2 \times d_{2x}^{\,2}\right)$$

where

$d_{1x} = y$ distance between Y and y'

$$= \frac{4r}{3\pi} + 2 = \frac{4 \times 16}{3 \times \pi} + 2 = \ 8.79 \ in.$$

$A_1 = \pi r^2 / 4 = \pi \times 16^2 / 4 = \ 201.06 \ in^2$

$d_{2x} = 4 + 2 = 6 \ in.$

$A_2 = 8 \times 8 = 64 \ in^2$

giving

$$I_Y = (3597.92 + 201.06 \times 8.79^2) - (341.33 + 64 \times 6^2)$$

$$= 19132.64 - 2645.33 \ = \ 16487.31 \ in^4$$

Step 3: Answers and physical interpretation

$I_X = 11{,}502.28 \ in^4$

$I_Y = 16{,}487.31 \ in^4$

These values represent the magnitude of resistance offered by the area to rotate about the X and Y axes respectively. It is seen that the area is further away from the Y axis than the X axis; hence its resistance to rotate about the Y-axis is greater.

1.4 Summary

A quick and a brief review of the most relevant topics of Statics have been presented in this chapter. These topics are amongst the most used ones in the course of Mechanics of Materials. In order to understand any subject clearly it is, first and foremost, very important to understand the meaning of some of the keywords. The keywords introduced in this chapter are given below.

1. **Centroidal axis:** A set of orthogonal (perpendicular axes) passing through the centroid of an area.
2. **Determinate structure:** A structure which has the number of reactions equal to the available equations of equilibrium.
3. **Distributed load:** A distributed load acts over a length of a beam in a continuous manner and has the units of a force per unit length, such as *k/ft.*
4. **Indeterminate structure:** A structure in which the number of reaction forces are greater than the number of available equations of equilibrium
5. **Moment of Area:** Physically, this represents the concept of a moment, which is a product of a quantity (area) and a distance. In the equation shown below Q_y is the moment of area about the y-axis; x is the distance of the infinitesimal area dA from the y-axis

$$Q_y = \bar{x}A = \int xdA = \sum x_i A_i$$
$$Q_x = \bar{y}A = \int ydA = \sum y_i A_i$$

Eqn (1.1)

6. **Moment of Inertia:** The moment of inertia in physical terms represents the resistance (inertia) to a moment (bending). From a purely mathematical perspective, the moment of inertia is defined as the second moment of an area.
7. **Multi-force body:** A *multi force member* is one where forces act at more than two points. Equilibrium of these members can readily be handled by usual procedure of drawing a free body diagram and using the three equations of equilibrium to solve for the unknowns.
8. **Parallel Axis Theorem:** The most common method of determination of moments of inertia of composite shapes is the *Parallel Axis Theorem.* This theorem enables the determination of the moment of inertia of the area about any axis parallel to its own centroidal axis.
9. **Two force body:** A *two force* member is one in which a member is acted upon by forces at *only two points* (this is different from just two forces acting on the member). The equilibrium condition for a two force member is represented by joining the two points where the forces act by a straight line and getting the angle of the line.
10. **Stability:** Stability is a criterion associated with buckling of members loaded in compression. Buckling in a member occurs due to instability in the member.
11. **Stiffness:** Stiffness of a structure is a measure of its resistance to deformation. A structure is said to be stiff if the deformations in it are small due to the applied loads.
12. **Strength:** The structure is said to be safe in its strength behavior if the computed internal stresses are lesser than the allowable values

1.5 Problems

1.1 Determine the reactions for the beam loaded as shown. Draw a clear free body diagram for the beam.

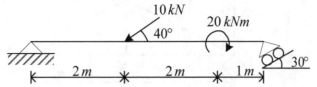

1.2 Draw a clear free body diagram and determine the reactions at the fixed support A.

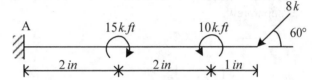

1.3 Define a free body diagram in your own words.

1.4 Determine the reactions and member forces in truss shown. Use method of joints. State whether they are in compression or tension.

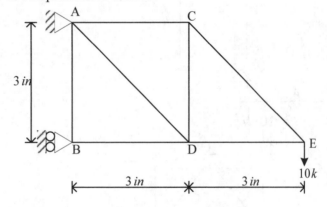

1.5 Using method of sections determine the forces in members CI, DE and JI.

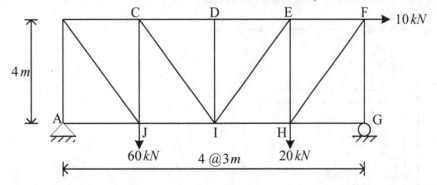

1.6 Using a combination of method of joints and sections determine the member forces of the truss shown. State whether the members are in tension or compression.

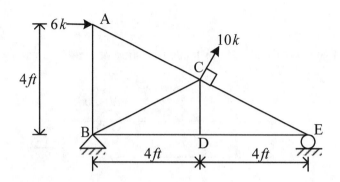

1.7 Determine the forces in each member of the frame structures shown below. Draw the final forces in each member separately.

a.

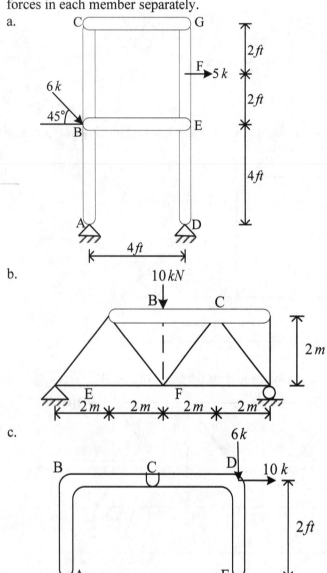

b.

c.

1.8 Determine the centroid of the area shown.

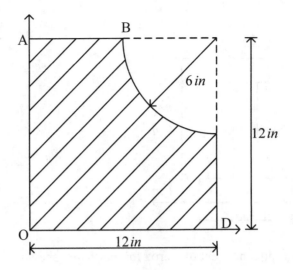

1.9 Determine the reactions of the structure loaded as shown.

a.

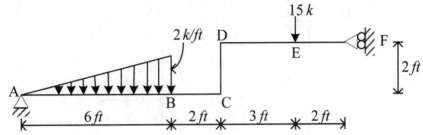

b.

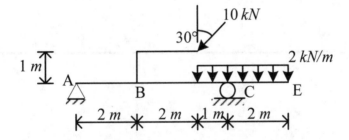

1.10 Determine the moment of inertia about the x and y axis shown for the composite shape.

a.

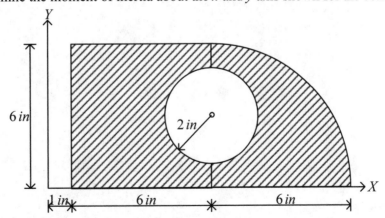

b.

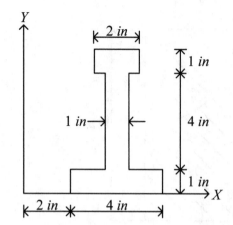

1.11 Determine the centroidal moment of inertia for the shapes shown.

a. 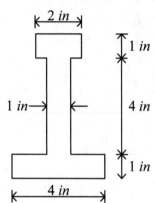   b.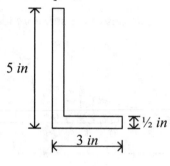

Chapter 2

Stress and Strain

Goal: The learning objectives in this chapter are as follows:

1. Description of *intensities of force (stress)* and *deformation (strain)*
2. Quantification of stress and strain
3. Physical and mathematical description of the types of stresses and strains
4. Basic application of these measures to simple problems
5. Usage of these measures in design problems

2   Stress and Strain

2.1 Introduction

The previous chapter dealt with the fundamentals of Statics as used in a course on mechanics of materials. The basics of finding the forces on members of a truss or a frame, the forces at the connections etc. were described. This chapter takes the next step of describing the use of finding the forces in the structure.

The main objective of this chapter is to clearly outline the concepts of *stress* and *strain*. Stress is intensity of force and strain is intensity of displacement. In the analysis of any structure, forces and displacements are inadequate quantities in order to come up with an efficient and structurally safe design. It will be seen shortly, how important the knowledge of stress and strain is to an engineer. This chapter outlines the different types of stresses and strains, namely the *axial* and the *shear*.

There are three different kinds of problems that a reader can expect in any engineering environment and they are addressed in the form of examples in this and other chapters.
1. The first type of problem is the straight forward one in which all the data pertaining to the geometry of the structure and the loads are completely specified. The question would involve the direct determination of the quantities such as stress and strain using appropriate principles and equations.
2. The second type of problem is of an indirect type. In such problems some of the data pertaining to either the geometry or forces is missing but stress or strain data is given. The question would be to find the missing geometry or force information. The reader should keep in mind that while these problems might appear more difficult on paper, if the principles and steps are followed as in the first type of problem the solution process becomes relatively simpler.
3. The third type of problem is design based. In such questions, the allowable values of stress and strain quantities and the forces acting on the structure are given. The unknown is the geometry of the sections such the cross section details.

In this chapter stress and type of stresses are discussed first followed by strain.

2.2 Stress

Stress is such a commonly used term in one's daily life that nobody really thinks about it when using it. A good beginning to try to understand the meaning of stress is to verbalize your definition of stress and write it down in the space below.

To Do: Define stress in your own words

Definition: *Stress* can be broadly defined as the *intensity of force*. Stress is the internal distribution of forces within a body that balances and reacts to the loads applied to it. Mathematically a stress is calculated as a force divided by an area on which the force is acting.

$$\text{Stress} = \frac{\text{Force}}{\text{Area}}$$

Relating this to your own daily experience, you do not feel stressed unless you are faced with numerous deadlines in a short period. Stress in your body is something you can only experience and describe. Similarly, stress in any object is a hypothetical quantity that is internal to it. Force is real and definite while stress is something that is calculated based on many factors that will be shortly described.

Types of Stresses

There are two basic types of stresses – based on the physical action – that are used through out this subject. They are:
1. Axial or Normal Stress
2. Shear Stress

The basic steps involved in the definition and computation of any stress are
1. Isolating an object in equilibrium under a set of external forces
2. Sectioning (cutting a slice) the object into two independent parts – to expose an area on which the stress is desired
3. Using equilibrium principles to compute the internal force on the area
4. Using principles described in this chapter – calculate the stresses from the internal force and the area resisting the internal force

2.2.1 Axial or Normal Stress

Consider a circular rod subjected to two equal and opposite forces acting along the axial direction, as shown in Figure 2.1. The axial direction has a special meaning in mechanics of materials. Consider a line drawn through the centroid of areas of the cross-section at the two ends of an object. This line is called the *axial direction* as shown in Figure 2.1.

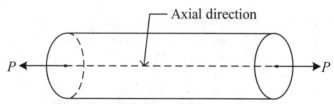
Figure 2.1: Definition of the axial direction

Now, cut the rod into two parts by passing a section that exposes an area that is *perpendicular* to the axial direction as shown. By considering the equilibrium of either section, it can be readily seen that the *internal forces* P_1 that act on either section must be equal and opposite of the external force in that particular section. This is illustrated in the drawing shown below. Thus it can be seen that the internal force P_1 in each section is equal in magnitude and is acting in the direction opposite of the external force P.

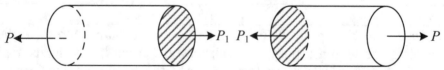
Figure 2.2: Method of sections to expose an internal area and the internal force

These internal forces cause stresses in the rod. Since the force causing this stress is acting in axial direction or in other words, the force is acting normal (synonymous to perpendicular) to the cross-section, this stress is termed as *axial* or *normal* stress. The Greek letter σ is typically used to identify the normal stress. The *axial* or *normal* stress can be expressed in equation form as follows.

$$\sigma = \frac{P_1}{A}$$ Eqn (2.1)

There are two types of axial or normal stress that an internal area can experience. These depend on the direction of the two equal and opposite external forces. If the two external forces act in order to pull the rod apart then the axial stress is *tensile* in nature (*rod is in tension*). On the other hand if the two external forces tend to compress the rod, the axial stress experienced by an internal area perpendicular to this force is *compressive*. The Figure 2.3 shown below illustrates the difference between *tensile* and *compressive normal stresses*.

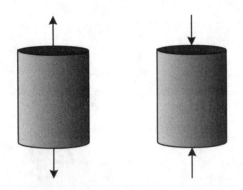

(a) Rod in tenion   (b) Rod in compression
Figure 2.3: Difference between tensile and compressive stress

2.2.2 Shear Stress

The second basic type of stress is called the *shear* stress – based on the shearing action it causes to the internal area. Consider two plates connected by a single bolt and being pulled apart by two equal and opposite forces *P* as shown in the Figure 2.4. The area of the bolt in between the two plates experiences a shearing action and the stress the bolt area experience is called *shear stress*.

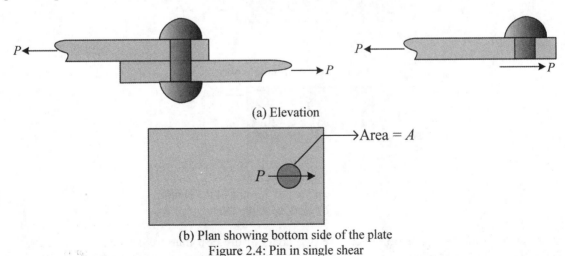

(a) Elevation

(b) Plan showing bottom side of the plate
Figure 2.4: Pin in single shear

The internal force on the bolt is computed by taking a section in between the two plates as shown in Figure 2.4. This process exposes the internal force. The internal force itself is computed by considering the force equilibrium of the section. Here the internal force in the bolt is also P. The shear stress on the area (represented by the Greek letter τ) is given as

$$\tau = \frac{P}{A}$$ Eqn (2.2)

Single Shear: Figure 2.4 shows the example of a pin in single shear. The action implies that the entire force is taken up by one sectional area of the bolt (the area in between the two plates). Equation 2.2 shown above is used to compute this stress.

Double Shear: Figure 2.5 shows the transfer of a force from one plate to two plates, all connected by a single bolt.

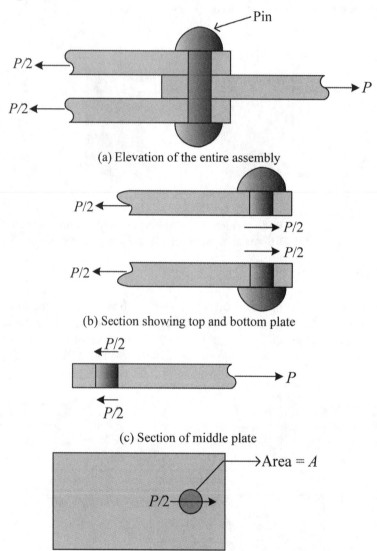

(a) Elevation of the entire assembly

(b) Section showing top and bottom plate

(c) Section of middle plate

(d) Plan showing the bottom side of the plate
Figure 2.5: Pin in Double Shear

Due to nature of the connection, there are two areas of the bolt that are effective in carrying the force P. Figure 2.5(b) shows a section showing the top and bottom plates (each taking up the half the force P). The shear stress in the bolt computed from this section is

$$\tau = \frac{\text{Force}}{\text{Area}} = \frac{P/2}{A} = \frac{P}{2A} \qquad \text{Eqn (2.3)}$$

Another way to look at it is by considering the free body diagram of the middle plate, shown in Figure 2.5(c). In contrast to the top and bottom plate here, there are two areas of the bolt that are resisting the force. The shear stress in the bolts can be computed as follows

$$\tau = \frac{\text{Force}}{\text{Area}} = \frac{P}{2A} \qquad \text{Eqn (2.4)}$$

Considering either the top or the middle plate, it is seen that the shear stress is the same. This form of action of the bolt is called *double shear*.

2.2.3 Bearing Stress

The term bearing stress is used to denote a stress that is:
➢ Compressive in nature
➢ Perpendicular to the surface
➢ Occurs between two surfaces

Two cases of bearing stress are presented here as an illustration. The first case represents the transfer of a compressive force between two bodies, while the second case represents the bearing stress that occurs between a bolt and a plate.

Case 1: Bearing between a column and a pedestal
Figure 2.6 shows a column transmitting a force to a pedestal. The column transmits an axial force P and has a cross sectional area as shown. The bearing stress on the pedestal acts uniformly over the entire bearing area which is also shown in Figure 2.6

$$\sigma = \frac{\text{Force}}{\text{Bearing Area}} = \frac{P}{b \times d} \qquad \text{Eqn (2.5)}$$

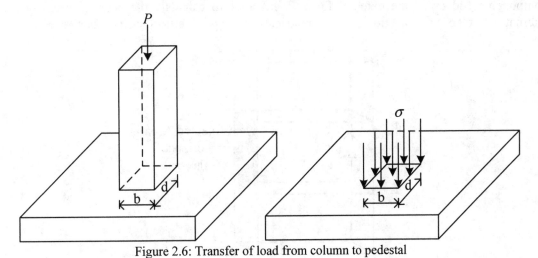

Figure 2.6: Transfer of load from column to pedestal

Case 2: Bearing between bolt and a plate

Figure 2.7: Bolt in shear and bearing

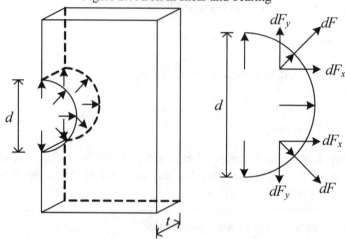

Figure 2.8: Actual bearing stress experience by the hole

When the circular bolt bears against the surface of the hole, the stress theoretically acts along the radial direction over the entire semi-circular area as seen in Figure 2.8. However, the vertical components of the force acting on each symmetric area cancel out and only the horizontal components add up to the external force P. In order to calculate the bearing stress one can alternatively take the projection of the cylindrical area onto a vertical surface as shown in Figure 2.9.

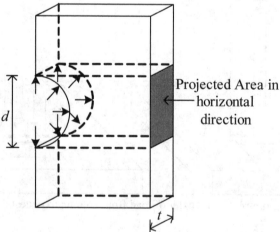

Figure 2.9: Projected area for stress computation

The bearing stress on the surface can be computed using the following expression

$$\sigma = \frac{\text{Force}}{\text{Projected Area}} = \frac{P}{d_{hole} \times t_{plate}}$$

Eqn (2.6)

2.2.4   Practical Units of Stress

As a student's training to be an engineer progresses, it will be realized that units of any physical measure are what gives it a meaning. Here, since stress is a force unit divided by an area unit, the *basic unit of stress* is
- Pounds per square feet - *psf* - in U.S. Customary units
- Newton per square meter - N/m^2 - in SI Units

U.S. Customary Units:
Since *psf* is a rather small quantity (one pound acting on a square foot of area) there are other derivatives of this unit which are more frequently used. The list below gives some frequently used units for stress
- *psi* - Pound per square inch
- *ksi* - kilo Pound (1000 *lbs.*) per square inch
- *msi* - million Pounds (1,000,000 *lbs.*) per square inch

SI Units:
In SI Units, one Pascal (*Pa*) defined as a Newton force acting on one square meter of area.

To Do: The stress your weight exerts per square meter of floor area = _____ *Pa*.

From the above numerical value it can be clearly seen that a *Pa* is not a practical unit to use. A *Pascal* is a very small stress value. Even normal stress values would run into seven to eight digit numbers. Some of the frequently used units and its multiples for stress in SI units are given below
- *kPa* - kilo Pascal - $10^3 N/m^2 = 1 kN/m^2$
- *MPa* - Mega Pascal - $10^6 N/m^2 = 1 N/mm^2$
- *GPa* - Giga Pascal - $10^9 N/m^2 = 1000 MPa$

2.2.5   Dependence of Stress on Force and Area

The example shown below illustrates an interesting dependence of stress on the force and an area. It is illustrated in the example that while the internal forces in the section of the rod and the physical rod itself is identical, different cross-section areas of the rod experience different kinds of stress. The student is encouraged to think and understand this example to get a better insight into the concept of stress.

Example 2-1: Illustration of the Concept of Area and Force and Stress

Problem Statement: A rectangular bar of dimensions $2\ in \times 3\ in \times 24\ in$ is subjected to an axial force of 6000 *lbs* as shown in the figure. At point 'A' on the bar as shown, determine the stresses at 'A' for the following two cases.

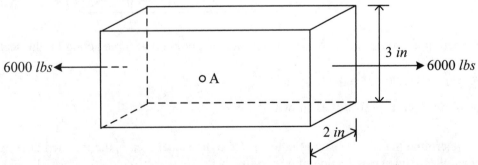

Required: 1) Find the stresses at 'A', if the cross sectional area is cut perpendicular to the axial direction.

2) Find the stresses at 'A', if the cross sectional area is cut at an angle of 30 degrees to the horizontal as shown.

Solution: Part 1

Step 1: Section the bar at point A and determine the net internal force acting on the section cut from the force equilibrium equation.

Sign Convention: If the internal forces on the sectioned area are shown acting away from the area the physical action is *tension* (considered *positive* here).

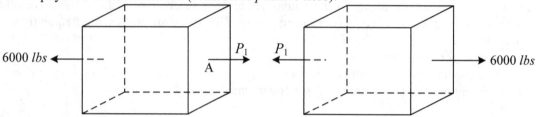

In the above figure the two sections can be defined as the left section and the right section. From the left section free body diagram the following equilibrium equation can be written

$$\rightarrow \sum F_x = 0: \quad \therefore -6000 + P_1 = 0$$

$P_1 = +6000$ *lbs.* (+ve hence tension)

Step 2: Determine the area resisting the force

$A_1 = 3 \times 2 = 6 \ in^2$

Step 3: Since the force P_1 *acts perpendicular and away* from the area, there is only one stress acting on this area – which is the axial or normal stress. Hence the stress at 'A' is given as

$$\sigma = \frac{6000 \ lbs.}{6 \ in^2} = 1000 \ psi \text{ (tensile)}$$

Solution: Part 2

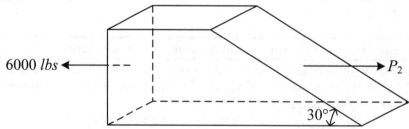

Step 1: Section the rod at point 'A' and determine the net internal force acting on the section cut from equilibrium

$$\rightarrow \sum F_x = 0: \quad \therefore -6000 + P_2 = 0$$

$P_2 = +6000$ *lbs.* (acting outwards as shown)

Step 2: Determine the area resisting the force. Here the actual area is the inclined area, which is greater than the visible cross section of 6 in^2 of the bar.

$$A_2 = \frac{3 \times 2}{\cos 60°} = 12 \; in^2$$

Step 3: Since the force P_2 *acts neither perpendicular nor parallel* to the area, this force is resolved into components perpendicular $P_\perp$ (to get the normal stress) and parallel P_P (to get the shear stress).

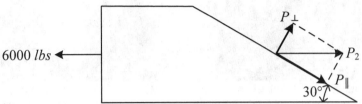

$$P_\perp = P_2 \sin 30 = 6000 \sin 30° = 3000 \; lbs$$
$$P_\parallel = P_2 \cos 30 = 6000 \cos 30° = 5196.15 \; lbs$$

Step 4: Determine the stress due to the parallel (shear stress) and perpendicular (normal stress) components of the forces acting on the area

$$\sigma = \frac{P_\perp}{A_2} = \frac{3000 \; lbs.}{12 \; in^2} = 250 \; psi \; \text{(tensile)}$$

$$\tau = \frac{P_P}{A_2} = \frac{5196.15 \; lbs.}{12 \; in^2} = 433 \; psi \; \text{(shear)}$$

Note: The point A is the same, but the stresses acting at the point depend on how the area is sectioned. It could be either normal or a combination of normal and shear. Hence, we never refer to stress at a point, rather a point on a given area. The significance of this concept will be illustrated in a later chapter of stress transformations.

Q: From Example 2-1 an important question may arise in your mind. Why should we be concerned with the determination of stress values on two different planes? A detailed answer to this will be evident as you go through related topics that appear later in the course. However, a brief explanation is given at this point.

Any material typically has different *failure stress* values in tension, compression and shear. Simplistically, this can be thought of as an experimentally determined limiting stress value, which when exceeded causes failure or fracture in a material. Ductile materials such as aluminum and steel tend to have a lower failure stress value in shear as compared to tension. On the other hand, brittle materials such as cast iron, chalk, concrete etc. tend to have a lower tensile failure stress value compared to shear.

Figure 2.10 shows the failure/fracture of two geometrically identical specimen; one of which is made of aluminum which is a ductile material (tends to fail in shear first as it has a lower shear failure stress value) while the second specimen is made of cast iron (tends to fail in tension first).

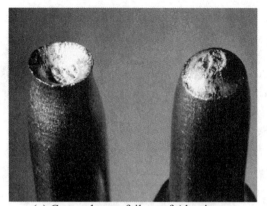 

(a) Cup and cone failure of Aluminum   (b) Brittle failure in cast iron

Figure 2.10: Failure modes in a ductile (Aluminum) and brittle (Cast Iron) specimen in tension

When a pure axial force is applied to the rod, note that the failure mode for the aluminum specimen has a diagonal shape, while the cast iron specimen fractures along a plane perpendicular to the axial force. This clearly indicates that the shear stress on an inclined plane of the aluminum failed before a normal stress on a plane perpendicular to the normal force reached its failure value. The case is reversed for the brittle specimen, where the normal stress on a plane perpendicular to the axial force reached its limiting value before the shear stress on an inclined plane could reach its limiting value. This concept along with more details associated with this topic will be addressed in a subsequent chapter on stress transformations.

2.2.6 Force, Traction and Stress

So far we have seen the relationship between a force and two kinds of stresses, namely the normal and shear stress. It has been shown that a stress is either parallel or perpendicular to an area. There are three terms that are frequently used in this subject. They are *force, traction vector, stress tensor.* The distinction between these terms is described in Figure 2.11.

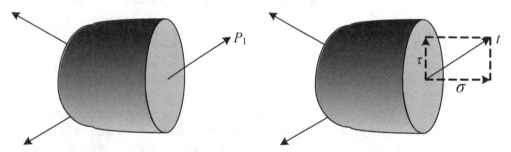

Figure 2.11: Internal force, Traction vector and Stress components

Force: The net internal force on the area sectioned in the body, is calculated from equilibrium consideration of each section. This resultant force is a vector quantity. In Figure 2.11 this is depicted by the vector P_1.

Traction (Stress) Vector: This quantity has the units of stress but has the characteristics of a vector. It is defined mathematically as

$$\vec{t} = \frac{\vec{P}}{\text{Area}}$$

This quantity is in the direction of the resultant force and has the units of stress, hence it is also known as the stress vector. In this subject this term is not used frequently.

Stress: Once the internal resultant force P_1 is resolved into parallel and perpendicular components and these components are divided by the cross-section area in order to get the two stress components that have been discussed so far. Figure 2.11 illustrates the stress terms.

Example 2-2: Tensile stress, shear stress and bearing stress

Problem Statement: A pin is used to transmit the force from the middle plate to the two plates at the top and bottom as shown. Determine the different kinds of stresses acting on the plate and the bolt in the process of transmitting this force. The thickness of each of the plates is 0.5 *inches*.

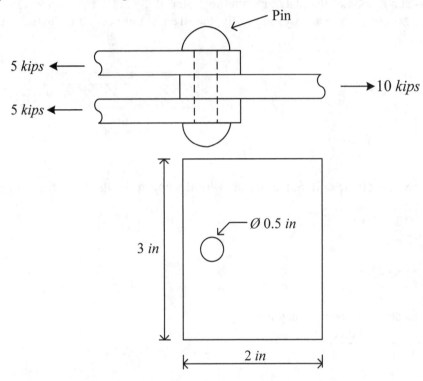

Required: Find the following stresses
        a) Stress in the plate at a section away from the home
        b) Stress in the plate at a section taken at the center of hole
        c) Shear Stress in the bolt
        d) Bearing stress on the top plate
        e) Bearing stress on the middle plate

Solution:

Step 1: Determine the nature and magnitude of stress in the plate at a section away from the hole. This stress is tensile in nature. In order to determine the stress the following section FBD is used, the internal force determined and the stress computed by dividing the force by the area resisting the force.

$$\sigma = \frac{10\ k}{3 \times 0.5\ in^2} = 6.67\ ksi$$

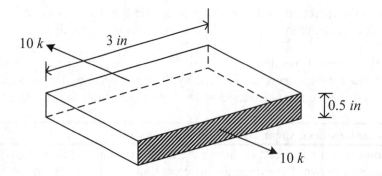

Step 2: Stress at a section of the plate through the center of the hole: This concept is important as the area at this section is the least. Consequently, the stress at this section is the maximum stress.

$$\sigma = \frac{\text{Force}}{A_{net}}$$

$$A_{net} = A_{gross} - d_{hole} \times t_p$$

$$= 3 \times 0.5 - 0.5 \times 0.5 = 1.25 \ in^2$$

$$\sigma = \frac{10 \ k}{1.25 \ in^2} = 8 \ ksi \ (\text{Tensile})$$

Step 3: Shear Stress on the bolt. Since two areas of the bolt resist the force this bolt is in double shear

$$\tau = \frac{\text{Force}}{2A} = \frac{10 \ k}{2 \times \pi \times r^2}$$

$$= \frac{10 \ k}{2 \times \pi \times 0.25^2} = 25.46 \ ksi$$

Step 4: Bearing stress on the middle plate

$$\sigma = \frac{\text{Force}}{\text{Bearing Area}} = \frac{\text{Force}}{d_{bolt} \times t_{plate}}$$

$$= \frac{10 \ k}{0.5 \ in \times 0.5 \ in} = 40 \ ksi$$

Step 5: Bearing stress on the top and bottom plate

$$\sigma = \frac{\text{Force}}{\text{Bearing Area}} = \frac{\text{Force}}{d_{bolt} \times t_{plate}}$$

$$= \frac{5 \ k}{0.5 \ in \times 0.5 \ in} = 20 \ ksi$$

Example 2.3: Design problem using a frame problem

Problem Statement: Given that the diameter of the bolt at C connecting the two members of the frame is 0.5 *in*, determine the shear stress acting in the bolt.

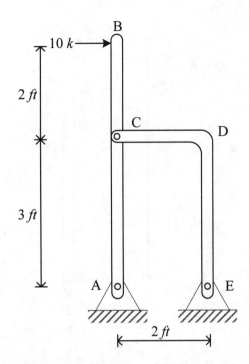

Required: Find the shear stress in the bolt.

Solution:

Step 1: Determine the force acting at C. For this a frame analysis is required. From the figure it can be seen that member ABC is a multi-force member while member CDE is a 2-force member.

Equilibrium of a 2F member: Forces are acting at C and E only. Hence, the resultant force goes along the line joining C and E. From geometry, the angle that this line makes and hence the resultant, is as shown in the figure.

$$\tan \theta = \frac{3}{2}$$

$$\theta = 56.31°$$

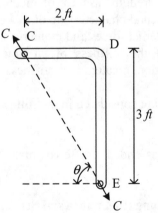

Step 2: Draw the free body diagram of the multi force member ABC, determine the force at C. The force at C is the force acting in the bolt.

$$\sum M_A = 0$$

$$\therefore -(C\sin\theta)\times 3 - 10\times 5 = 0$$

$$\therefore -(C\sin 56.31°)\times 3 - 10\times 5 = 0$$

$$C = -20.03 \; kips$$

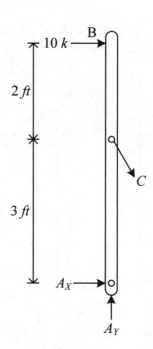

Step 3: The shear stress in the bolt is then

$$\tau = \frac{B}{A_{bolt}} = \frac{20.03 \; kips}{\pi(0.5)^2/4} = 102 \; ksi$$

2.3 Deformation

So far we have discussed the 'strength' aspects of mechanics of materials. As outlined in the introduction, the second fundamental characteristic of this course is the stiffness aspect. When an object is subjected to a set of external forces and moments it changes in shape. In other words, the object deforms. A measure of the stiffness of an object is the amount of deformation it experiences. Lesser the deformation, greater is the stiffness of the body.

Two basic types of deformation are considered in the following sections. They are,
1. Axial Deformation
2. Shear Deformation
These two types of deformations and the different measures that exist are described in detail below.

2.3.1 Axial Displacement, Elongation and Axial Strain

We will consider bodies subjected to an axial force in this chapter. There are three fundamentally different measures to describe the deformation of any body. The three terms can be briefly defined as follows:
1. **Displacement** $\rightarrow$ of a *point*. A specific point is said to displace when the object deforms. The displacement is measured in feet, meters, inches, mm etc. Displacement can be positive or negative. A positive displacement indicates that the point has moved in the positive axis direction. This term will be denoted with the letter u. For example u_A denotes the displacement of point A.
   ➢ **Sign Convention:** + ve indicates a displacement in the + ve axis direction.

> ➤ **Units:** Length units (Example: *ft.* in US units or *mm* in SI Units).

2. **Elongation** → of a *region*. This measures the stretch of a region in the bar. It can be visualized as the change in distance between two points after a deformation has occurred. This term will be denoted by the Greek letter Δ. For example Δ_{AB} denotes the elongation of region AB.

> ➤ **Sign Convention:** +ve indicates elongation of the bar whereas -ve indicates compression of the bar.
> ➤ **Units:** Length units (Example: *ft.* in US units / *mm* in SI Units).

3. **Axial Strain** → in the *region*. The axial strain in a region is defined as the *intensity of elongation.* It is defined as the elongation of region divided by its original length. This term will be denoted using the Greek letter ε. For example, ε_{AB} denotes the axial strain in region AB. The axial strain is mathematically defined as follows

$$\varepsilon_{AB} = \frac{\Delta_{AB}}{L_{AB}} \qquad \text{Eqn (2.6)}$$

> ➤ **Sign Convention:** +ve indicates elongation of the bar / -ve indicates compression of the bar.
> ➤ **Units:** No units. However, (*in. /in.*), (*mm/mm*) etc. are frequently used.

The following example clearly illustrates the difference between the three measures.

Consider a circular rod subjected to an axial force as shown in Figure 2.12. Furthermore, consider two points on the rod A and B that are half *inch* apart. Point A is one *inch* from the origin O. After elongation the points now are located as shown.

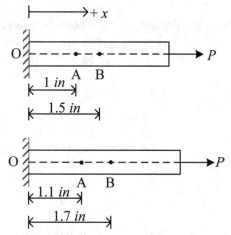

Figure 2.12: Axial displacement, elongation and strain

Original locations:
> ➤ Point A: 1 *inch* from the origin O
> ➤ Point B: 1.5 *inches* from the origin O

After deformation:
> ➤ Point A: 1.1 *inches* from the origin O
> ➤ Point B: 1.7 *inches* from the origin O

Various deformation measures are defined as follows.

Displacement of points:
- $u_A = 1.1 - 1.0 = +0.1$ *in*
- $u_B = 1.7 - 1.5 = +0.2$ *in*

Elongation of AB:

- $\Delta_{AB} = l_{A'B'} - l_{AB} = 0.6 - 0.5 = +0.1 \ in$ (extension)

Axial Strain in AB:

- $\varepsilon_{AB} = \dfrac{l_{A'B'} - l_{AB}}{l_{AB}} = \dfrac{0.6 - 0.5}{0.5} = +0.2 \ in/in$

General Definition of Axial (Extensional) Strain

Consider a line AB in an object as shown in the Figure 2.13 subjected to a combination of forces. After the application of forces the line elongates (or contracts) to A'B',

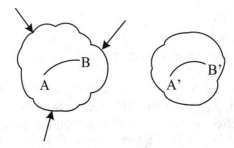

Figure 2.13: Object and line AB before and after deformation

Let the length of the line in the originally undeformed body be L and the length after deformation be L_1. If ε is the extensional strain at any point on the line then the incremental change (ΔL) of any infinitesimal length of the line (dL) can be used to define the new length of the infinitesimal segment (dL_1) as follows

$$dL_1 = dL + \Delta L$$

$$\Delta L = \varepsilon dL$$

Important: In the above equation we consider an infinitesimal segment since the extensional strain at any point on the line can have a *different* value. Consequently, the new length of the line can be expressed in an integral form as

$$L_1 = \int_A^B dL_1 = \int_A^B (1+\varepsilon)dL$$

$$L_1 = \int_A^B dL + \int_A^B \varepsilon dL$$

$$L_1 = L + \int_A^B \varepsilon dL$$

In general, ε can be any function, which can then be integrated.

Special Case: Axially Loaded Bar subjected to a constant axial force
Consider a bar having a constant cross sectional area subjected to a constant axial force through out as shown in Figure 2.14.

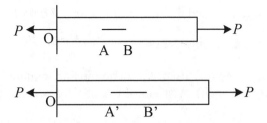

Figure 2.14: Axially loaded bar

Two situations are now considered to derive the expressions for change in length.

a) **Small Strain Deformation:** If the elongation in the bar is such that change in the total elongation is very small, it is reasonable to assume that the extensional strain value ε is *constant* throughout the bar. In this condition the change in length can be written as follows

$$\Delta L = \int \varepsilon dL = \varepsilon \int dL = \varepsilon L$$

or

$$\varepsilon = \frac{\Delta L}{L} = \frac{\text{change in length}}{\text{original length}}$$

b) **Large Strain Deformation:** However, if the elongation of the bar is such that the new length is significantly larger than the original length (say a one *inch* segment becomes 1.5 *inch*) then the strain equation defined by Equation (2.6) cannot be used. In this case it must be noted that reference length (L) keeps changing. Within this length L, consider an infinitesimally small length L_1 which changes to L_2. Hence the strain (called the true strain) can be expressed as

$$\varepsilon_{true} = \int_{L_1}^{L_2} \frac{dL}{L} = \ln(L)\,|_{L_1}^{L_2}$$

$$= \ln(L_2) - \ln(L_1) = \ln(\frac{L_2}{L_1}) = \ln(\frac{L_1 + \Delta L}{L_1}) \qquad \text{Eqn (2.7)}$$

$$= \ln(1 + \varepsilon)$$

In the equation (2.7) above the true strain (also called as log strain) value has been expressed in terms of the small strain. The problem of large strains is not addressed in this book and will be discussed in advanced courses such as Continuum Mechanics.

Small strains and True Strains

The conceptual example shown below gives an insight into how the strain definition in a large strain problem must be viewed. Consider a twelve *inch* rod, as shown in the figure below subjected to an axial force as shown. Assume that a gage length AB of one *inch* becomes 1.5 *inch* after the application of the load.

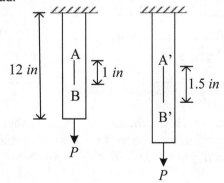

The computation of small strain ε_0 and the true strain is shown below.

$$\text{Small (Engineering) strain: } \varepsilon_o = \frac{\Delta l}{l_o} = \frac{(1.5-1.0) \ in}{1.0 \ in} = 0.5$$

It can be seen that the gage length l_o used, the denominator, remains constant through out the entire deformation process (one inch). A strain of 0.5 or fifty percent is clearly an example of a rod undergoing large deformations.

In the computation of large strains the gage length is not constant. The computation is shown below where the problem is broken down into ten segments wherein the gage length is increased to the new value for every computation of the strain. It has to be kept in mind that the equation used to define and compute strain as the change in length divided by the gage length is valid only for small strains; hence the usage in the manner shown below is valid. In other words, the computation of strain (true strain) for the large deformation case is broken down into many small strain problems.

$$\text{Strain Definition: } \varepsilon_x = \frac{\Delta l}{l}$$

l	Δl	ε_x
1.0		
1.05	0.05	$\frac{0.05}{1} = 0.05$
1.1	0.05	$\frac{0.05}{1.05} = 0.0476$
1.15	0.05	$\frac{0.05}{1.1} = 0.04545$
1.2	0.05	$\frac{0.05}{1.15} = 0.0435$
1.25	0.05	$\frac{0.05}{1.2} = 0.0416$
1.3	0.05	$\frac{0.05}{1.25} = 0.04$
1.35	0.05	$\frac{0.05}{1.3} = 0.0385$
1.4	0.05	$\frac{0.05}{1.35} = 0.037$
1.45	0.05	$\frac{0.05}{1.4} = 0.0357$
1.5	0.05	$\frac{0.05}{1.45} = 0.0345$
		$\sum \varepsilon_x = 0.4132$

Table 3.1: True strain

True Stress-True Strain Curve: The mathematical equation representing true strain has been shown to be defined by a logarithmic equation. In a similar manner the true stress can also be shown be related to the engineering stress definition as shown below

$$\varepsilon_{true} = \ln(1 + \varepsilon_o)$$
$$\sigma_{true} = \ln(1 + \sigma_o)$$

The difference between the stress-strain graphs for the small deformation case $(\sigma_o - \varepsilon_o)$ and the large deformation case $(\sigma_{true} - \varepsilon_{true})$ is shown below. Note that in the large deformation case no portion of the stress strain graph goes into a descending portion.

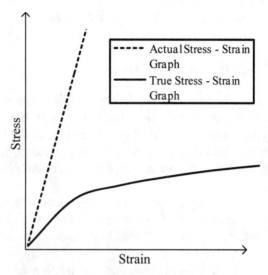

Figure 2.15: Graph of true stress vs. true strain

It can be seen that if the segments is increased to twenty or more the true strain value can be exactly obtained.

2.3.2   Shear Strain

The other basic type of strain, caused by shear stresses, is called shear strain. Unlike axial strain which measures the change in the length of a line element, the shear strain is a measure of the change in an angle.

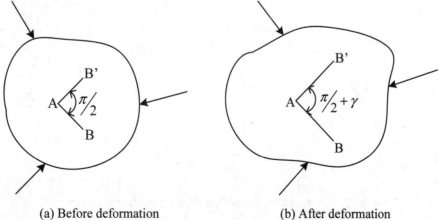

(a) Before deformation   (b) After deformation
Figure 2.16: Physical definition of shear strain

Consider an object subjected to forces as shown in Figure 2.16. Within this object consider two lines, AB and AB', which are perpendicular to each other. When the forces act on the object the angle between the two lines changes and let the new angle be ($\frac{\pi}{2} + \gamma$). The *change in the angle* γ is defined as the *shear strain*.

➢ **Sign Convention:** +ve sign indicates that the angle between the two lines has increased and a –ve sign indicates a decrease in the angle.
➢ **Units:** *Radians* (all engineering angular units are measured in radians). '*Radians*' is a dimensionless quantity.

2.4 Hooke's Law Relating Stresses and Strains

In the chapter so far, we have discussed two primary physical quantities, namely stresses and strains. Stress is a measure of the intensity of the force while strain is a measure of the intensity of deformation. In order to have a tool to predict the deformation in the body subjected to a set of forces, we need a relationship which connects the stresses to strains. *Such a relationship cannot be derived and is determined purely by experiments, hence is called a law.*

Isotropic Material: An isotropic body is considered to be made of a material, which is assumed to be uniform in its material properties in all directions. Examples of isotropic materials are steel, brass, aluminum etc. All these materials can be visualized to be homogeneous and uniform.

This section describes some basic experiments that are performed in order to determine the relationship between stresses and strains. Two basic types of stresses and strains have been defined here relating
➢ Axial strains and axial stresses
➢ Shear strains and shear stresses

2.4.1　Young's Modulus and Poisson's Ratio

There are two basic and independent elastic constants that can be determined from a simple uniaxial test on a standard specimen. A uniaxial test represents a state of axial stress and axial strain in the specimen. Figure 2.17 shows a schematic representation of the uniaxial tension test.

Figure 2.17: Schematic representation of a uniaxial tension test

No specific material (such as aluminum or steel) is considered in this explanation. The experimental observations typically are recorded as a force (P) and elongation (ΔL) relationship. Elongation is measured by using either a clip gage or a strain gage with a fixed and specified gage length (L). The axial stress and strain at any data point is then determined from the following equation.

$$\sigma = \frac{P}{A}; \quad \varepsilon = \frac{\Delta L}{L}$$

where, A is the area of cross section of the bar. Figure 18 shows a typical stress-strain curve for a tension test on a metallic specimen.

Hooke's Law: It can be seen from Figure 2.18 that in the region where the strains are low the experimental curve can be represented as a linear curve. This linear relationship, called Hooke's Law, can be expressed as

$$\sigma = E\varepsilon \hspace{4cm} \text{Eqn (2.8)}$$

where, E is an elastic constant called the *Young's modulus* or *modulus of elasticity*. The slope of the line represents the modulus of elasticity and has the same units as that of stress. However it is typically three orders in magnitude to that of the stress value.

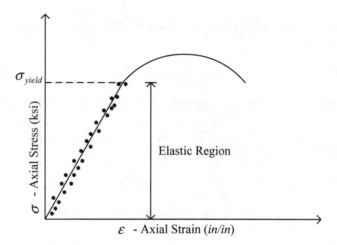

Figure 2.18: Results from a uniaxial tension test

Another observation that is recorded in a tension test corresponds to the observation that the cross sectional area at the middle of the specimen decreases as the elongation in the longitudinal direction occurs. This phenomenon, known as the *Poisson's effect*, represents the decrease in the lateral dimension due to a longitudinal elongation. Figure 2.19 shows a schematic representation of the axial strain and Poisson's effect.

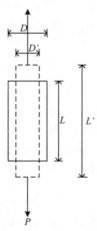

Figure 2.19: The axial strain and Poisson's effect

The strain in the longitudinal ($\varepsilon_{longitudinal}$) and the lateral ($\varepsilon_{lateral}$) can be defined as follows

$$\varepsilon_{longitudinal} = \frac{\Delta L}{L} = \frac{L' - L}{L}$$

$$\varepsilon_{lateral} = \frac{D' - D}{D}$$

In a typical tension test the longitudinal strain is positive (elongation) while the lateral strain is negative (contraction). Poisson's effect is now defined using a physical or elastic constant called *Poisson's Ratio (v)* (Greek letter – pronounced as 'nu' or 'new').

$$v = -\frac{\varepsilon_{lateral}}{\varepsilon_{longitudinal}}$$

The negative sign is introduced in order to have a positive constant value. For most metals the value of Poisson's Ratio ranges between 0.25 and 035. It will be shown in a later section that the value of this ratio can never exceed 0.5.

Table 2.2 gives typical values of the Elastic Modulus and Poisson's ratio for some commonly used materials in engineering.

Material	Young's Modulus		Poisson's Ratio
	ksi	*GPa*	
Aluminum	10,000	70	0.33
Brass	14-16,000	96-110	0.34
Concrete (compression)	2,500-4,500	18-30	0.1-0.2
Steel	29,000	210	0.28-0.3

Table 2.2: Table of material properties of some common materials

Material behavior and material properties are described in greater detail in a later chapter.

2.4.2 Shear Modulus

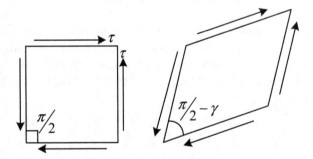

Figure 2.20: Shear stress-strain

Consider a cube subjected to a shearing action (shear stress τ) as shown in Figure 2.20, which shows the two dimensional elevation of the cube. Due to the action of the forces the bottom left right angle changes and this change in the angle is called the *shear strain* (γ). Considering the cube to be made of a metal, as the shear stress is increased it can be observed that the shear strain also changes and the relationship between the two is a linear one. This linear relationship can be expressed as

$$\tau = G\gamma$$

where, G is called the *Shear Modulus* or *Modulus of Rigidity,* and is the third elastic constant defined so far in this chapter. For any material, the elastic behavior can be *completely defined* by only *two elastic constants*. It will be shown in a subsequent chapter that the relationship between the shear modulus, elastic modulus and Poisson's ratio can be expressed as

$$G = \frac{E}{2(1+v)}$$

Example 2.4: Determination of elastic constants

Problem Statement: A circular rod made of aluminum is 2.25 *inches* in diameter and 12 *inches* in length is subjected to an axial force of 32 *kips*. At the end of the tension test the rod length was measured to be 12.00938 *inches* and its diameter at the center decreased to 2.249415 *inches*. Determine the two elastic constants for aluminum, namely Young's modulus E and the Poisson's ratio v.

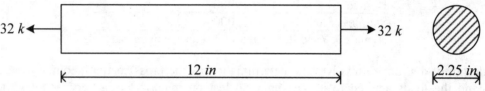

Required: Find the Young's modulus and Poisson's ratio of aluminum

Solution:

Step 1: Determine the change in length and diameter of the bar

$$\Delta l = 12.00938 \ in - 12 \ in = 0.00938 \ in$$

$$\Delta d = 2.249415 \ in - 2.25 \ in = -0.000585 \ in$$

Step 2: Determine the axial and transverse strain

$$\varepsilon_x = \frac{\Delta l}{l} = \frac{0.00938 \ in}{12 \ in} = 0.000782 \ in/in.$$

$$\varepsilon_{transverse} = \frac{\Delta d}{d} = \frac{-0.000585 \ in}{2.25 \ in} = -0.00026 \ in/in.$$

Step 3: Since this is a uniaxial test the equation of Poisson's ratio $v = -\dfrac{\varepsilon_{transverse}}{\varepsilon_{longitudinal}}$ can be used.

The elastic modulus and the Poisson's ratio is now determined

$$v = -\frac{\varepsilon_{transverse}}{\varepsilon_{longitudinal}} = -\frac{\varepsilon_{transverse}}{\varepsilon_x} = -\frac{-0.00026}{0.000782} = 0.333$$

$$E = \frac{\sigma_x}{\varepsilon_x}$$

$$\sigma_x = \frac{P}{A} = \frac{32 \ kips}{\pi(1.125)^2} = 8,030 \ psi$$

$$E = \frac{\sigma_x}{\varepsilon_x} = \frac{8,030 \ psi}{0.000782} = 10,268 \ psi$$

Hence

$$E = 10,300 \ ksi \text{ and } v = 0.333$$

2.5 Design Issues

The goal of the study of mechanics of materials is to establish the fundamental principles based on which any structure such as buildings, bridges, cars, micro devices etc. can be designed. It will be eventually seen that actual designs, while based on principles of mechanics of materials, incorporate many practical conditions and issues.

Material	Yeild Stress	
	psi	*MPa*
Aluminum	35000	
Red Brass	18000	
Bronze	19000	
Stainless Steel	55000	

Table 2.3: Yield stress values for some common materials

The design of a structure involves the determination of the cross section geometry necessary to withstand the loads applied to it. The uniaxial test on materials is a very popular method to determine the yield stress f_y of any material. For isotropic materials this is statistically a constant value. The design process however uses the *allowable stress* values which is the yield stress value divided by a factor of safety *(FOS)*. The factor of safety accounts for uncertainties in material properties and actual loads. Table 2.3 gives a partial list of some commonly used materials and their yield stress values. The factors of safety can also vary with the type of behavior that the structure is experiencing.

The basic design procedure for axially loaded members or bolts in shear or in bearing is to first find the force acting on the member P and then divide the force by the allowable stress value f_{all} in order to find the area as shown below

$$A_{req.} = \frac{P}{f_{all.}}$$

From the area required either the bolt diameter or the thickness and the width of the plate required are determined.

Consider a simple example of a circular rod, as shown in the figure, made of steel and is required to carry an axial force of 6 *kips*. Given that the yield stress of steel is 50 *ksi* and using a factor of safety of 1.5, it is required to find the diameter of the steel rod.

6 *k*

$$f_{all.} = \frac{f_y}{FOS} = \frac{50\ ksi}{1.5} = 33.33\ ksi$$

$$A_{req.} = \frac{P}{f_{all.}} = \frac{6\ k}{33.33\ ksi} = 0.18\ in^2 = \frac{\pi d^2}{4}$$

$$d \geq 0.478\ in$$

$$\therefore \text{Provide } d = 0.5\ in.$$

Gross and Net Areas: In tension members the concept of gross and net areas is an important entity. The section taken across the net area is the least area available for the material to resist the force; hence it experiences the greatest stress value. Consequently, the allowable stress value is first reached in the net section. Hence, the designer must exercise care in using the net area in order to determine the width or the thickness of the section.

Consider the plate with a hole subjected to tensile forces, as shown in the figure. If the thickness of the plate to be designed is ½ *in* determine the width of the plate. The plate is made of steel as in the previous problem and is subjected to a force of 40 *kips*.

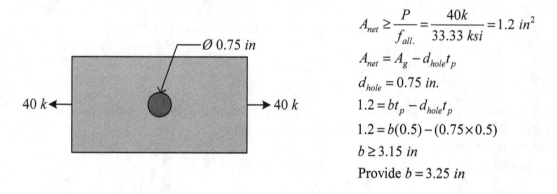

$$A_{net} \geq \frac{P}{f_{all.}} = \frac{40k}{33.33\ ksi} = 1.2\ in^2$$

$$A_{net} = A_g - d_{hole}t_p$$

$$d_{hole} = 0.75\ in.$$

$$1.2 = bt_p - d_{hole}t_p$$

$$1.2 = b(0.5) - (0.75 \times 0.5)$$

$$b \geq 3.15\ in$$

$$\text{Provide } b = 3.25\ in$$

Example 2.5: Design problem

Problem Statement: If the frame in the problem is made of members that are 3/4 *in.* thick, if the allowable stresses are $\tau_{all} = 24\ ksi$ and $f_{bearing} = 33.33\ ksi$, determine the diameter of the bolt required.

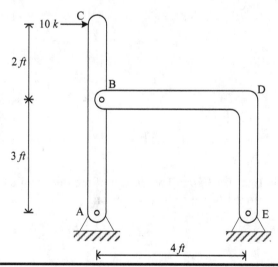

Required: Find the diameter of the bolt

Solution:

Step 1: Determine the force acting at C. For this a frame analysis is required. From the figure it can be seen that member ABC is a multi-force member while member CDE is a 2-force member.

Equilibrium of a 2F member: Forces are acting at C and E only. Hence, the resultant force goes along the line joining C and E. From geometry, the angle that the resultant is shown in the figure.

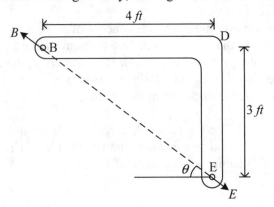

$$\tan \theta = \frac{3}{4}$$

$$\theta = 36.87^{o}$$

Step 2: Draw the free body diagram of the multi force member ABC, determine the force at C. The force at C is the force acting in the bolt.

$$-B \sin \theta (3) - 10 (5 \, ft) = 0$$

$$B = -20.83 \, kips$$

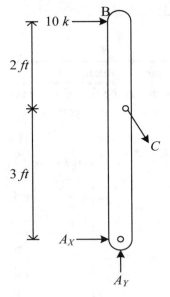

Step 3: The force in the bolt is 20.83 *kips*. The design of the bolt diameter is to be determined from both the shear stress and the bearing stress criterion.

From the shear stress criterion:

$$A_{bolt} = \frac{B}{\tau_{all.}} = \frac{20.83\ kips}{24\ ksi} = 0.87\ in^2$$

$$0.87\ in^2 = \frac{\pi d^2}{4}$$

$$d \geq 1.1\ in$$

$\therefore$ Provide $d = 1\frac{1}{8}\ in.$

From the bearing stress criterion:

$$A_b = \frac{B}{f_{all.}} = \frac{20.83\ kips}{33\ ksi} = 0.625\ in^2$$

$$A_b = d_{bolt} t_{plate}$$

$$d_{bolt} \geq \frac{0.625}{0.75}$$

$$d \geq 0.8332\ in$$

Provide $d = 1\frac{1}{8}\ in$

It can be seen that shearing stress criterion gives a greater diameter, which is the diameter to be provided.

2.6 Summary

The key terms introduced in this chapter are summarized below.

1. **Tension (Normal Stress):** This type of stress is caused by force acting at the centroid of the section, in a direction perpendicular and away from the area. The effect on the body is to stretch it.

2. **Compression (Normal Stress):** This type of stress is caused by a force acting at the centroid of the section, in a direction perpendicular and into from the area. The effect on the body is to crush it.

3. **Single Shear:** A shear stress acts parallel to an area. A pin is said to be in single shear if only one cross section area of the bolt is effective in resisting the force.

4. **Double Shear:** A pin or bolt is said to be in double shear if two areas of the bolt are effective in resisting the applied force as seen in Figure 2.5.

5. **Bearing Stress (Normal Stress):** A bearing stress is compressive nature. However, this is a stress on the surface between two objects. The characteristic of this stress that it acts perpendicular to the surface and into the surface.

6. **Displacement:** A specific point is said to displace when the object deforms. The displacement term is used to denote the actual movement of a *point*.

7. **Elongation - of a *region*:** This measure the stretch of a region in the bar

8. **Axial Strain - in the *region*:** The axial strain in a region is defined as the elongation of region divided by its original length

9. **Shear Strain:** When the forces act on the object the angle between the two lines changes. The *change in the angle* γ is defined as the *shear strain* and is measure in radians.

10. **Elastic or Material Properties:** The elastic properties of a material are its Young's modulus, Poisson's ratio, Shear Modulus and the Bulk Modulus,

11. **Isotropic Material:** A homogeneous material with a uniform form is said to isotropic if it has identical material properties in all directions.

12. **Young's Modulus:** The Young's modulus or the Elastic modulus (E) is a measure of the initial stiffness of the material and is determined from the slope of the stress strain graph from a tension test of the material. It has the units of *GPa* or *ksi*.

13. **Poisson's Ratio:** The Poisson's ratio quantifies the Poisson's effect which is the phenomenon of the transverse diameter shortening upon being pulled in the longitudinal direction. It has no units.

14. **Shear Modulus:** The shear modulus (G) relates the shear strain to the shear stress and represents the material's ability to resist a shear strain.

2.7 Problems:

2.1   Define axial direction.

2.2   Define a normal stress.

2.3   A steel bar has a radius of 10 *mm* and is axially loaded by force of 4 *kN*. Determine the axial stress and express your answer in *MPa* units.

2.4   An aluminum rod of 0.5 *in* diameter is experiencing an axial stress of 30 *ksi*. What is the axial force in the bar?

2.5   Determine the axial stress in a rectangular bar of cross section area 10*mm* x 50*mm* and loaded by a force of 20 *kN* as shown in the figure.

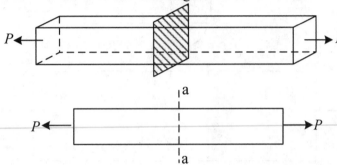

2.6   Determine the axial stress and shear stress on the area along section a-a and b-b. The rectangular bar is having the cross section area and loading same as in problem 2.5.

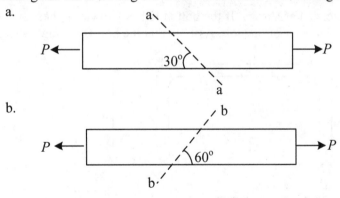

2.7   The figure shown in problem 2.6, if the shear stress on section a-a is 350 *MPa*, determine:
a)   Axial force in the rod.
b)   Axial stress on the section b-b

2.8   Two pieces are glued as shown in the figure, given that the cross section of the wood at the ends is 1½ *in* x 3½ *in* and if the maximum shearing stress that the glue can take is 3 *psi* determine the maximum *P* that can be applied to the bar.

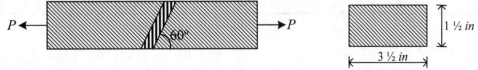

2.9 In the above example if the maximum axial stress in the wood is 5 *psi* determine the maximum *P* that can be applied to the bar.

2.10 Using the data and information from problem 2.8 and 2.9, if the maximum tensile stress in the glue is 5 *psi*, determine the maximum load *P* that can be applied.

2.11 Two plates are connected as shown in the figure. If the width of the plates is 3 *in*, the thickness is ½ *in* and the diameter of the bolt is ¾ *in* determine
    a)   maximum tensile stress in the plate
    b)   shear stress in the bolt
    c)   bearing stress on the plate

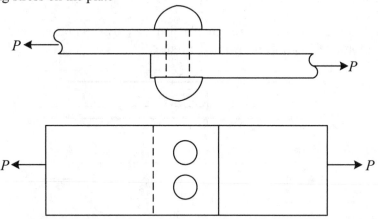

2.12 In problem 13, if the maximum tensile in the plate and the maximum shear stress in the bolt is 6 *ksi* and 25 *ksi*, determine the maximum load *P* that can be applied to the plate.

2.13 The frame in the figure is loaded as shown. If the bolt at C has allowable shear stress of 20 *ksi*, determine the required diameter of the bolt. Assume that the bolt is in single shear.

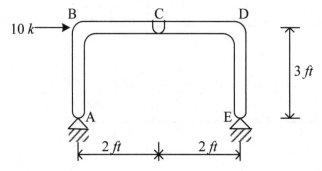

2.14 A circular rod made of aluminum is 2 *inches* in diameter and 10 *inches* in length is subjected to an axial force of 25 *kips*. At the end of the tension test the rod length was measured to be 10.0025 *inches* and its diameter at the center decreased to 1.9415 *inches*. Determine the elastic constants for aluminum, namely Young's modulus *E*, the Poisson's ratio ν and Shear Modulus *G*.

Chapter 3

Axial Force Diagram

Goals: The learning objective of this chapter

1. Determining axial stresses and strain in statically determinate axially loaded bars
2. Determining elongations and displacements in statically determinate axially loaded bars
3. Defining statically indeterminate systems in axially loaded situations
4. Establishing equilibrium and compatibility principles to solve reactions, stresses, strains and elongations in axially loaded statically indeterminate systems

3   <u>Axial Force Diagram</u>

3.1   Introduction

It was seen in Chapter 2 that there are two fundamental strength related quantities, namely *Axial Force* and *Axial Stress*, while there are three fundamental stiffness related measures, namely; *displacement, elongation* and *strain*. Another concept that was introduced in Chapter 2 was the relationship between the axial stress and axial strain by means of an experimental law called *Hooke's Law*. In this chapter, following topics are discussed.
1. Determining elongations and displacements in statically determinate axially loaded bars
2. Determining axial stresses and strain in statically determinate axially loaded bars

3.2   Axial Force Diagram

The necessity and concept of an Axial Force Diagram (AFD) is demonstrated along with the method used to draw these diagrams. Consider a bar as shown in Figure 3.1 which has varying geometry, as measured by the lengths and the diameters of the bars, and is loaded by different sets of axial forces as shown.

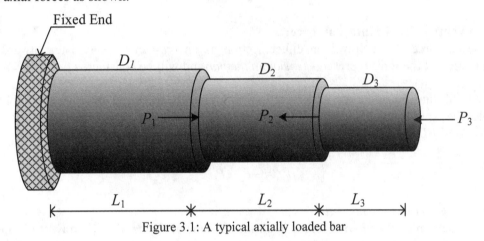

Figure 3.1: A typical axially loaded bar

In Figure 3.1 the forces are assumed to act through the centroid of each cross section of the bar. The internal forces (here only an axial force) in the bar are determined by the *method of sections.*

3.2.1   Method of Sections

The plot of the internal forces in the bar on the *y*-axis with the *x*-axis representing the location where the force is acting on the bar is called the *Axial Force Diagram*. The steps involved in the method of sections are described below, followed by a numerical example.

Step 1: Determine the Reaction at A.

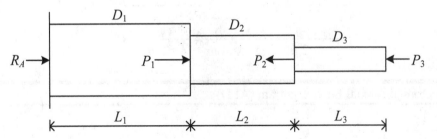

$$\sum F_x = 0 \rightarrow$$
$$R_A + P_1 - P_2 - P_3 = 0$$
$$R_A = P_2 + P_3 - P_1$$

Step 2: Determine the axial force in the central bar using method of sections

This is accomplished by splitting (sectioning) the central bar, such that the entire object is separated into two independent objects as shown below. This sectioning results in a *left section* free body diagram and a *right section* free body diagram. The force P_{aa}, shown in each section, is the internal axial force at that section.

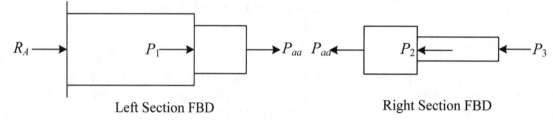

Left Section FBD   Right Section FBD

Sign Convention for the internal force:

The internal force P_{aa} is drawn on either section as an *outward arrow*. The outward arrow representation of the force represents *tension in the bar* and will be considered *positive*.

Force equilibrium equation for either section will give the required internal axial force. For example, the equilibrium equation and the resulting expression for the internal axial force in the *right section FBD* are as follows:

$$-P_{aa} - P_2 - P_3 = 0$$
$$P_{aa} = -P_2 - P_3$$

Q: How many sections are needed?

In order to determine the internal forces in all the sections of the bars, as we traverse from left to right, a new section is taken whenever
➢ The cross section changes
➢ A new axial force is introduced

Example 3.1: Axial Force Diagram

Problem Statement: The bar shown below is axially loaded at B, C and D by the forces given in the figure. The entire bar is made up of steel.

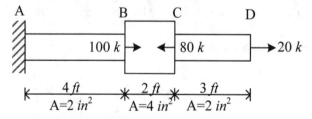

Required: Draw the Axial Force Diagram (AFD)

Solution:

Step 1: Determine the reaction at A using the FBD as shown below

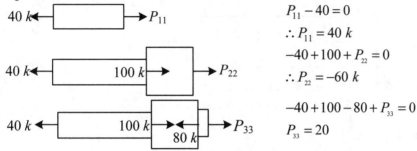

$A_x + 100 - 80 + 20 = 0$

$A_x = -40$

$\therefore A_x = 40 \ k \leftarrow$

Step 2: Determine the internal forces.

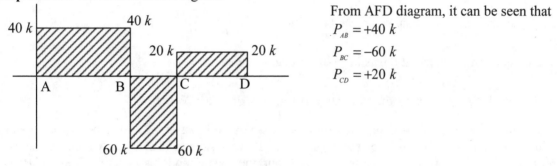

$P_{11} - 40 = 0$

$\therefore P_{11} = 40 \ k$

$-40 + 100 + P_{22} = 0$

$\therefore P_{22} = -60 \ k$

$-40 + 100 - 80 + P_{33} = 0$

$P_{33} = 20$

Step 3: Draw the Axial Force Diagram.

From AFD diagram, it can be seen that

$P_{AB} = +40 \ k$

$P_{BC} = -60 \ k$

$P_{CD} = +20 \ k$

Note: ← force, Jump up in the Axial Force Diagram.

        → force, Jump down in the Axial Force Diagram.

3.3   Displacements and Elongations in Axially Loaded Members

The fundamental case of a homogeneous rod (constant cross-sectional and material properties) subjected to a uniform axial force sets up the basis for numerous calculations that will follow. Let the rod AB of length L, having a uniform cross section area A, made of a material with a modulus of elasticity E be subjected to a concentrated axial force P at end B as shown in Figure 3.2

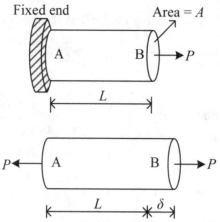

Figure 3.2: Homogeneous rod subjected to uniform axial force

Internal Axial Force in the bar $= P$

Stress in the bar: $\sigma = \dfrac{P}{A}$

From Hooke's Law the axial strain can be written as: $\varepsilon = \dfrac{\sigma}{E} = \dfrac{P}{AE}$

From equation in chapter 2 the axial strain can be written as: $\varepsilon = \dfrac{\delta}{L}$

From the above expressions the elongation δ can be written as: $\delta = \varepsilon L = \dfrac{PL}{AE}$

It should be noted that this expression for elongation could be used only for a homogeneous bar with a constant axial force throughout its length. If we now consider a bar, which has several portions L_1, L_2, L_3 with areas given by A_1, A_2, A_3 and the elastic modulus as E_1, E_2, E_3 and if P_1, P_2, P_3 are the internal axial forces in each of these segments, then the total elongation of the rod may be expressed in a summation form as

$$\delta = \sum \frac{P_i L_i}{E_i A_i}$$
Eqn (3.1)

Example 3.2: Axial Force Diagram, Elongation and Displacement

Problem Statement: The bar shown is axially loaded at B, C and D by the given forces.

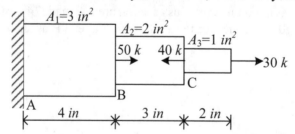

The entire bar is made of steel with an Elastic Modulus value 30×10^3 *ksi*.

Required: Determine the displacements at A, B, C and D and elongations of regions AB, BC and CD for the bar axially loaded as shown.

Solution:

Step 1: Determine the reaction at A using the FBD shown below:

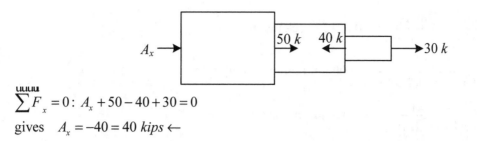

$$\sum F_x = 0 : \ A_x + 50 - 40 + 30 = 0$$

gives $\ A_x = -40 = 40 \ kips \leftarrow$

Step 2: Determine the internal forces and draw the Axial Force Diagram

$-40 + P_1 = 0$

or $P_1 = +40 = 40 \ kips$ (tension)

$-40 + 50 + P_2 = 0$

or $P_2 = -10 = 10 \ kips$ (compression)

$-40 + 50 - 40 + P_3 = 0$

or $P_3 = +30 = 30 \ kips$ (tension)

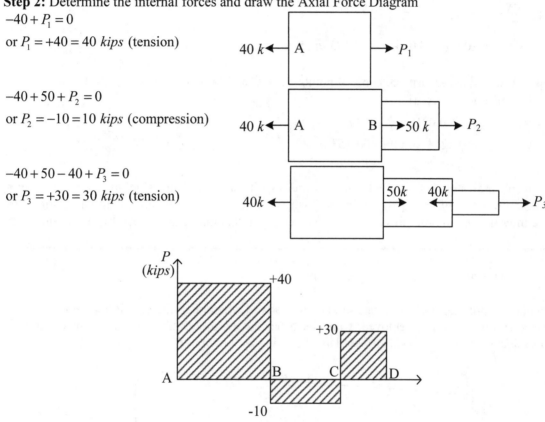

Step 3: Determine the axial stress in various sections of the bar

$$\sigma_{AB} = \frac{P_{AB}}{A_{AB}} = \frac{+40 \ kips}{3 \ in^2} = +13.33 \ ksi \ \text{(tension)}$$

$$\sigma_{BC} = \frac{P_{BC}}{A_{BC}} = \frac{-10 \ kips}{2 \ in^2} = -5.0 \ ksi \ \text{(compression)}$$

$$\sigma_{CD} = \frac{P_{CD}}{A_{CD}} = \frac{+30 \ kips}{1 \ in^2} = +30.0 \ ksi \ \text{(tension)}$$

Step 4: Determine the elongation/compression of each region

$$\Delta_{AB} = \frac{P_1 L_1}{E_1 A_1} = \frac{(40 \ kips)(48 \ in)}{(30 \times 10^3 \ ksi)(3 \ in^2)} = +0.0213 \ in \ (\text{elongation})$$

$$\Delta_{BC} = \frac{P_2 L_2}{E_2 A_2} = \frac{(-10 \ kips)(36 \ in)}{(30 \times 10^3 \ ksi)(2 \ in^2)} = -0.006 \ in \ (\text{compression})$$

$$\Delta_{CD} = \frac{P_3 L_3}{E_3 A_3} = \frac{(30 \ kips)(24 \ in)}{(30 \times 10^3 \ ksi)(1 \ in^2)} = +0.024 \ in \ (\text{elongation})$$

Hence the total elongation of the rod is

$$\Delta_{AD} = \sum \frac{P_i L_i}{E_i A_i} = \Delta_{AB} + \Delta_{BC} + \Delta_{CD}$$

$$= 0.0213 - 0.006 + 0.024 = +0.0393 \ in \ (\text{elongation})$$

Step 5: Determine the displacements of points A, B, C and D

$u_A = 0$ (this point is fixed)

$u_B = u_A + \Delta_{AB} = 0 + 0.0213 = 0.0213 \ in$

$u_C = u_B + \Delta_{BC} = 0.0213 - 0.006 = 0.0153 \ in$

$u_D = u_C + \Delta_{CD} = 0.0153 + 0.024 = 0.0393 \ in$

This result indicates that although some of the regions are in compression and some in tension, the net movement of each point is in the positive direction. The net movement calculations are sometimes needed in order to satisfy clearance criterion that may exist especially at the ends.

3.3.1 General Expression for Elongation

A general expression for the elongation is now derived wherein all the conditions imposed in the previous section are now removed. Consider a bar having an arbitrary cross sectional variation and subjected to an arbitrary distributed axial loading as shown in Figure 3.3

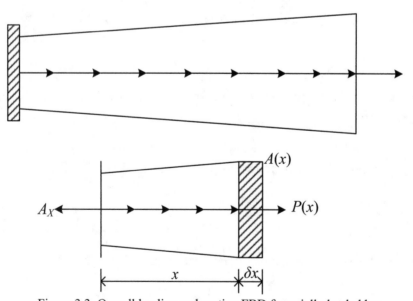

Figure 3.3: Overall loading and section FBD for axially loaded bar

Figure 3.3 also shows an arbitrary section at a distance x from the support A. The axial force $P(x)$ remains constant only over a small length of the section dx. The strain, which is constant only in this infinitesimal section, can be expressed as

Hence, the total elongation of the entire bar can be expressed in an integral form as

$$\Delta = \int \delta x = \int_L \varepsilon(x)dx = \int_L \frac{P(x)}{E(x)A(x)}dx \qquad \text{Eqn (3.2)}$$

In order to illustrate an application of the above Equation (3.2) we determine the total elongation of a bar due to its own self weight, as shown in Figure 3.4. Let the total weight of the bar be W and its total length be L. The self weight can be considered as a *uniformly distributed axial load* of magnitude

$$w = \frac{W}{L}$$

As seen in Figure 3.4, a section is cut at a distance x from the top and an infinitesimal element adjacent to it is considered. The force in this infinitesimal element is constant and is equal to the weight of the portion of the rod below it. Hence the force in this section is given as

$$P(x) = w(L - x)$$

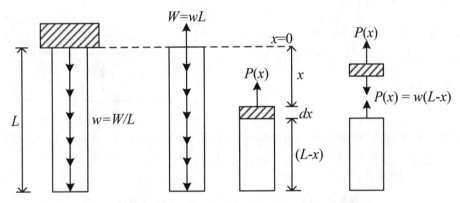

Figure 3.4: Elongation of a bar due to its own self weight

The elongation of the incremental portion is given by the integral equation expression given in Equation 3.2. Hence, the total elongation of the bar is given as

$$\Delta = \int_0^L \frac{P(x)}{EA}dx = \int_0^L \frac{w(L-x)}{EA}dx = \frac{wLx}{EA} - \frac{wx^2}{2EA}\Big|_0^L \qquad \text{Eqn (3.3)}$$

$$\Delta = \frac{wL^2}{EA} - \frac{wL^2}{2EA} = \frac{wL^2}{2EA} = \frac{(wL)L}{2EA} = \frac{WL}{2EA}$$

It can be seen from Equation 3.3 that the total elongation is equal to one half of the elongation of the bar with a force W acting at the end of the bar.

Example 3.3: Elongation and Displacement in a Frame Problem

Problem Statement: The frame shown in the figure is subjected to a force P on member AB. Links CA and DB are made of aluminum and steel respectively.

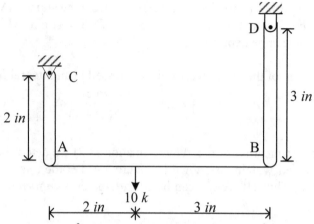

Bar CA: Elastic modulus 10.4 x 10³ ksi, cross section area = 0.25 in²
Bar DB: Elastic modulus 29.0 x 10³ ksi, cross section area = 0.5 in²

Required: Determine the stress in the aluminum and steel bars and the final displacement of the midpoint of the bar AB.

Solution:

Step 1: Determine the reaction at A using the FBD shown below

$$\uparrow \sum F_Y = 0 : R_A + R_B - 10 = 0$$

$$\sum M_A = 0 : (R_B \ kips)(5 \ in) - (10 \ kips)(2 \ in) = 0$$

$$\therefore R_B = +4 = 4 \ k \uparrow$$

$$\therefore R_A = +6k = 6 \ k \uparrow$$

Step 2: Determine the elongation of links CA and DB

$$\Delta_{CA} = \frac{R_A L_{CA}}{E_{CA} A_{CA}} = \frac{(6 \ kips)(12 \ in)}{(10.4 \times 10^3 \ ksi)(0.25 \ in^2)} = 0.0276 \ in$$

$$\Delta_{DB} = \frac{R_B L_{DB}}{E_{DB} A_{DB}} = \frac{(4 \ kips)(24 \ in)}{(29 \times 10^3 \ ksi)(0.5 \ in^2)} = 0.0066 \ in$$

Step 3: From geometry of deformation determine the displacement of the midpoint of member AB.

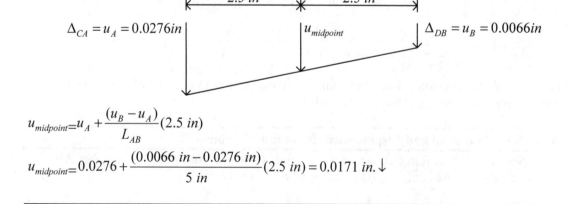

$$u_{midpoint} = u_A + \frac{(u_B - u_A)}{L_{AB}}(2.5 \ in)$$

$$u_{midpoint} = 0.0276 + \frac{(0.0066 \ in - 0.0276 \ in)}{5 \ in}(2.5 \ in) = 0.0171 \ in. \downarrow$$

3.4 Temperature related deformations

The effect of temperature on the behavior of materials is now considered. As long as there is *no change in temperature*, there is no effect on the structure or the material. However, when there is a change in the ambient temperature, it causes deformations or stresses or both. When the ambient temperature increases by an amount ΔT, the thermal energy is conducted through the material, resulting in a *uniform* tensile *strain in all directions* provided that there are no constraints to expansion of the object. In a similar manner, if the temperature reduces, a uniform compressive *strain* occurs in all directions. The effect of the change in temperature on the typical engineering structures is now illustrated.

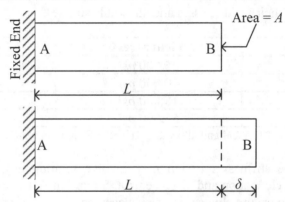

Figure 3.5: Bar subjected to temperature change

Figures 3.5 show a statically determinate homogeneous bar, fixed at end A and free to displace at end B. Let the cross section area of the bar be A, the modulus of elasticity be E and its length L. When the temperature of the surrounding atmosphere rises by ΔT (Centigrade or Fahrenheit), both the diameter and the length of the bar increases. The change in length is now considered. The strain in the longitudinal direction is given as

$$\varepsilon_{th} = \alpha \, \Delta T$$

Where, α is the *coefficient of thermal expansion* of the material and has the units of *strain quantity per degree Fahrenheit or Centigrade*. Hence, the elongation of the bar in the longitudinal direction is given as

$$\delta_{th} = \varepsilon_{th} L = \alpha \Delta T L$$

3.5 Design Considerations in Axially Loaded Members

The two main themes of this chapter on the behavior of axially loaded bars has been
➢ Strength criterion $\Rightarrow$ involving stress computations
➢ Stiffness criterion $\Rightarrow$ involving displacement and elongation computation

Both of the above mentioned criteria are essential in the design of any structure. In what is known as the Allowable Stress Design (ASD) both these criteria play a very important role. The design aspect in any problem could involve the determination of the size of the members for a given set of forces or alternatively it could be to determine the maximum load that can be applied given the geometry of the structure and the allowable strength and stiffness criterion.

Strength Criterion: The stress criterion typically takes the following form

$$\sigma_{actual} \leq \sigma_{allowable}$$

$$\frac{P}{A} \leq \sigma_{allowable}$$

The allowable stress is a quantity determined from experiments and human judgment. For example the allowable stress for Grade 40 steel, with a yield stress of 40 *ksi*, is 20 *ksi*. In most cases the allowable stress is determined by

$$\sigma_{all} = \frac{\sigma_y}{\text{Factor of Safety}}$$

This ensures that the actual stresses in the bar remain within the elastic region. Table 3.1 gives some common materials, their yield stresses and allowable stresses.

Material	Yield Stress	Allowable Stress
Aluminum	35,000 *psi*	21,000 *psi*
Bronze	19,000 *psi*	11,000 *psi*
Red Brass	18,000 *psi*	11,000 *psi*
Stainless Steel	55,000 *psi*	30,000 *psi*

Table 3.1: Yield and allowable stresses of common materials

Stiffness Criterion: The stiffness criterion may involve limiting any of the three stiffness measures namely; strain, elongation and displacement. Strain limits are not frequently employed. However, it is common to ensure elongation or displacement limits. Often, these limits are based on either certain tolerances that are necessary or the physical comfort level of the owner and use of the structure. Mathematically, this criterion may be expressed as follows:

$$\Delta \leq \Delta_{all} \text{ or } u \leq u_{all}$$

Example 3.4: Indirect Problem

Problem Statement: The rod shown in the figure is subjected to force *P*. The cross sectional are of the bar is 2 *in*². The entire bar is made up of steel with Elastic Modulus value of 30 x10³ *ksi*. The maximum allowable stress of the rod is 20 *ksi* and the maximum allowable displacement at B is 0.02 *in*.

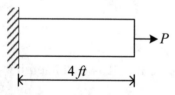

Required: To find the maximum force P that can be applied.

Solution:

Step 1: Find Reaction at A

$$\sum F_x = 0 : A_x + P = 0$$

gives : $A_x = -P = P \leftarrow$

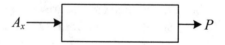

Step 2: Draw a AFD.

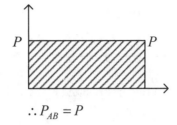

$$\therefore P_{AB} = P$$

Step 3: Find Elongation and Stress.

$$\Delta_{AB} = \frac{PL}{EA} = \frac{(P)(48\ in)}{(30 \times 10^3\ ksi)(2\ in^2)} = 0.0008P\ in$$

$$\sigma = \frac{P}{A} = \frac{P}{2}\ ksi$$

Step 4: Find displacement at B.

$$U_B = U_A + \Delta_{AB} = 0 + 0.0008P = 0.0008P$$

Step 5: Check against constraints

$$U_B = 0.02\ in = 0.0008P \Rightarrow P = \frac{0.02}{0.0008} = 25\ kips$$

$$\sigma_{all} = 20\ ksi = \frac{P}{A} = \frac{P}{2\ in^2} \Rightarrow P = 40\ kips$$

The least of the two values is chosen so that both the stress and displacement are with the limits given.

$$\therefore P = 25\ kips$$

3.6 Statically Indeterminate Problems

In the previous sections, only those problems have been considered where the reactions at the support were fully determined using equations of equilibrium alone. Such problems are called statically determinate problems. In short, if all the reactions cannot be determined from equations of Statics alone, the problems are defined as a statically indeterminate problem. In this section, the problem of determination of all the reactions for a statically indeterminate structure is addressed.

3.6.1 Definition of Indeterminacy

Consider the beam AB shown in Figure 3.6, which is supported at the two ends by pin connections and is loaded as shown. Figure 3.6(b) shows the Free Body Diagram of the beam AB where the supports have been replaced by two reactions at A and B respectively. It can be seen that for this two dimensional body, only three equations of equilibrium are available; namely $\sum F_X = 0$; $\sum F_Y = 0$; $\sum M_A = 0$; but there are four unknown reactions to be determined, namely A_X, A_Y, B_X and B_Y. Hence, this is a problem that is statically indeterminate, *i.e., all reactions cannot be determined from equations of statics alone.*

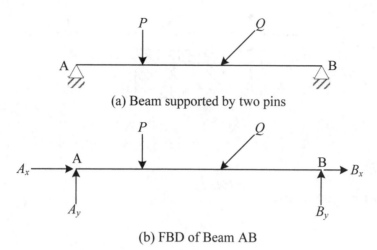

(a) Beam supported by two pins

(b) FBD of Beam AB

Figure 3.6: Indeterminate beam

This problem has a degree of indeterminacy, *DOI=n-r*, where *n* is the number of unknown reactions and *r* is the available equations of statics. In the above example the degree of indeterminacy is one. This implies that one more equation is needed in order to determine all the reactions. Consequently, there are two types of conditions from which the reactions are determined. These are:

a) Equations of equilibrium
b) Condition of (displacement) compatibility

The equations of equilibrium are the standard equations that one has learnt from statics, in which one must ensure that there is no x-motion, y-motion and no rotation, which is applied by using two force equations and one moment equation. The condition of compatibility uses the concept of displacement computations that has been introduced in this chapter and uses some form of existing end displacement condition.

3.6.2 Equilibrium and Compatibility

The concept of equilibrium and compatibility is illustrated in this example. Consider a homogeneous axially loaded (elastic modulus *E*; cross section area *A*) bar as shown in Figure 3.7, which has one axial force *P* acting as shown. The two ends of the bar are fixed.

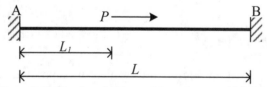

Figure 3.7: Fixed ended bar subjected to an axial force

Figure 3.7 (a) shows the free body diagram of the bar with one reaction each at the ends in the *x*-direction (the other reactions, including the force and moment reaction are not shown as they are zero in this case due to the nature of the external loads). It is seen that there are two unknowns A_X and B_X. However, only one equation of equilibrium is available namely,

$$\sum F_X = 0: \ A_X + P + B_X = 0$$

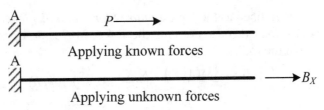

Figure 3.7(a): Free Body Diagram of the bar

The application of the compatibility condition is done as follows. The fixed end B is released so that this end can freely displace. This removal of the fixed end is accompanied by placing an unknown reaction force B_X, as shown in Figure 3.7(b). The bar AB is now subjected to two sets of forces, one set known (here it is P) and other set is the unknown reaction (B_X).

Figure 3.7(b): End B released from the bar

The, now statically determinate, problem can be split up into two parts in order to determine the displacement at B. In the first set only known loads are applied and a known value of displacement (Δ_{B1}) is determined. In the second set, only the unknown reaction force is applied and the displacement at B (Δ_{B2}) is determined in terms of this unknown force. This is shown in Figure 3.7(c)

A

$P \longrightarrow$

Applying known forces

A

$\longrightarrow B_X$

Applying unknown forces

Figure 3.7(c): Application of the known and unknown forces

However, in the original problem the displacement at B is zero. This is the compatibility condition, which can be expressed mathematically as

$$\Delta_{B1} + \Delta_{B2} = 0$$

Applying the displacement values in the compatibility condition expressed above, the unknown reaction can be determined as follows.

$$\frac{PL_1}{EA} + \frac{B_X L}{EA} = 0$$

$$B_X = -\frac{PL_1}{L}$$

From the equilibrium equation the other reaction can now be determined as follows

$$A_X + B_X + P = A_X - \frac{PL_1}{L} = 0$$

$$A_X = P(1 - \frac{L_1}{L})$$

3.6.3   Flexibility and Stiffness

Statically indeterminate problems with a high degree of indeterminacy are often solved using numerical techniques, such as the force or flexibility and displacement or stiffness method. These techniques involve the idealization of the given physical problems as a suitable numerical entity. In the case of structures members are often idealized as elastic springs.

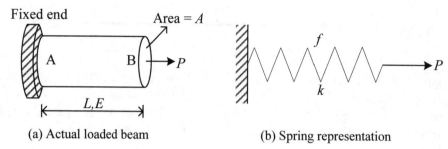

(a) Actual loaded beam   (b) Spring representation

Figure 3.8: Spring representation of an axially loaded bar

In Figure 3.8(a) a rod of cross sectional area A and length L and made of a material with an elastic modulus E is subjected to an axial force P. It can be easily seen that the entire rod is subjected to a uniform axial force P. The deformation of the rod, and also the displacement at B is given as:

$$u_B = \Delta = \frac{PL}{EA}$$

The rod can be idealized as a linear elastic spring, as shown in Fig. 3.8(b). The behavior of an elastic spring can be written as $P = k\Delta$, where P is the force in the spring and k is the spring constant. The definitions of stiffness and flexibility are outlined below.

Stiffness: Stiffness k can be defined as the *force required for a unit displacement.* In other words, stiffness of a linear axially loaded rod represents the force, in *lbs.* or *kips*, required to cause a displacement of one *inch* in the rod.

$$k = \frac{P}{\Delta} = \frac{EA}{L} = \frac{(ksi)(in^2)}{(in)} = \frac{kips}{inch} \quad (kips \text{ per } inch)$$

Flexibility: Flexibility f, which is the inverse of stiffness, represents the displacement caused by a unit force. Alternatively, it represents the displacement in *inches* caused by one *kip* of force.

$$f = \frac{\Delta}{P} = \frac{L}{EA} = \frac{(in)}{(ksi)(in^2)} = \frac{inch}{kip} \quad (inch \text{ per } kip)$$

$$\therefore \Delta = (f)(P).$$

Flexibility (Force) Method

One of methods to solve any statically indeterminate problem is called the flexibility or the force method. This method is ideally suited for hand calculations and problems with a low degree of indeterminacy. This method uses the definition of flexibility as outlined earlier in computing deflections. This technique is especially convenient in computing total displacements when there are linear springs in series. For example, consider a series of springs of flexibility f_1, f_2 and f_3 subjected to a constant force P.

The net displacement at the end of the three springs are given as

$$u_D = f_1 P + f_2 P + f_3 P = (f_1 + f_2 + f_3)P$$

The total displacement can be easily computed as the sum of three flexibilities multiplied by the force acting in the springs.

Example 3.5 gives an example of the approach adopted in the solution of a basic statically indeterminate problem with a degree of indeterminacy of one. A superposition method is used to determine all the unknown reaction values. The major steps can be outlined as follows

1. Draw the FBD of the overall structure and write the axial equilibrium equation. It will be seen that the number of unknown reactions are greater than the number of equations of statics.

2. One of the redundant supports is eliminated and replaced by an unknown reaction force. Thus the structure is treated as a combination of known and unknown forces, subjected to a zero deformation constraint at the redundant support.

Example 3.5: Statically Indeterminate Axially Loaded Bar (Force Method)

Problem Statement: A bar ABC is made of two materials aluminum and steel and has geometric properties as shown in the figure. The bar is fixed at ends A and B.

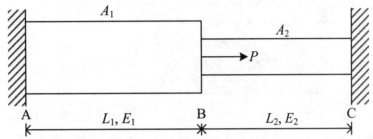

Bar AB: Aluminum: Elastic modulus E_1, cross section area $= A_1$
Bar BC: Steel: Elastic modulus E_2, cross section area $= A_2$

Required: Determine the reactions at A and C?

Solution:

Step 1: Draw the Free Body Diagram of the original structure and write the relevant equation of equilibrium

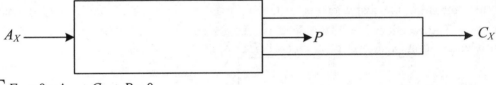

$$\rightarrow \sum F_X = 0: \ A_X + C_X + P = 0$$

It is noted that this is a *statically indeterminate* problem since there is one equation of equilibrium and two unknown reactions (A_X and C_X). Hence the degree of indeterminacy is one.

Step 2: Release end C of the original structure and replace it with an unknown reaction as shown in the above FBD. This structure is now statically determinate.

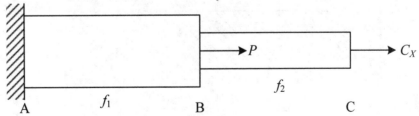

Flexibility of AB $= f_1 = \dfrac{L_1}{E_1 A_1}$

Flexibility of BC $= f_2 = \dfrac{L_2}{E_2 A_2}$

Step 2a: Determine the displacement at C (u_{C1}) on the released structure due to applied loads. The only applied load is P as shown in the figure. The reaction due to this load is also P acting at A in the opposite direction as shown. The resulting axial force diagram is also shown.

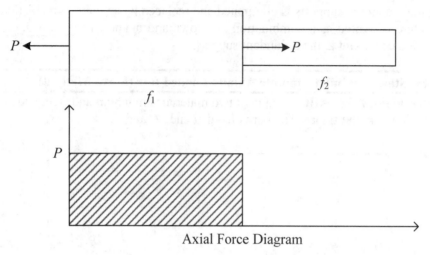

Axial Force Diagram

$$P_{AB} = P$$
$$P_{BC} = 0$$
$$\therefore\ u_{C1} = u_A + \Delta_{AB} + \Delta_{BC}$$
$$u_{C1} = 0 + f_1 P_{AB} + f_2 P_{BC}$$
$$u_{C1} = 0 + f_1 P_{AB} + 0 = f_1 P_{AB}$$

Step 2b: Determine the displacement at C (u_{C2}) on the released structure due to unknown reaction C_X. The reaction due to this load is also C_X acting at A in the opposite direction as shown. The resulting axial force diagram is also shown.

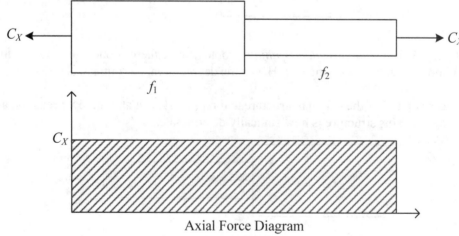

Axial Force Diagram

$$P_{AB} = C_x$$

$$P_{BC} = C_x$$

$$\therefore u_{c2} = u_A + \Delta_{AB} + \Delta_{BC}$$

$$u_{c2} = 0 + f_1 P_{AB} + f_2 P_{BC}$$

$$u_{c2} = 0 + f_1 C_X + f_2 C_X = (f_1 + f_2) C_X$$

Step 3: Apply the compatibility condition. This equation gives the reaction at C. In the original structure end C is fixed. Hence, the total displacement at C is zero.

$$u_{C1} + u_{C2} = 0$$

$$f_1 P + (f_1 + f_2) C_X = 0$$

$$\therefore C_X = -\frac{f_1 P}{(f_1 + f_2)} = \frac{f_1 P}{(f_1 + f_2)} \leftarrow$$

From the overall equilibrium equation from step 1, the other reaction at end A can then be determined.

$$\rightarrow \sum F_X = 0 : \mathrm{A}_X + C_X + P = 0$$

or

$$A_X = -P - C_X = -P - \left(-\frac{f_1}{f_1 + f_2} P \right)$$

$$\therefore \mathrm{A}_X = -\frac{f_2}{f_1 + f_2} P = \frac{f_2}{f_1 + f_2} P \leftarrow$$

Example 3.6: Statically Indeterminate Axially Loaded Bar (Force Method)

Problem Statement: A bar ABCD is made of steel and has geometric properties as shown in the figure. The bar is fixed at ends A and D.

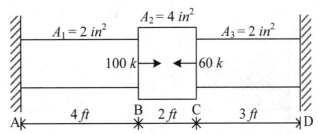

The entire bar is made of steel: Elastic modulus = 30×10^6 *psi*.

Required: Determine the reactions at A and D and the axial stress in each bar. Also, determine the final displacement of each point (draw the axial displacement diagram).

Solution:

Step 1: Draw the Free Body Diagram of the original structure and write the relevant equation of equilibrium

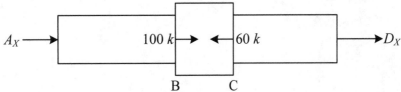

$$\rightarrow \sum F_X = 0: \ A_X + D_X + 100 - 60 = 0$$

There are two unknowns and one equation of equilibrium. Hence, the beam is statically indeterminate with a degree of indeterminacy of 1.

Step 2: Release end D of the original structure and replace it with an unknown reaction as shown in the above FBD. This structure is now statically determinate.

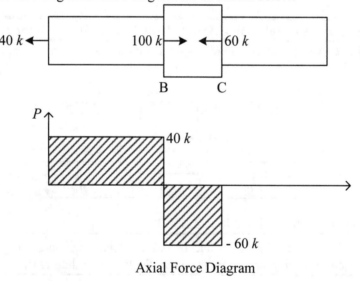

$$f_{AB} = \left(\frac{L}{EA}\right)_{AB} = \left(\frac{4 \times 12 \ in}{30 \times 10^6 \ psi \times 2 \ in^2}\right) = 8 \times 10^{-7} \ in./lb.$$

$$f_{BC} = \left(\frac{L}{EA}\right)_{BC} = \left(\frac{2 \times 12 \ in}{30 \times 10^6 \ psi \times 4 \ in^2}\right) = 2 \times 10^{-7} \ in./lb$$

$$f_{CD} = \left(\frac{L}{EA}\right)_{CD} = \left(\frac{3 \times 12 \ in}{30 \times 10^6 \ psi \times 2 \ in^2}\right) = 6 \times 10^{-7} \ in./lb.$$

Step 2a: Determine the displacement at D (u_{D1}) on the released structure due to applied loads. The reaction and the resulting axial force diagram are as shown below.

Axial Force Diagram

$P_{AB} = +40 \ k$

$P_{BC} = -60 \ k$

$P_{CD} = 0 \ k$

$\therefore \ u_{D1} = u_A + \Delta_{AB} + \Delta_{BC} + \Delta_{BC}$

$u_{D1} = 0 + f_{AB}P_{AB} + f_{BC}P_{BC} + f_{CD}P_{CD}$

$u_{D1} = 0 + (8 \times 10^{-7} \ in./lb)(40,000 \ lbs.) + (2 \times 10^{-7} \ in./lb)(-60,000 \ lbs.) + 0$

$u_{D1} = 0 + 0.032 - 0.012 = 0.02 \ in.$

Step 2b: Determine the displacement at C (u_{C2}) on the released structure due to unknown reaction C_X. The reaction due to this load is also C_X acting at A in the opposite direction as shown. The resulting axial force diagram is also shown.

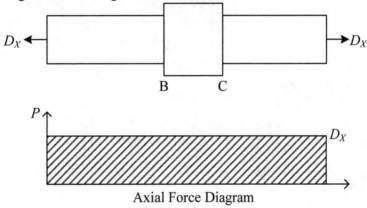

Axial Force Diagram

$P_{AB} = D_X$

$P_{BC} = D_X$

$P_{CD} = D_X$

$\therefore \ u_{D2} = u_A + \Delta_{AB} + \Delta_{BC} + \Delta_{CD}$

$u_{D2} = 0 + f_{AB}P_{AB} + f_{BC}P_{BC} + f_{CD}P_{CD}$

$u_{D2} = (16 \times 10^{-7})D_X \ in.$

Step 3: Apply the compatibility condition. The total displacement at D is zero in the original structure. This gives the second equation (the first was the equilibrium equation).

$u_{D1} + u_{D2} = 0$

$0.02 + 16 \times 10^{-7} D_X = 0$

$D_X = -12,500 \ lbs. = 12,500 \ lbs. \leftarrow$

From the overall equilibrium equation from step 1, the other reaction at A can then be determined.

$\rightarrow \sum F_X = 0: \ A_X + D_X + 40,000 = 0$

or

$A_X = -40,000 - D_X = -40,000 - (-12,500)$

$\therefore \ A_X = -27,500 = 27,500 \ lbs. \leftarrow$

Step 4: Draw the Final Axial Force Diagram and determine the axial stress in each bar from this diagram.

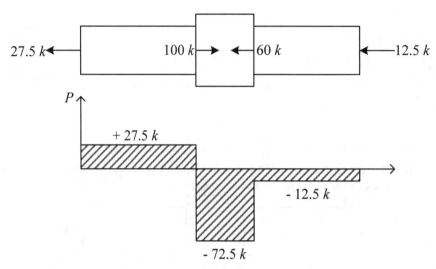

$$P_{AB} = +27.5 \ k; \ \sigma_{AB} = \frac{P_{AB}}{A} = \frac{+27.5 \ k}{2 \ in^2} = +13.75 \ ksi (\text{tension})$$

$$P_{BC} = -72.5 \ k; \ \sigma_{BC} = \frac{P_{BC}}{A} = \frac{-72.5 \ k}{4 \ in^2} = -18.125 \ ksi (\text{compression})$$

$$P_{CD} = -12.5 \ k; \ \sigma_{CD} = \frac{P_{CD}}{A} = \frac{-12.5 \ k}{2 \ in^2} = -6.25 \ ksi (\text{compression})$$

Step 5: Determine the axial displacement at each point. The elongations (Δ) for each region is first determined. The displacement at every point is then found from the elongation of that region added to the displacement of the first point of the region. The details of the calculations are shown below.

$$\Delta_{AB} = f_{AB} P_{AB} = (8 \times 10^{-7} \ in./lb)(27,500 \ lbs.) = 0.022 \ in.$$

$$\Delta_{BC} = f_{BC} P_{BC} = (2 \times 10^{-7} \ in./lb)(-72,500 \ lbs.) = -0.0145 \ in$$

$$\Delta_{CD} = f_{CD} P_{CD} = (6 \times 10^{-7} \ in./lb)(-12,500 \ lbs.) = -0.0075 \ in$$

$$\therefore$$

$$u_A = 0$$

$$u_B = u_A + \Delta_{AB} = 0.022 \ in.$$

$$u_C = u_B + \Delta_{BC} = 0.022 - 0.0145 = 0.0075 \ in.$$

$$u_D = u_C + \Delta_{CD} = 0.0075 - 0.0075 = 0$$

As verification, it can be seen that the total displacements at A and D are zero.

Example 3.7: Statically Indeterminate Axial Force Problem

Problem Statement: A hollow steel cylinder of height of 8 *inch* has an inside diameter of 8 *inch* and is ¼ *inch* thick. The steel cylinder is filled with concrete, which has a clearance of 0.001 *inch* at the top, as shown in the figure. The entire assembly is compressed by a rigid plate with an axial force of 150 *kips*. The elastic modulus of steel is 30×10^6 *psi*, while that of concrete is 2×10^6 *psi*.

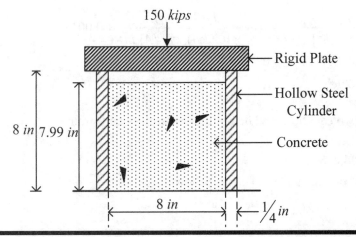

Required: Determine the compressive stress in each material and the strain in concrete and steel portions.

Solution:

Step 1: Draw the Free Body Diagram of the original structure and write the relevant equation of equilibrium

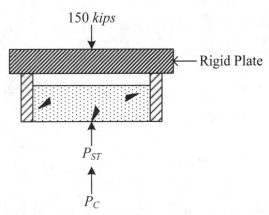

$$\uparrow \sum F_y = 0: \; P_C + P_{ST} - 150 \, k = 0$$

There are two unknowns and one equation of equilibrium. Although the forces in the steel cylinder act at along the peripheral area, the net effect can be represented as a single force at the centroid of the hollow cylinder, which is at the center of the cylinder.

Step 2: *Compatibility Condition*: A displacement-based equation (compatibility of deformations) is written based on the expected deformation pattern. In this case, it is expected that since the plate is rigid, once the plate comes in contact with the concrete core both the cylinder and concrete core deform together. Mathematically, this can be written as follows

$$\Delta_C = \Delta_{ST} + 0.001 \; in.$$

As the concrete and steel parts are undergoing purely axial deformation the compatibility equation can be expanded as follows

$$\frac{P_{ST}L_{ST}}{E_{ST}A_{ST}} = \frac{P_C L_C}{E_C A_C} + 0.001$$

$$\frac{P_{ST}(8\ in)}{(30\times10^3\ ksi)(\pi[8.5^2 - 8^2]/4)\ in^2} = \frac{P_c(7.99\ in)}{(2\times10^3\ ksi)(\pi8^2/4)\ in^2} + 0.001$$

$$0.0000411P_{ST} = 0.0000795P_c + 0.001$$

$$P_{ST} = 1.931P_c + 24.298$$

Step 3: Solve the two equations and determine the stresses and strain

$$P_C + P_{ST} = 150\ k$$

$$-1.931P_C + P_{ST} = 24.298$$

The final forces in concrete and steel are as follows

$$P_{ST} = 107.11\ kips$$

$$P_C = 42.887\ kips$$

The stresses can now be calculated from the forces as

$$\sigma_{ST} = \frac{P_{ST}}{A_{ST}} = \frac{107.11\ k}{6.47\ in^2} = 16.55\ ksi$$

$$\sigma_C = \frac{P_C}{A_C} = \frac{42.887\ k}{50.26\ in^2} = 0.853\ ksi$$

The final deformation and strains are then calculated as

$$\Delta_C = \frac{P_C L_C}{E_C A_C} = \frac{(42.887\ k)(7.99\ in)}{(2\times10^3\ ksi)(50.26\ in^2)} = 0.0034\ in$$

$$\Delta_{ST} = \Delta_C + 0.001 = 0.0044\ in$$

$$\varepsilon_{ST} = \frac{\Delta_{ST}}{L_{ST}} = \frac{0.0044}{8\ in.} = 5.5\times10^{-4}\ in./in.$$

$$\varepsilon_C = \frac{\Delta_C}{L_C} = \frac{0.0034\ in}{7.99\ in.} = 4.26\times10^{-4}\ in./in.$$

Note: As the modulus of steel is fifteen times that of concrete it should be noted that in order to sustain deformations of similar magnitude (0.0034 *inch* in concrete and 0.0044 *inch* in steel) the stresses in concrete and steel are very different (16.53 *ksi* in steel and 0.853 *ksi* in concrete – almost 1/15th of that of steel).

3.6.4 Statically Indeterminate Thermal Problems

We now consider a structure with redundant supports subjected to a thermal change. It was seen in section 3.4 that a statically determinate rod subjected to a temperature change is free to elongate and consequently experiences stress free deformation. However, if the same structure is constrained to displace at both ends as shown in Figure 3.9(a), it becomes a statically indeterminate problem.

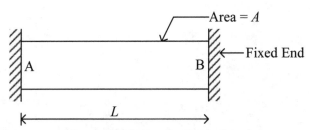

Figure 3.9(a): Bar fixed at both ends

If the bar is now subjected to a constant change in temperature of ΔT, it can be seen that bar will try to expand. However, since both the ends are constrained, it is prevented from doing so and will thus experience a compressive stress due to the temperature change. Figure 3.9(b) shows the schematic for the computation of this compressive stress by the method of superposition.

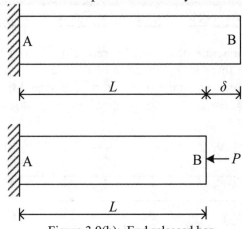

Figure 3.9(b): End released bar

End B in Figure 3.9(b) is released and the known change in temperature is now applied to bar. The free end displacement can be now computed, as shown in section 3.4, as follows:

$$\delta = (\alpha)(\Delta T)(L)$$

Since, the displacement of the end B in the original structure is zero, an imaginary force P can bring the thermal displacement at B back to zero, such that

$$P = \frac{\delta}{f} = \frac{\delta EA}{L} = \frac{(\alpha \Delta T L)(EA)}{(L)} = (\alpha \Delta T)(EA)$$

This force is now compressive in nature and thus the compressive stress induced in the bar due to a thermal change can be expressed as

$$\sigma = \frac{P}{A} = \frac{(\alpha \Delta T)(EA)}{A} = (\alpha \Delta T)E$$

Example 3.8: Statically Indeterminate Frame Problem

Problem Statement: A statically indeterminate frame is subjected to forces and moments as shown. Determine the reactions and the force in the rods. The links at B and D are made of steel.

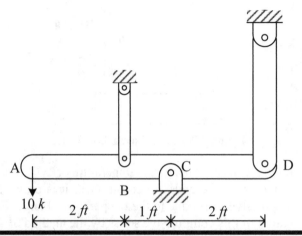

Required: Determine the reaction at the pin support at C and the stresses in rods at B and D?

Solution:

Step 1: Draw the free body diagram of the bar by replacing the pin by two unknown reactions and the rods by one unknown force in the direction of the rods. It can be seen that the forces are axial forces and could be tensile or compressive (it should be noted that the difference between a rod and a cable is that a rod can carry both compressive and tensile forces while a cable can resists only tensile forces.

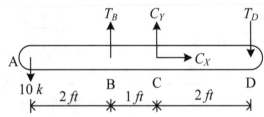

$$\rightarrow \sum F_X = 0: \ C_X = 0$$

$$\uparrow \sum F_y = 0: \ -10\,k + T_B + C_y - T_D = 0$$

$$\sum M_C = 0: \ +(10\,k)(3\,ft) - T_B(1\,ft) - T_D(2\,ft) = 0$$

There are three equations from statics (static equilibrium) and four unknowns (C_X, C_Y, T_B, T_D). Also, it is assumed that the force in the rod B is tensile (shown as arrow pointing away from B) and the force in the rod at D is compressive (force pointing towards D).

Step 2: A displacement compatibility condition is written based on an expected deformation pattern of the structure. For this, we assume that the rod ABCD is rigid under the action of the forces (*i.e.* the rod remains straight after deformation). This assumption is true if forces and consequently the deformations are small. The displaced configuration of the structure and the geometric compatibility equation are shown below.

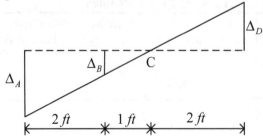

$$\frac{\Delta_B}{1\,ft} = \frac{\Delta_D}{2\,ft}$$

$$\Delta_D = 2\Delta_B$$

Since the rods are being axially deformed the compatibility equation can be written as follows

$$\frac{T_B L_B}{E_B A_B} = 2\left(\frac{T_D L_D}{E_D A_D}\right)$$

$$\frac{T_B 8\,in}{E_B(0.25\,in^2)} = 2\left(\frac{T_D 16\,in}{E_D(0.2\,in^2)}\right)$$

$$T_B = 5T_D$$

Step 3: Solve the unknowns by combining the equilibrium equations with the relationship between the forces in the two rods, derived from the compatibility condition.

$$C_X = 0$$

$$\uparrow \sum F_y = 0: \ -10\,k + 5T_D + C_y - T_D = 0$$

$$\sum M_C = 0: \ +(10\,k)(3\,ft) - 5T_D(1\,ft) - T_D(2\,ft) = 0$$

$$\therefore 7T_D = 30$$

$$\therefore T_D = 4.28\,k \ \text{(compression)}$$

$$T_B = 5(4.28\,k) = 21.4\,k \ \text{(tension)}$$

$$C_Y = 10\,k - 21.4\,k + 4.28\,k = -7.12\,k = 7.12\,k \downarrow$$

Hence, the stresses in the rods are given as

$$\sigma_B = \frac{T_B}{A_B} = \frac{21.4\,k}{0.25\,in^2} = 85.6\,ksi\,\text{(tension)}$$

$$\sigma_D = \frac{T_D}{A_B} = \frac{4.28\,k}{0.20\,in^2} = 21.4\,ksi\,\text{(compression)}$$

Example 3.9: Design aspects

Problem Statement: A bar ABC is made of steel (E =29,000 ksi) with geometric properties as shown in the figure and is subjected to two forces. The allowable axial stress should not exceed 30 ksi and the displacement at C should not be greater than 0.02 in. Determine the minimum design diameters of the two bars if the area of the smaller bar should be half that of the bigger bar.

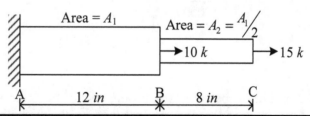

Required: Determine the diameters of the two bars?

Solution:

Step 1: Draw the Free Body Diagram of the original structure and write the relevant equation of equilibrium

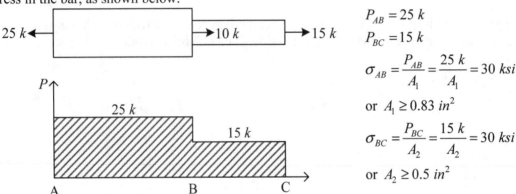

$$\rightarrow \sum F_X = 0:\ A_X + 10 + 15 = 0$$

or $A_X = -25\ k = 25\ k \leftarrow$

Step 2: *Strength Design:* This step is to ensure that the strength of the bar is never exceeded, in terms of the actual stresses being always less than the allowable stresses. This is done by drawing the axial force diagram and determining the axial force and axial stress in each portion. In order to find the required areas the axial stress in each portion of the bar is equated to the allowable stress in the bar, as shown below.

$P_{AB} = 25\ k$

$P_{BC} = 15\ k$

$$\sigma_{AB} = \frac{P_{AB}}{A_1} = \frac{25\ k}{A_1} = 30\ ksi$$

or $A_1 \geq 0.83\ in^2$

$$\sigma_{BC} = \frac{P_{BC}}{A_2} = \frac{15\ k}{A_2} = 30\ ksi$$

or $A_2 \geq 0.5\ in^2$

Since it is required that the area $A_2 = A_1/2$, it follows that the area A_2 is the greater of $0.5 in^2$ and $A_1/2 = 0.83/2 = 0.415\ in^2$. Hence, $A_2 = 0.5\ in^2$ and $A_1 = 1.0\ in^2$

Step 3: *Stiffness Design:* This step ensures that the displacements and elongations in the bar are within the required limits. For this problem, the stiffness condition specified is that the displacement at the end of the bar should be less than $0.02\ in$. Hence, the displacement at the end of the bar is now determined in terms of the unknown areas.

$$u_C = u_A + \Delta_{AB} + \Delta_{BC}$$

$$0.02\ in = 0 + \left(\frac{PL}{EA}\right)_{AB} + \left(\frac{PL}{EA}\right)_{BC}$$

$$0.02\ in = 0 + \left(\frac{(25\ k)(12\ in)}{(29,000\ ksi)(A_1)}\right) + \left(\frac{(15\ k)(8\ in)}{(29,000\ ksi)(A_1/2)}\right)$$

gives

$$A_1 \geq 0.931\ in^2$$

Step 4: Determine the design diameters based on the results from the strength and stiffness criteria. In this case it can be seen that the area required by the strength criterion ($1.0\ in^2$) is greater than that required by the stiffness criterion ($0.931\ in^2$). Hence, the design diameters are given as follows

Strength Criterion:

$$A_1 = 1.0 \ in^2 = \frac{\pi d_1^2}{4} \Rightarrow d_1 \geq 1.12 \ in.$$

$$A_2 = 0.5 \ in^2 = \frac{\pi d_2^2}{4} \Rightarrow d_2 \geq 0.798 \ in$$

Stiffness Criterion:

$$A_1 = 0.931 \ in^2 = \frac{\pi d_1^2}{4} \Rightarrow d_1 \geq 1.09 \ in$$

$$A_2 = 0.4655 \ in^2 = \frac{\pi d_2^2}{4} \Rightarrow d_2 \geq 0.77 \ in$$

Here strength criterion governs.

Example 3.10: Statically Indeterminate Temperature Problem

Problem Statement: A solid rod made of brass is connected to a hollow rod made of aluminum. The inner diameter of the hollow rod is $1 in$ and it is 0.25 in thick, while the solid rod is 1 in in diameter. If the ambient temperature increases by $30^\circ F$, determine the stresses in the two bars.

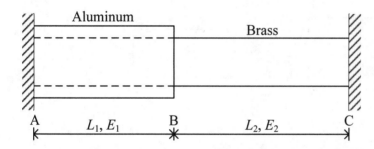

Data:

$E_1 = 10400 \ ksi$

$E_2 = 15000 \ ksi$

$L_1 = 12 \ in$

$L_2 = 15 \ in$

$\alpha_1 = \alpha_{Al} = 13.3 \times 10^{-6} \ /^\circ F$

$\alpha_2 = \alpha_{Br} = 11.6 \times 10^{-6} \ /^\circ F$

Required: Determine the stresses in the aluminum and brass bars.

Solution:

Step 1: Draw the Free Body Diagram of the original structure and write the relevant equation of equilibrium

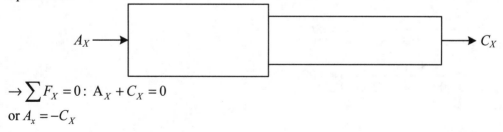

$$\rightarrow \sum F_X = 0 : \ A_X + C_X = 0$$

or $A_x = -C_X$

Step 2: Release one of the redundant end free, end C here, and determine the displacement at C due to the temperature increase.

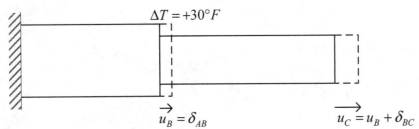

$$\delta_B = \Delta_{AB} = \alpha_1 \Delta T L_1$$
$$= (13.3 \times 10^{-6} \ /^\circ F)(30 \ ^\circ F)(12 \ in)$$
$$= 0.004788 \ in$$
$$\delta_C = \delta_B + \Delta_{BC} = \delta_B + \alpha_2 \Delta T L_2$$
$$= \delta_B + (11.6 \times 10^{-6} \ /^\circ F)(30 \ ^\circ F)(15 \ in)$$
$$= 0.00478 + 0.00522 = 0.01 \ in$$

Step 3: Determine the reaction force at C required to displace the end C back to its original position. This is done by determining the displacement caused at end C by the reaction at C and equating it to 0.01 in. This is the compatibility condition.

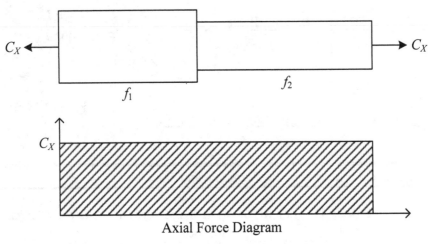

Axial Force Diagram

$$f_1 = \left(\frac{L}{EA} \right)_1 = \left(\frac{12 \ in}{10,400 \ ksi \times 0.982 \ in^2} \right) = 0.00117 \ in/k$$

$$f_2 = \left(\frac{L}{EA} \right)_2 = \left(\frac{15 \ in}{15,000 \ ksi \times 0.785 \ in^2} \right) = 0.00127 \ in/k$$

$$P_{AB} = P_{BC} = C_X$$
$$u_C = u_A + \Delta_{AB} + \Delta_{BC}$$
$$= 0 + f_1 C_X + f_2 C_X = 0.00244 C_X \rightarrow$$

Applying the compatibility condition the reaction force at C is found as follows

$$u_C = 0 = 0.01 + 0.00244 C_X$$

$$\therefore C_X = \frac{-0.01}{0.00244}$$

$$\therefore C_X = -4.1 \ k = 4.1 \ k \leftarrow$$

Step 4: Since the only forces acting on the bars are at the supports, 4.1 k acting inwards, the entire bar is subjected to a uniform compressive force of 4.1 k in compression. The stresses in the bars are then determined as follows.

$$\sigma_{AB} = \frac{P_{AB}}{A_1} \Rightarrow \frac{-4.1\ k}{0.982\ in^2} = -4.17\ ksi$$

$$\sigma_{BC} = \frac{P_{BC}}{A_2} \Rightarrow \frac{-4.1\ k}{0.785\ in^2} = -5.22\ ksi$$

Hence, the forces in the aluminum and brass bars are the same but the stresses are 4.17 ksi and 5.22 ksi in compression respectively.

3.7   Summary

In chapter 3 the concept of axial force in a member was introduced and studied. The keywords introduced in this chapter are as follows.

1. **Axial Force Diagram:** The plot of internal forces in the bar on y-axis and x-axis representing the location where the force is acting on the bar is called the Axial Force Diagram.

2. **Section FBD:** When the free body diagram of the entire body is separated or splitted into two independent objects, it results in two section FBDs, namely; Left section FBD and Right section FBD.

3. **Axial elongation:** The elongation a bar or any body undergoes when it is loaded along its axial direction is called Axial Elongation.

$$\delta = \frac{PL}{AE}$$

4. **Strength criterion:** It is the design criterion which involves stress computations. In this criterion, the actual stress in the body is kept less than the allowable stress of that body.

$$\sigma_{actual} \leq \sigma_{allowable}$$

where $\sigma_{allowable}$ is the yield stress divided by factor of safety.

5. **Stiffness criterion:** This is the design criterion which involves limiting any of the three stiffness measures namely; strain, elongation and displacement. Mathematically, this can be written as

$$\Delta \leq \Delta_{allowable} \text{ or } U \leq U_{allowable}$$

6. **Compatibility condition:** The additional physical condition which provides the additional equation necessary to solve statically indeterminate problems. This condition usually involves some form of displacement compatibility criterion.

7. **Stiffness:** Force required to cause a unit displacement. It is the measure of the resistance to deform of an object.

$$k = \frac{P}{\Delta} = \frac{EA}{L} = \frac{kips}{inch}$$

8. **Flexibility:** Displacement caused by a unit force. It is the measure of deformation under a force.

$$f = \frac{\Delta}{P} = \frac{L}{EA} = \frac{inch}{kip}$$

$$\therefore \Delta = (f)(P).$$

3.8 Problems

Use the following figures for problems 3.1 & 3.2

i.

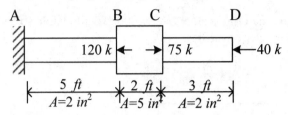

ii.

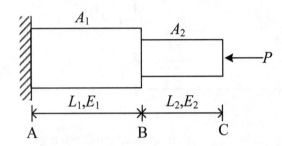

iii.

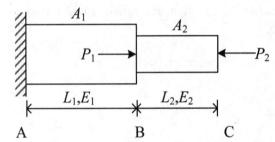

iv.

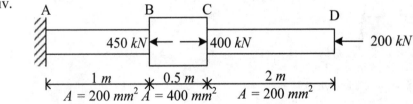

v.

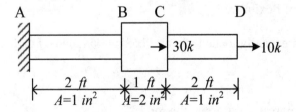

3.1 For each of the figures shown above
   a. Draw the axial force diagram
   b. Determine the maximum axial force in tension and compression
   c. Determine the maximum compressive and tensile stresses in each case

3.2 If the material in the figures shown above is made of steel (E=29,000 ksi / 210 GPa) determine
   a. Displacement at the free end

b. Maximum elongation and tensile strain in the bars
c. Maximum tensile and compressive strain in the bars
d. Draw the axial displacement diagram

3.3 In the figure shown below, given that the material is steel (E=29,000 *ksi*, allowable stress σ_{all}=24 *ksi*), determine the minimum diameter of the bar.

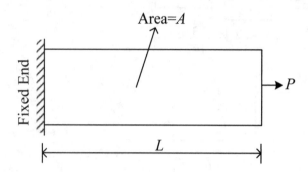

3.4 If the bar in problem 3 is also subjected to the stiffness criterion in which the displacement at the free end is limited to 0.01 *in.*, determine the bar diameter which would satisfy both the strength and stiffness criterion

3.5 Determine the axial stiffness and flexibility of the rod shown below

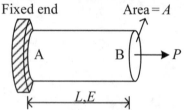 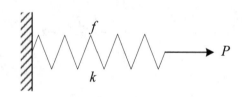

a. E=29,000 *ksi* , A= 1 *in²*, L=3 *ft.*
b. E=29,000 *ksi*, A = 2 *in²*, L=6 *ft.*
c. E= 210 *GPa*, A= 100 *mm²*, L=2 *m.*
d. E= 210 *GPa*, A=200 *mm²*, L=4m.

3.6 Redo problem 3.2 using the concepts of flexibility.

3.7 The rods shown in the figures below are axially loaded and are fixed at both ends. For each of the figures shown,
a. Determine the reactions
b. Draw the axial force diagram
c. Find the maximum tensile and compressive stress in the rod

i.

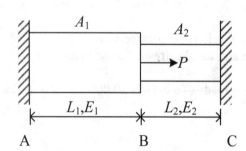

ii.

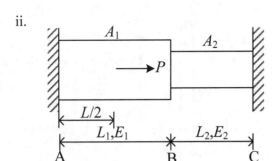

3.8 In the following figure, if the temperature change in the surrounding is $+20^oF$, determine the stress in the bars. (E=29,000 *ksi*, A=1 in^2, L=3 *ft.*, δ=0.01 *in*).

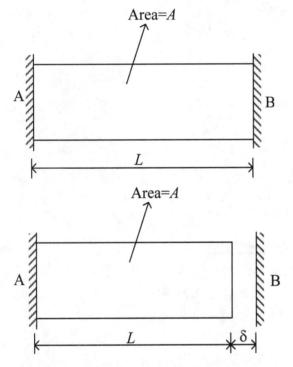

3.9 In problem 7, if the bar experiences a temperature drop of 10^oF, in addition to the forces, determine the maximum tensile and compressive stress in the bar.

3.10 In the frames loaded as shown below,
    a. Determine the forces in the link rods
    b. Determine the deflections at the
        i) point of attachment of the link to the rod and
        ii) load locations.

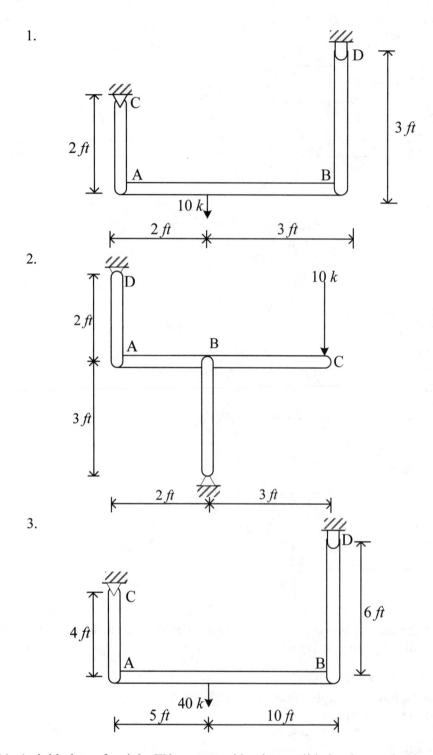

1.

2.

3.

3.11 A rigid plate of weight W is supported by three solid circular steel columns of diameter 250 *mm* each. The outer two columns are 2 *m* long while the inner column is 0.25 *mm* short. If E_{st}=210 *GPa* and the allowable stress in steel is 250 *MPa*, determine
a) The safe load W that can be supported
b) The safe load that can be supported if the inner column did not exist

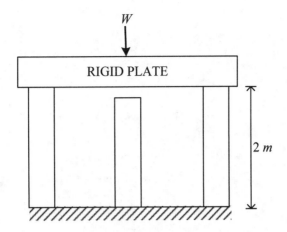

3.12 A composite section made of a concrete column of size 12 *in* x 12 *in* has 4 steel reinforcing bars of 1 *inch* diameter as shown. If E_c = 3,600 *ksi* and E_{st} = 29,000 *ksi*, determine the maximum axial load that the section can carry.

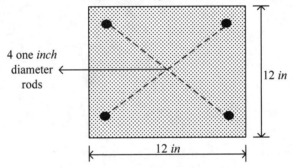

3.13 A rigid bar ABCD is supported by two steel rods of one inch diameter at A and B as shown. If the maximum stress in the rods is limited to 24 *ksi*, determine
   a) Maximum P that can be supported
   b) For the calculated maximum P load, find the deflection of the rigid bar at D.

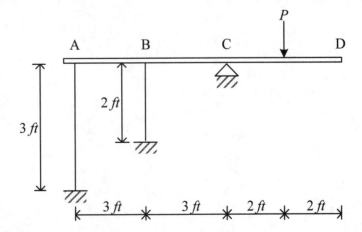

3.14 For the frame in problem 3.13, if *P*=10 *K* determine
   a) Stress in the bar
   b) Deflection at D

NOTES:

Chapter 4

Multi-Axial Loading

Goal: The learning objectives of this chapter are as follows:

1. Describing examples of multi-axial loading
2. Describing a general state of stress
3. Deriving generalized Hooke's Law equation
4. Describe the four elastic constants
5. Derive inter-relationships between the four elastic constants

4   Multi-Axial Loading

4.1   Introduction

The concept of stress at a point and its diagrammatic representation on an element for a uniaxial loading was illustrated in chapter 2. It was seen that for the uniaxial case, only one normal stress, acting in the axial/longitudinal direction exists while strains develop in both the longitudinal and lateral directions due to the Poisson's effect. In this chapter, we extend this concept to a generalized loading situation, in which any given element could be subjected to a set of up to six independent stresses (three normal and three shear stresses).

Consider a very common example shown in Figure 4.1, which shows a thin cylindrical pressure vessel storing a liquid inside it. In this case, the closed ends are subjected to a hydrostatic internal pressure, which acts outwards and consequently subjects the cylindrical portion to tensile forces. The hydrostatic pressure of the fluid on the walls of the cylinder, acting in the radial direction, results in the cylinder being subjected to hoop stresses. The stresses in the thickness direction itself is negligible, as this is a thin plate and so it is in a state of plane stress. Hence, any element on the cylindrical portion is subjected to a multi-axial state of stress, as shown in Figure 4.1.

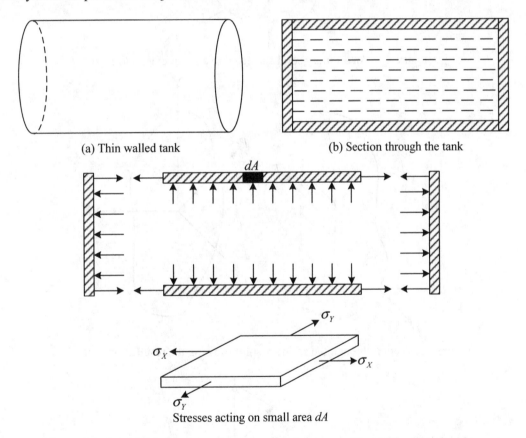

(a) Thin walled tank   (b) Section through the tank

Stresses acting on small area *dA*

Figure 4.1: A cylindrical pressure vessel, subjected to a multi-axial loading situation

4.2   Definition of general state of stress

Figure 4.2 shows a solid object subjected to a set of arbitrary external forces. In order to determine the stress at any internal point A, we cut the body such that the section passes through point A and cuts the body into two independent parts, as shown in Figure 4.3. In general, the resultant internal force in the section (left or right) is equal and opposite to the resultant of the external forces acting on that section (Figure 4.3). This internal force can be resolved into a force normal and parallel to the section (Figure 4.3). The force that is normal to the section causes the normal stress, while the stress parallel to the section causes shearing stresses. The force parallel to the section can be further resolved in two perpendicular forces on the plane of the section such that their directions are along the coordinate axis directions, as shown in Figure 4.4. Consequently, there are two independent shear and one normal stress acting on the plane at point A.

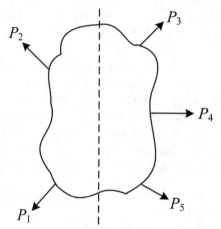

Figure 4.2: An arbitrary solid subjected to a set of external forces

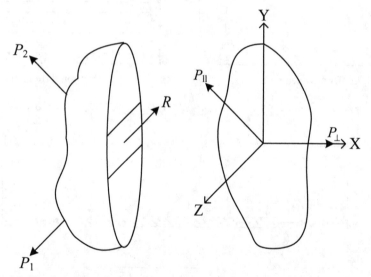

Figure 4.3: Section through the arbitrary solid showing the resultant internal force

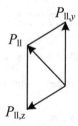

Figure 4.4: Resolving the force parallel to the section into two orthogonal shear stresses

4.3   Stresses in solids subjected to multi-axial normal stresses

A representative three-dimensional infinitesimal cube, at a point on the solid, represents the element in which all the stresses acting on it are described The notations and the sign-convention used to describe the state of stress are now illustrated. Figure 4.5 shows the stresses on three faces of the cube, which represents the element.

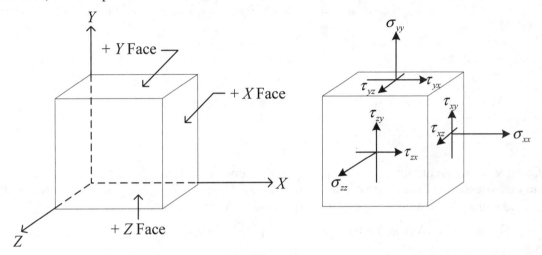

Figure 4.5: Positive stresses shown on the three faces of the cubic element

Definitions:
1. **Positive face:** A positive face is defined as the face/area of the cube that is perpendicular to the positive axis. The positive x, y and z faces are as shown Figure 4.5.
2. **Negative face:** Similarly, the faces that are perpendicular to the negative axes are called negative faces. It is the face perpendicularly opposite to the positive face.
3. **Stress tensor notation:** The stresses are of two types, namely the normal stress denoted by σ and the shear stress denoted by τ. The stress values have two subscripts with the first subscript denoting the face on which the stress acts and the second subscript denoting the direction in which it acts- $\tau_{face,direction}$. The following list describes the six independent stress types that exist.
    a. σ_{xx} - normal stress acting on the positive x face & positive x-direction.
    b. σ_{yy} - normal stress acting on the positive y face & positive y-direction
    c. σ_{zz} - normal stress acting on the positive z face & positive z-direction
    d. τ_{xy} - shear stress acting on the positive x face & positive y-direction
    e. τ_{xz} - shear stress acting on the positive x face & positive z-direction
    f. τ_{yz} - shear stress acting on the positive y face & positive z-direction
4. **Positive stresses:** Stresses acting as described in item 3 are considered positive stresses. Also, the corresponding stresses acting on the negative face and negative directions are also considered as positive.

From Figure 4.5 it can be seen that there are 9 stresses, namely $\sigma_x, \sigma_y, \sigma_z, \tau_{xy}, \tau_{yx}, \tau_{xz}, \tau_{zx}, \tau_{yz}, \tau_{zy}$. However, the internal element must satisfy equilibrium conditions, of force and moment equilibrium.

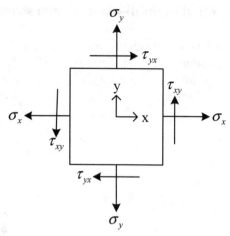

Figure 4.6: Two-dimensional representation of the cube.

Consider a two-dimensional representation of the cube as shown in Figure 4.6, which shows the normal stresses and shear stresses acting in the x-y plane on the x and y faces. We specifically consider the shear stresses τ_{xy} and τ_{yx}. The stresses can be converted to forces (F_{xy}, F_{yx}) by multiplying by the cross-sectional area of the respective faces as follows

$$F_{xy} = \tau_{xy}(dxdz)$$
$$F_{yx} = \tau_{yx}(dydz)$$

Consider the moment equilibrium of the section. Only the shear stresses cause a moment.

$$\sum M_z = 0:$$
$$F_{xy}(dx) - F_{yx}(dy) = 0$$
$$(\tau_{xy}dxdz)dy - (\tau_{yx}dydz)dx = 0$$

or

$$\tau_{xy} = \tau_{yx}$$

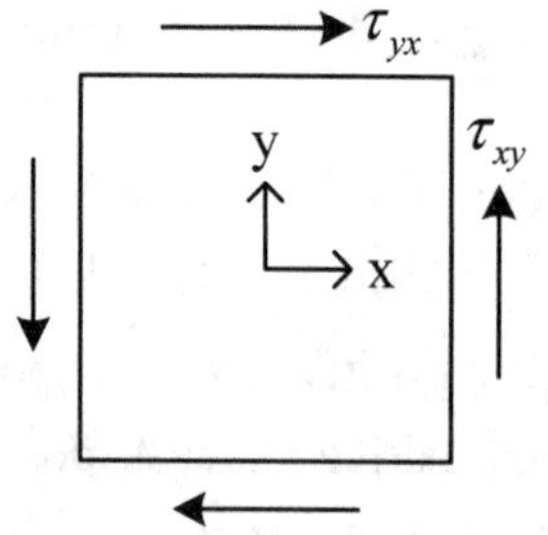

Figure 4.7: Shear Stresses in a cube.

So now we can see that out of the 9 stresses acting on the cube, just 6 are independent stresses. They are $\sigma_{xx}, \sigma_{yy}, \sigma_{zz}, \tau_{xy}, \tau_{yz}$ and τ_{zx}.

4.3.1 Superposition Principle

For the case of multi-axial loading, in which an element behaving elastically is subjected to stresses in all the three directions, the stress-strain relations are now derived. For most materials under elastic behavior and undergoing small deformations, the principle of superposition can be used to determine the stress-strain relations.

Consider a rectangular element, made of a material with an elastic modulus of E and having a Poisson's ratio v, subjected to stresses in three directions as shown in Figure 4.8. We would like to determine the axial strains in the three directions due to these stresses. In order to determine this, consider the element subjected to a uniaxial stress in each direction individually as shown in Figure 4.9. For the case of uniaxial stress, the equations derived in chapter 2 for an elastic material can be used and applied as shown below. For each case two effects are used, namely the axial effect which gives the strain in the axial direction and the Poisson's effect which gives the magnitudes of the other two lateral strain in terms of the strain in the axial direction.

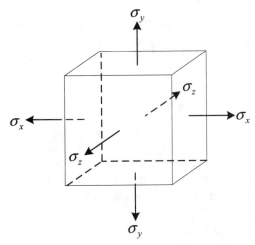

Figure 4.8: A representative element subjected to a multi-axial state of stress

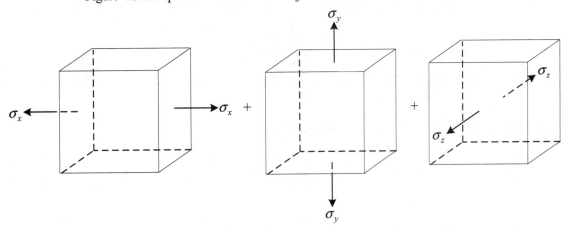

Figure 4.9: Three cases in which the element is subjected to individual uniaxial stresses

Case 1: Cubic element subjected to an axial stress σ_x. The strain are given as

$$\varepsilon_{x1} = \frac{\sigma_x}{E} \text{ (uniaxial strain due to uniaxial stress)}$$

$$\varepsilon_{y1} = -v\varepsilon_{x1} = -v\frac{\sigma_x}{E}$$

$$\varepsilon_{z1} = -v\varepsilon_{x1} = -v\frac{\sigma_x}{E} \text{ (these are due to Poisson's effect)}$$

Case 2: Cubic element subjected to an axial stress σ_y. The strain are given as

$$\varepsilon_{y2} = \frac{\sigma_y}{E} \text{ (uniaxial strain due to uniaxial stress)}$$

$$\varepsilon_{x2} = -\nu\varepsilon_{y2} = -\nu\frac{\sigma_y}{E}$$

$$\varepsilon_{z2} = -\nu\varepsilon_{y2} = -\nu\frac{\sigma_y}{E} \text{ (these are due to Poisson's effect)}$$

Case 3: Cubic element subjected to an axial stress σ_z. The strain are given as

$$\varepsilon_{z3} = \frac{\sigma_z}{E} \text{ (uniaxial strain due to uniaxial stress)}$$

$$\varepsilon_{x3} = -\nu\varepsilon_{z3} = -\nu\frac{\sigma_z}{E}$$

$$\varepsilon_{y3} = -\nu\varepsilon_{z3} = -\nu\frac{\sigma_z}{E} \text{ (these are due to Poisson's effect)}$$

The combined effect of the three stresses can be derived by superposition principle, which states that the total axial strain in any direction is the sum of the individual strains in any direction. Mathematically the combination can be expressed as follows.

$$\varepsilon_x = \varepsilon_{x1} + \varepsilon_{x2} + \varepsilon_{x3} = \frac{\sigma_x}{E} - \nu\frac{\sigma_y}{E} - \nu\frac{\sigma_z}{E} = \frac{1}{E}\{\sigma_x - \nu(\sigma_y + \sigma_z)\} \qquad \text{Eqn (4.1)}$$

$$\varepsilon_y = \varepsilon_{y1} + \varepsilon_{y2} + \varepsilon_{y3} = \frac{\sigma_y}{E} - \nu\frac{\sigma_x}{E} - \nu\frac{\sigma_z}{E} = \frac{1}{E}\{\sigma_y - \nu(\sigma_x + \sigma_z)\} \qquad \text{Eqn (4.2)}$$

$$\varepsilon_z = \varepsilon_{z1} + \varepsilon_{z2} + \varepsilon_{z3} = \frac{\sigma_z}{E} - \nu\frac{\sigma_x}{E} - \nu\frac{\sigma_y}{E} = \frac{1}{E}\{\sigma_z - \nu(\sigma_x + \sigma_y)\} \qquad \text{Eqn (4.3)}$$

The above set of equations can be used to find the strain in any direction, given the stresses in a multi-axial loading case.

4.4   Shear stress-shear strain relationships

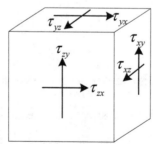

Figure 4.10: Element subjected to shear stresses in all three dimensions

Figure 4.10 shows the representative element subjected to the three shear stresses. The strains caused by the shear stresses are now determined. The determination is motivated by two main observations.

1.   The shear stress in any one plane causes shear strain in that plane only. The object does not deform in the other two planes. This is depicted in Figure 4.11

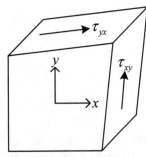

Figure 4.11: Deformation pattern caused by shear stress τ_{xy} on the three dimensional element

2. There is a linear relationship (as in the case of uniaxial stress-strain behavior) between the shear stress τ and the shear strain γ, as shown in Figure 4.12. The slope of the linear curve represents the third elastic constant, namely the shear modulus G. The relationship between the two quantities are given by

$$\tau = G\gamma \qquad \text{Eqn (4.4)}$$

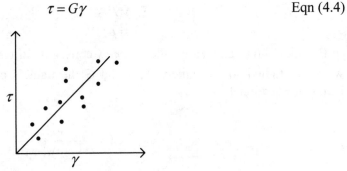

Figure 4.12: Graph showing the elastic behavior of the shear stress-shear strain

Hence, the shear strains in each of the three planes can now be expressed as follows.

$$\gamma_{xy} = \frac{\tau_{xy}}{G}$$

$$\gamma_{xz} = \frac{\tau_{xz}}{G} \qquad \text{Eqn (4.5)}$$

$$\gamma_{yz} = \frac{\tau_{yz}}{G}$$

4.5 Generalized Hooke's law equations

In summary, for an element subjected to all the six independent stresses, as shown in Figure 4.5 the generalized Hooke's law, which enables the computation of strains in the element, can be expressed by the following equations.

$$\varepsilon_x = \frac{1}{E}\{\sigma_x - v(\sigma_y + \sigma_z)\}$$

$$\varepsilon_y = \frac{1}{E}\{\sigma_y - v(\sigma_x + \sigma_z)\}$$

$$\varepsilon_z = \frac{1}{E}\{\sigma_z - v(\sigma_x + \sigma_y)\}$$

$$\gamma_{xy} = \frac{\tau_{xy}}{G}$$

$$\gamma_{xz} = \frac{\tau_{xz}}{G}$$

$$\gamma_{yz} = \frac{\tau_{yz}}{G}$$

The six equations expressed in equation above can be rearranged and reorganized in order to get the stresses if the strains are known. The set of six equations are shown below.

$$\sigma_x = (\lambda + 2\mu)\varepsilon_x + \lambda(\varepsilon_y + \varepsilon_z)$$

$$\sigma_y = (\lambda + 2\mu)\varepsilon_y + \lambda(\varepsilon_x + \varepsilon_z)$$

$$\sigma_z = (\lambda + 2\mu)\varepsilon_z + \lambda(\varepsilon_x + \varepsilon_y)$$

$$\tau_{xy} = \mu\gamma_{xy}$$

$$\tau_{xz} = \mu\gamma_{xz}$$

$$\tau_{yz} = \mu\gamma_{yz}$$

Eqn (4.6)

In Equation 4.6 λ and μ are called *Lame's* constants. In terms of the three elastic constants that we have studied so far namely, E, v and G the Lame's constants can be expressed as shown below in Equation 4.7

$$\mu = G$$

$$\lambda = \frac{vE}{(1-2v)(1+v)}$$

Eqn (4.7)

4.6   Relationship between the three elastic constants

It is to be noted that for an isotropic elastic material, there are only two *independent* elastic constants. It can be shown from stress-strain and strain-transformation relations (to be described in the following chapters) that the three elastic constants are related as follows:

$$G = \frac{E}{2(1+v)}$$

Eqn (4.8)

Hence, for an elastic material the shear modulus G is always less than the elastic modulus E.

Example 4.1: Plane stress and plane strain problem

Problem Statement: The state of stress at a point is as shown in the element below. The material has an elastic modulus of 30,000 *ksi* and a Poisson's ratio of 0.25.

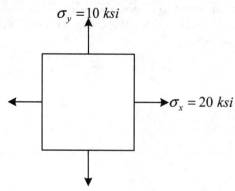

$\sigma_y = 10\ ksi$

$\sigma_x = 20\ ksi$

Required: Assuming plane stress and plane strain conditions respectively, determine the strains $\varepsilon_x, \varepsilon_y$ and ε_z.

Solution:

Step 1: Solving the problem assuming plane stress. Plane stress situations often occur in structures made of thin sections, where the stress in the thickness direction is negligible (or zero). For plane stress: $\sigma_z = 0; \tau_{xz} = \tau_{yz} = 0$. From the problem it can be seen that $\sigma_x = +20\ ksi$ and $\sigma_y = +10\ ksi$

The equations of the generalized Hooke's law can be written as follows

$$\varepsilon_x = \frac{1}{E}\{\sigma_x - v(\sigma_y + \sigma_z)\} = \frac{1}{30,000}\{20 - 0.25(10+0)\} = 5.83 \times 10^{-4}$$

$$\varepsilon_y = \frac{1}{E}\{\sigma_y - v(\sigma_x + \sigma_z)\} = \frac{1}{30,000}\{10 - 0.25(20+0)\} = 1.66 \times 10^{-4}$$

$$\varepsilon_z = \frac{1}{E}\{\sigma_z - v(\sigma_x + \sigma_y)\} = \frac{1}{30,000}\{0 - 0.25(20+10)\} = -2.5 \times 10^{-4}$$

Step 2: For the case of plane strain condition, the primary requirement is that the deformation, hence the strain in the thickness direction is zero. In this example this implies that $\varepsilon_z = 0$ (Note that for plane strain $\sigma_z \neq 0$). The first step is to determine σ_z from the corresponding strain equation as shown below.

$$\varepsilon_z = \frac{1}{E}\{\sigma_z - v(\sigma_x + \sigma_y)\} = \frac{1}{30,000}\{\sigma_z - 0.25(20+10)\} = 0$$

$$\therefore \sigma_z = 7.5\ ksi$$

Using the value of $\sigma_z = 7.5\ ksi$ the other two generalized Hooke's law equations can be written as follows

$$\varepsilon_x = \frac{1}{E}\{\sigma_x - v(\sigma_y + \sigma_z)\} = \frac{1}{30,000}\{20 - 0.25(10+7.5)\} = 5.208 \times 10^{-4}$$

$$\varepsilon_y = \frac{1}{E}\{\sigma_y - v(\sigma_x + \sigma_z)\} = \frac{1}{30,000}\{10 - 0.25(20+7.5)\} = 1.04 \times 10^{-4}$$

From this example it can be clearly seen that the strains in the case of plane stress and plane strain problems are quite different.

Example 4.2: Plane stress example

Problem Statement: A plate of size $8\ in \times 12\ in \times \frac{1}{4}\ in$. is shown in the figure. The sides of the plate are subjected to a uniform distributed load as shown. It is observed that the plate measures $8.00768\ in \times 12.00864\ in$ after the loads are applied. Given that the plate is made of steel with a modulus of elasticity of $30,000\ ksi$ and a shear modulus of $12,000\ ksi$, determine the magnitudes of the distributed loads.

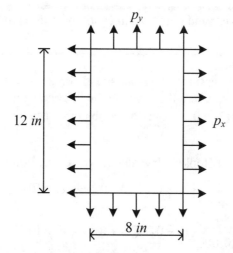

Required: Determine the distributed load magnitudes p_x, p_y applied to the plate.

Solution:

Step 1: Since the plate is a thin plate (the thickness being very small compared to the other two dimensions), this can be idealized as a plane stress problem ($\sigma_z = 0$). The strains in the x and y directions are determined first.

$$\varepsilon_x = \frac{\Delta L_x}{L_x} = \frac{8.00768 - 8}{8} = 0.00096$$

$$\varepsilon_y = \frac{\Delta L_y}{L_y} = \frac{12.00864 - 12}{12} = 0.00072$$

Step 2: Determine the Poisson's ratio.

$$G = \frac{E}{2(1+\nu)}$$

$$\nu = \frac{E}{2G} - 1 = \frac{30,000 \ ksi}{2(12,000 \ ksi)} - 1 = 0.25$$

One must exercise care in the determination of Poisson's ratio. In this example the expression for Poisson's ratio given by $\nu = -\dfrac{\varepsilon_{lateral}}{\varepsilon_{longitudinal}}$ cannot be used since this expression is valid and defined only for a uniaxial case.

Step 3: Using generalized Hooke's law, determine the stresses. Since this is a plane stress problem

$$\varepsilon_x = \frac{1}{E}\left\{\sigma_x - \nu(\sigma_y + \sigma_z)\right\}$$

$$\therefore 0.00096 = \frac{1}{30,000}\left\{\sigma_x - 0.25\sigma_y\right\}$$

$$\varepsilon_y = \frac{1}{E}\left\{\sigma_y - \nu(\sigma_x + \sigma_z)\right\}$$

$$\therefore 0.00072 = \frac{1}{30,000}\left\{\sigma_y - 0.25\sigma_x\right\}$$

Rearranging the above equations to get two equations in terms of σ_x and σ_y

$$\sigma_x - 0.25\sigma_y = 28.8$$

$$-0.25\sigma_x + \sigma_y = 21.6$$

Solving the equations simultaneously we get,

$$\sigma_x = 36.48 \ ksi$$

$$\sigma_y = 30.72 \ ksi$$

$$\sigma_z = 0$$

Step 4: The distributed loads are found from the stress values by multiplying them by the thickness of the plate

$$p_x = \sigma_x t = 36.48 \ ksi \times 0.25 \ in = 9.12 \ k/in$$

$$p_y = \sigma_y t = 30.72 \ ksi \times 0.25 \ in = 7.68 \ k/in$$

Example 4.3: 3-D Multi-axial stress problem

Problem Statement: A solid block of dimensions a=100 *mm*, b=50 *mm* and c=50 *mm* is made of an isotropic elastic material with a Poisson's ratio of 0.25. Three forces act axially as shown and have magnitudes $P_x = 150 \ kN$; $P_y = -100 \ kN$ and $P_z = -50 \ kN$. If instead of three forces acting, only a force in *x*-direction is acting, determine the magnitude of that force such that the deformations in the *x*-direction in the two cases are identical.

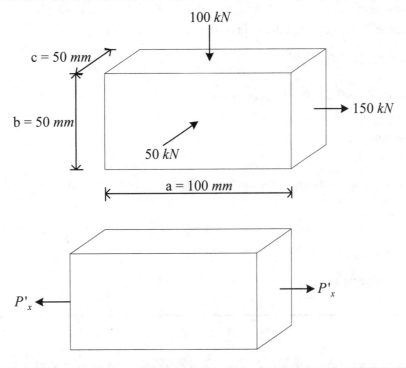

Required: Magnitude of force P_x' which would cause same deformation in the *x*-direction as the three forces together would cause in the first case.

Solution:

Step 1: Choose an appropriate unit set and determine the state of stress in the given case. For force units of *N* (1 *kN*=1000 *N*) is chosen and the units of length is chosen to be *mm*.

$$\sigma_x = \frac{P_x}{A_x} = \frac{150,000 \ N}{50 \times 50 \ mm^2} = 60 \ N/mm^2 = 60 \ MPa$$

$$\sigma_y = \frac{P_y}{A_y} = \frac{-100,000 \ N}{100 \times 50 \ mm^2} = -20 \ N/mm^2 = -20 \ MPa$$

$$\sigma_z = \frac{P_z}{A_z} = \frac{-50,000 \ N}{100 \times 50 \ mm^2} = -10 \ N/mm^2 = -10 \ MPa$$

Step 2: Determine the elongation in the x-direction.

$$\Delta L_x = \varepsilon_x L_x = \varepsilon_x a$$

$$\Delta L_x = \frac{1}{E}\left\{\sigma_x - \nu(\sigma_y + \sigma_z)\right\}a$$

$$= \frac{1}{E}\left\{60 - 0.25(-20 - 10)\right\}(100 \ mm)$$

$$= \frac{6,750}{E} \ mm$$

Step 3: For the second case, if only forces are acting only along the x-direction the stresses $\sigma_y = \sigma_z = 0$. The extension along the x-direction can now be determined as follows

$$\sigma_x = \frac{P_x'}{A_x} = \frac{P_x'}{50 \times 50 mm^2} = 0.0004 P_x'$$

Hence, the strain and elongation in the x-direction is

$$\Delta L_x = \frac{1}{E}\left\{\sigma_x - \nu(\sigma_y + \sigma_z)\right\}a$$

$$= \frac{1}{E}\left\{0.0004 P_x' - 0.25(0 + 0)\right\}(100 mm)$$

$$= \frac{0.04 P_x'}{E} \ mm$$

Step 4: Equating the elongations in x-direction in the two cases, the equivalent x-direction force can be determined

$$\Delta L_x = \frac{6,750}{E} = \frac{0.04 P_x'}{E}$$

or

$$P_x' = 168,750 \ N = 168.75 \ kN$$

4.7 Bulk Modulus

The fourth elastic constant, called the *Bulk Modulus K*, expresses the effect of the three axial stresses in the change in the volume of the material. Consider a cubic element as shown in Figure 4.8 subjected to three axial stresses σ_x, σ_y and σ_z. If the original lengths of the three sides are l_x, l_y and l_z and the axial strains are $\varepsilon_x, \varepsilon_y$ and ε_z then the new lengths of the three sides can be expressed as follows

$$l_x' = l_x + \varepsilon_x l_x = l_x(1 + \varepsilon_x)$$
$$l_y' = l_y + \varepsilon_y l_y = l_y(1 + \varepsilon_y)$$
$$l_z' = l_z + \varepsilon_z l_z = l_z(1 + \varepsilon_z)$$

Hence, the change in volume can be expressed as

$$\delta V = V_{final} - V_{initial}$$
$$= l_x(1 + \varepsilon_x)l_y(1 + \varepsilon_y)l_z(1 + \varepsilon_z) - l_x l_y l_z$$
$$= l_x l_y l_z + l_x \varepsilon_x + l_y \varepsilon_y + l_z \varepsilon_z + \ldots - l_x l_y l_z$$
$$= l^3(\varepsilon_x + \varepsilon_y + \varepsilon_z) \text{ assuming } l_x = l_y = l_z$$

In the derivation shown it is assumed that strains are very small which allows us to neglect the product of strain terms or the higher order terms. Hence, the *dilatational strain e* or the strain that represents the change in volume per unit volume may be expressed as shown below

$$e = \frac{\delta V}{V} = \frac{l^3(\varepsilon_x + \varepsilon_y + \varepsilon_z)}{l^3} = (\varepsilon_x + \varepsilon_y + \varepsilon_z) \qquad \text{Eqn (4.9)}$$

Using the generalized Hooke's law the dilatational strain expression can be expanded as

$$e = \frac{1}{E}\{\sigma_x - \nu(\sigma_y + \sigma_z)\} + \frac{1}{E}\{\sigma_x - \nu(\sigma_y + \sigma_z)\} + \frac{1}{E}\{\sigma_x - \nu(\sigma_y + \sigma_z)\}$$
$$= \frac{1}{E}(\sigma_x + \sigma_y + \sigma_z) - \frac{2\nu}{E}(\sigma_x + \sigma_y + \sigma_z)$$
$$= \frac{1 - 2\nu}{E}(\sigma_x + \sigma_y + \sigma_z)$$

For the special case of what is known as a hydrostatic state of stress, in which all the axial stresses are equal $\sigma_x = \sigma_y = \sigma_z = p$, the dilatational modulus reduces to

$$e = \frac{3p(1 - 2\nu)}{E} \qquad \text{Eqn (4.10)}$$

Hence, the Bulk Modulus *K*, which is ratio of the hydrostatic pressure *p* applied to volumetric or dilatational strain in the body, is given as

$$K = \frac{p}{e} = \frac{E}{3(1 - 2\nu)} \qquad \text{Eqn (4.11)}$$

Example 4.4: Change in volume problem

Problem Statement: A solid block of dimensions a= 100 *mm*; b= 50 *mm* and c= 50 *mm* is acted up on by three axial forces as shown in the figure. The solid block is made up of an isotropic material with a Poisson's ratio of 0.25 and Elastic modulus of 50 *GPa*.

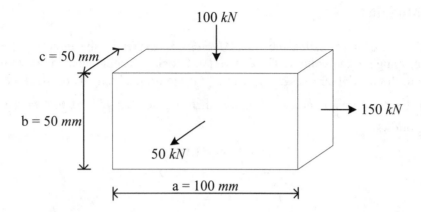

Required: Determine the change in the volume caused in the block due to the application of the forces.

Solution:

Step 1: Choose an appropriate unit set and determine the state of stress in the given case. For force units of N (1 kN=1000 N) is chosen and the units of length is chosen to be mm.

$$\sigma_x = \frac{P_x}{A_x} = \frac{150,000\ N}{50 \times 50\ mm^2} = 60\ N/mm^2 = 60\ MPa$$

$$\sigma_y = \frac{P_y}{A_y} = \frac{-100,000\ N}{100 \times 50\ mm^2} = -20\ N/mm^2 = -20\ MPa$$

$$\sigma_z = \frac{P_z}{A_z} = \frac{50,000\ N}{100 \times 50\ mm^2} = 10\ N/mm^2 = 10\ MPa$$

Step 2: Determine the strains in the three directions.

$$\varepsilon_x = \frac{1}{E}\{\sigma_x - v(\sigma_y + \sigma_z)\} = \frac{1}{50,000}\{60 - 0.25(-20 + 10)\} = 1.25 \times 10^{-3}$$

$$\varepsilon_y = \frac{1}{E}\{\sigma_y - v(\sigma_x + \sigma_z)\} = \frac{1}{50,000}\{-20 - 0.25(60 + 10)\} = -7.5 \times 10^{-4}$$

$$\varepsilon_z = \frac{1}{E}\{\sigma_z - v(\sigma_x + \sigma_y)\} = \frac{1}{50,000}\{10 - 0.25(60 + 20)\} = -2 \times 10^{-4}$$

Step 3: Determine the dilatational strain e.

$$e = \varepsilon_x + \varepsilon_y + \varepsilon_z$$

$$\therefore e = (1.25 \times 10^{-3}) + (-7.5 \times 10^{-4}) + (-2 \times 10^{-4})$$

$$= 3 \times 10^{-4}$$

Step 4: Determine the change in the volume.

$$V = 100 \times 50 \times 50 = 250,000\ mm^3$$

$$\delta V = e \times V = (3 \times 10^{-4}) \times 250,000$$

$$\therefore \delta V = 75\ mm^3$$

Limits of Poisson's Ratio: It can be seen from equation 4.12 that the Bulk Modulus must always be a positive quantity, since in increase or decrease in pressure must be associated with an increase or decrease in the volume, the denominator must always remain positive. It follows that

$$1 - 2v > 0 \text{ or } v < \frac{1}{2}$$

Also the Poisson's ratio is always greater than zero, as any longitudinal stretching is always associated with a lateral compression $\varepsilon_y = -v\varepsilon_x$, it follows that

$$0 < v < \frac{1}{2}$$

The right limit expresses a perfectly incompressible material ($v = 1/2$).

4.8   Summary

This chapter described the examples of situations where the body experiences a multi-axial state of stress. A generalized form of Hooke's law is derived and used for this purpose. The keywords and key concepts introduced in this chapter are as follows.

1. If a body is experiencing a *uniaxial* state of stress then the following equations relating the stress to the strain $\sigma = E\varepsilon$ and Poisson's effect relating the axial to the transverse strain $v = -\dfrac{\varepsilon_T}{\varepsilon_L}$ is valid.

2. If a body is experiencing a *multi axial* state of stress then the equations and concepts outlined in point (1), is no longer valid directly. The following *generalized Hooke's Law* equations govern the multi axial load case.

$$\varepsilon_x = \frac{1}{E}\left\{\sigma_x - v(\sigma_y + \sigma_z)\right\}$$

$$\varepsilon_y = \frac{1}{E}\left\{\sigma_y - v(\sigma_x + \sigma_z)\right\}$$

$$\varepsilon_z = \frac{1}{E}\left\{\sigma_z - v(\sigma_x + \sigma_y)\right\}$$

$$\gamma_{xy} = \frac{\tau_{xy}}{G}$$

$$\gamma_{xz} = \frac{\tau_{xz}}{G}$$

$$\gamma_{yz} = \frac{\tau_{yz}}{G}$$

3. **Lame's Constants:** The elastic constants λ and μ are called Lame's constants and are related to the other elastic constants by the following expression. Lame's constants are used to related stresses directly to the strains.

$$\sigma_x = (\lambda + 2\mu)\varepsilon_x + \lambda(\varepsilon_y + \varepsilon_z) \qquad \mu = G$$

$$\sigma_y = (\lambda + 2\mu)\varepsilon_y + \lambda(\varepsilon_x + \varepsilon_z) \qquad \lambda = \frac{vE}{(1-2v)(1+v)}$$

$$\sigma_z = (\lambda + 2\mu)\varepsilon_z + \lambda(\varepsilon_x + \varepsilon_y)$$

$$\tau_{xy} = \mu\gamma_{xy};\ \tau_{xz} = \mu\gamma_{xz};\ \tau_{yz} = \mu\gamma_{yz}$$

4. **Plane stress:** Plane stress situations often occur in structures made of thin sections, where the stress in the thickness direction is negligible (or zero). For plane stress: $\sigma_z = 0$ and $\tau_{xz} = \tau_{yz} = 0$

5. **Plane strain:** For the case of plane strain condition, the primary requirement is that the deformation, hence the strain in the thickness direction is zero. It it implies that $\varepsilon_z = 0$ then for plane strain, $\sigma_z \neq 0$.

6. **Shear Modulus (G):** The shear modulus is similar to Young's modulus which relates the shear stress τ to the shear strain γ by the equation $\tau = G\gamma$. It has the units GPa (Giga Pascals) or *ksi.*

7. **Volumetric Strain (e):** The volumetric strain e is the change in volume experienced by a volume when subjected to a hydrostatic pressure p. The volumetric strain can be related to the axial strains by the following expression.

$$e = \frac{\delta V}{V} = \left(\varepsilon_x + \varepsilon_y + \varepsilon_z\right)$$

8. **Bulk Modulus:** The *Bulk Modulus K,* expresses the effect of the three axial stresses to the change in the volume of the material. It can be related to the elastic modulus E and the Poisson's ratio v by the following expression.

$$K = \frac{p}{e} = \frac{E}{3(1-2v)}$$

9. **Hydrostatic Pressure (p):** The hydrostatic pressure is a hypothetical state in which a volume experiences equal compressive stress p in all its faces. The hydrostatic pressure is also determined as follows:

$$\sigma_m = \frac{\sigma_x + \sigma_y + \sigma_z}{3} = p$$

4.9 Problems:

4.1 A circular rod has a diameter of 1 *in* and is subjected to a uniaxial axial force of 40 *kips*. An extensometer which is attached to the rod has a gage length of 1 *in* and registers an extension of 0.0017 *in*. Simultaneously the rod decreases in diameter to 0.99943 *in*. Determine the a) elastic modulus b) Poisson's ratio c) Shear modulus and d) Bulk Modulus of the material.

4.2 A circular rod has a diameter of 25 *mm* and is subjected to an axial force of 180 *kN*. An extensometer which is attached to the rod has a gage length of 25 *mm* and registers an extension of 0.0043 *mm*. Simultaneously the rod decreases in diameter to 24.985 *mm*. Determine the a) elastic modulus b) Poisson's ratio c) Shear modulus and d) Bulk Modulus of the material.

4.3 Explain the difference between longitudinal and lateral strain in your own words and figures.

4.4 Draw a schematic stress strain diagram of a ductile and a brittle material and explain the difference in their behavior.

4.5 The state of stress at a point in an element is as shown in the figures below. The material has an elastic modulus of 70 *GPa* (30,000 *ksi*) and a Poisson's ratio of 0.25. Assuming plane stress and plane strain conditions respectively, determine the strains. Determine the shear stresses if they exist.

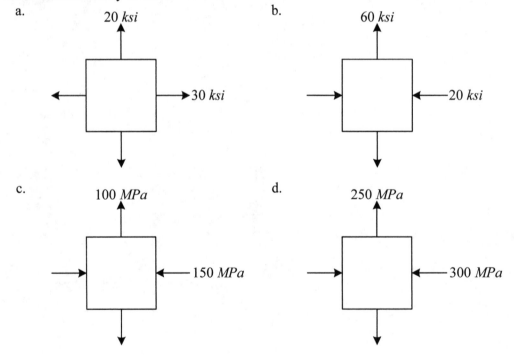

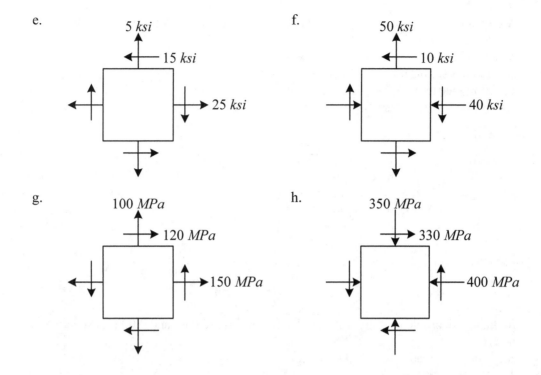

e. 5 ksi 15 ksi 25 ksi

f. 50 ksi 10 ksi 40 ksi

g. 100 MPa 120 MPa 150 MPa

h. 350 MPa 330 MPa 400 MPa

4.6   A plate of size 8 *in*. x 6 *in*. x ¼ *in*. is shown in the figure. The sides of the plate are subjected to a uniform distributed load as shown. It is observed that the plate measures 8.00768 *in*. x 12.00864 *in*. after the loads are applied. Given that the plate is made of steel with a modulus of elasticity of 30,000 *ksi* and a shear modulus of 12,000 *ksi*, determine the magnitudes of the distributed load applied to the plate.

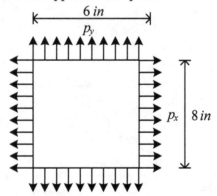

4.7   A cubic block has dimensions of 6 *in* x 8 *in* x 10 *in* along the *x*, *y* and *z* directions respectively. If the forces applied along the three directions is and given the material has an elastic modulus of $E = 20,000$ *ksi* and $v = 0.25$, determine the
a. Change in dimensions and
b. Volumetric strain *e*

4.8   In the Figure shown below, the stress in the *x* and *y* directions $\sigma_x = 15$ *ksi*, $\sigma_x = 10$ *ksi* and it is known that the strain in the *z*-direction $\varepsilon_z = 0$. If the material has an elastic modulus of $E = 20,000$ *ksi* and $v = 0.25$, determine the stress σ_z and the strains in the *x* and *y* directions.

4.9 A 8 *in* cube made of concrete is tested in axial compression as shown. If the load *P*=90 *kips*, determine
   a. Axial strain
   b. Lateral strain
   c. Volumetric strain
      if (v= 0.2) (E= 3,600 *ksi*)

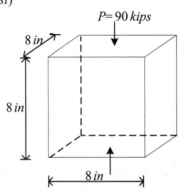

4.10 In the above problem, if the axial and lateral strains are 0.01 and 0.0025 respectively, determine:
   a. The axial load, if P = 120 *kips*
   b. Poisson's ratio
   c. Volumetric strain

4.11 An aluminium bar (E=70 *GPa*, v=0.23) has a cross section of 25 *mm* x 25 *mm* and is 1000 *mm* long. It is subjected to forces as shown. Determine:
   a. Change in volume
   b. New dimensions of the bars
      a.

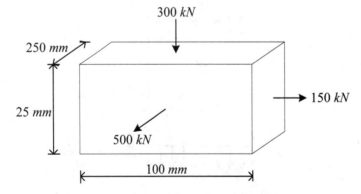

      b.

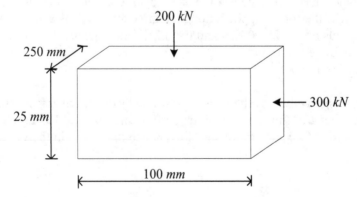

Chapter 5

Torsion and Shear Stress

Goals: The learning objectives in this chapter are as follows:

1. Describing the phenomenon of torsion and its effect on circular shafts
2. Describing the nature and magnitude of the shear stress caused by torsion
3. Describe the kinematics of torsion, namely the shear strain and angle of twist
4. Solve statically determinate problems of circular rods subjected to torsion
5. Solve statically indeterminate problems of rods subjected to torsion
6. Describe the behavior of composite shafts subjected to torsion
7. Describe the behavior of thin walled shafts subjected to torsion

5   Torsion and Shear Stress

5.1   Introduction

The previous chapters have considered one form of stress and strain in detail, namely the axial stress and the axial strain, and deformations associated with it. This chapter deals with the second form of stress and strain, namely the shear stress and strains. One of the primary applications where shear stresses occur is torsion or twisting moment in circular rods or shafts. Figure 5.1 shows the nature of a torque applied in a shaft. The circular shaft is subjected to shear stresses and strains in the process. For sections subjected to twisting moments or torques, a circular cross section is the most efficient section.

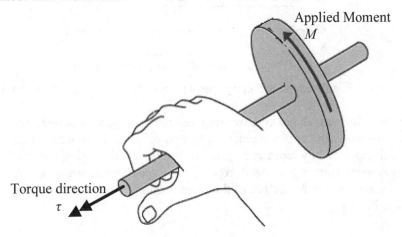

Figure 5.1: Representation of a torque in a circular shaft

The rest of the chapter is organized as follows.
1. Definition of torque and the geometric properties of the cross section needed to derive the associated shear stresses are outlined first.
2. The strain and deformation, such as the angle of rotation, are then described.
3. Hooke's law for shear stresses and strain are then used to correlate the stresses to the strains – in order to determine the deformation quantities from the given torques and the cross section properties.
4. Considerations involved with statically indeterminate shafts are described subsequently.
5. Designs of shafts subjected to torques are then described.
6. The chapter finally closes with a description of closed thin walled sections subjected to torsion.

5.2   Torque and Shear Stresses in Circular Shafts

Figure 5.2 shows a circular shaft subjected to a twisting moment also referred to as *torque*. A three dimensional representation of a circular shaft is shown along with its longitudinal axis. The two ends of the shaft are subjected to a moment about the longitudinal x-axis – the moment at the two ends act in accordance with the right hand rule. As shown in Figure 5.1, if the fingers of the right hand are curled along the direction of the moment, then the thumb points outwards, that is away from the surface. In this manner, at the right end the thumb points to the right and at the left end the thumb points towards the left. A two-dimensional representation of the same shaft is shown in Figure 5.2 (b). A double arrow will be henceforth used to depict a torque in a two dimensional representation.

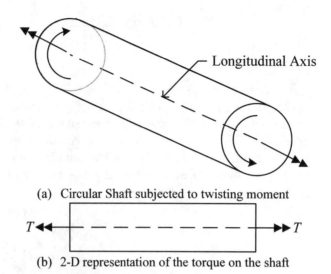

(a) Circular Shaft subjected to twisting moment

T ◄◄ — — — — — — — — — — — ► ► T

(b) 2-D representation of the torque on the shaft

Figure 5.2: Three and two-dimensional representation of torque on a shaft

Positive Twisting Moment: A positive twisting moment or torque is defined as shown in Figure 5.2 (a) and (b). Although the two moments act in two different directions (one is clockwise and the other is anticlockwise) they represent a positive torque. Analogous to the axial force, a double arrow pointing *away* from the surface represents a *positive twisting moment*. This action effectively causes a stress on the surface of the cross section, which is in the same direction as the twisting moment itself.

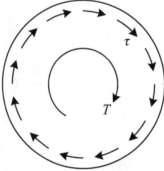

Figure 5.3: Shear stresses on the cross-section due to a twisting moment

Shear Stresses on the Cross Section: Figure 5.3 shows a circular cross section subjected to a positive torque T (a counter clockwise moment in this representation). The shear stresses, denoted by the Greek letter τ (tau), that develop on the surface acts at every material point as shown in the direction of the torque and is always perpendicular to the radius.

5.2.1   Shear Stress due to a Twisting Moment on a Circular Shaft

We now proceed to derive the relationship between the shear stress τ, the torque T and the geometric property of the circular cross-section namely the radius r for a linearly elastic material behavior. In order to do this a few basic assumptions are made below. The physical and consequently the mathematical implications of the assumption are also detailed.

Basis and Assumptions:

1. The fundamental assumption, which is valid for linearly elastic materials undergoing small deformations, is the so-called *plane section hypothesis.* This hypothesis states that plane sections remain plane after the final deformation. In the case of twisting of a circular cross-section this implies that there is *no warping* of the cross section. The plane section hypothesis physically means that all points on the cross-section remain in the same plane after deformation, meanwhile in a warped cross-section points that were in the same plane before deformation need not be in the same plane after deformation. Figure 5.4 illustrates the plane section hypothesis and also shows a warped section.

Figure 5.4: A plane and a warped section

2. The shear stresses are in the direction of the torque and are always perpendicular to the radius.
3. The outermost material point will undergo the largest twist and hence will have the maximum shear stress τ_{max}. Also, the material point at the center has no deformation, and hence, has zero shear stress. This is illustrated in Figure 5.5.
4. For a linear elastic material it is also assumed that the variation of the shear stress is linear between the center of the circle and the outer most point.

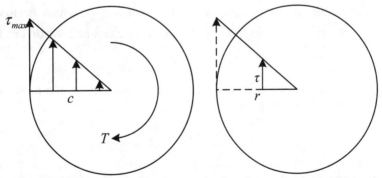

Figure 5.5: Shear stress at outer point and at any internal point on the section

This assumption of the linear variation of the magnitude of shear stresses as shown in Figure 5.5 can be expressed in mathematical form as follows.

$$\tau = \frac{r}{c}\tau_{max}$$

5. The total internal torque as determined by the shear stresses is equal to the total external torque acting on the body.

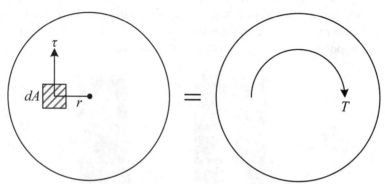

Figure 5.6: Relating the shear stress to torque

The force due to the shear stress acting on the incremental area dA is given as
$$dF = \tau dA$$
The incremental moment due to this force is
$$dT = rdF = r\tau dA$$

$$dT = r(\tau_{max}\frac{r}{c})dA$$

From Figure 5.6 the total internal torque is equal to the total external torque. This fact can be now expressed as

$$T = \int dT = \int r(\tau_{max}\frac{r}{c})dA$$

$$= \frac{\tau_{max}}{c}\int r^2 dA$$

$$= \frac{\tau_{max}}{c}J$$

where, c is the radius of the circular shaft and $J = \int r^2 dA$ is the polar moment of inertia of the rod. In order to determine the maximum shear stress τ_{max}, which occurs at the outermost points on the circular rod, the expression derived above can be rewritten as follows,

$$\tau_{max} = \frac{Tc}{J} \qquad \qquad \text{Eqn (5.1)}$$

Finally, the general expression for shear stress τ, which occurs at a point, which is located at a distance r from the center, can be expressed as

$$\tau = \tau_{max}\frac{r}{c} = \frac{Tc}{J}\frac{r}{c} = \frac{Tr}{J}$$

Polar Moment of Inertia:

The polar moment of inertia, as studied in Statics, for a circular and an annular cross section is briefly summarized here. For a solid circular cross section, as shown in Figure 5.7, polar moment of inertia can be derived as follows:

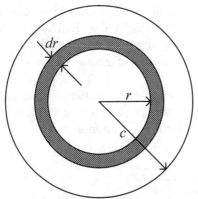

$$J = \int r^2 dA$$

where,

$dA = 2\pi r dr$ (considering an annular area)

$$\therefore J = \int_0^c r^2 2\pi r dr = 2\pi \int_0^c r^3 dr = 2\pi \frac{r^4}{4}\bigg|_0^c$$

or

$$J = \frac{\pi c^4}{2} = \frac{\pi d^4}{32} \qquad\qquad \text{Eqn (5.2)}$$

Figure 5.7: Solid circular cross section

For an annular section shown to the left, the polar moment of inertia can be determined by using the concept of subtracting the inertia of the inner circle (radius c_1) from the outer circle (radius c_2). The expression for the polar moment of inertia is hence,

$$J = \frac{\pi}{2}(c_2^4 - c_1^4) = \frac{\pi}{32}(d_2^4 - d_1^4) \qquad\qquad \text{Eqn (5.3)}$$

where, d_2 and d_1 are the diameters of the outer and inner circles, respectively.

What is the physical meaning of the Polar Moment of Inertia?
As seen from physics, the term inertia represents the resistance offered to any specific motion. For example, in Newton's second law $F = ma$, m is the mass of the object and is the term that quantifies the inertia or the resistance to accelerate. If the mass is higher the inertia is higher. Similarly, the Polar Moment of Inertia represents the resistance to twist about a pole point (the center of the circle in this example) when subjected to a twisting moment. In the case of the twisting moment the deformation expected in the cross-section is a twist.

Example 5.1: Shear stresses due to torsion

Problem Statement: A solid shaft of diameter 4 *in.* is subjected to a set of four torques, as shown below. Draw the Twisting Moment Diagram (TMD) and determine the maximum shear stress in the shaft.

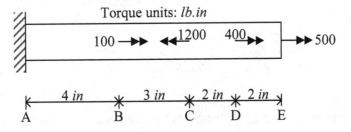

Required: To determine the maximum shear stress in the shaft.

Note: A positive twisting moment is defined as follows. A shaft subjected to a counterclockwise moment (as you look towards each section individually) on both sides of the shaft is said to experience *positive twisting moment*. A 3-dimensional view showing the twisting moments and a 2-dimensional view showing the twisting moments represented as double arrows is shown in Figure 5.2.

Step 1: Draw the Twisting Moment Diagram (TMD). This step is very similar to the procedure in drawing the Axial Force Diagram, using the method of sections. Instead of one arrow that is used to represent the axial force here a double arrow is used to represent the twisting moment.

a)   Determine the Reaction at the fixed end.

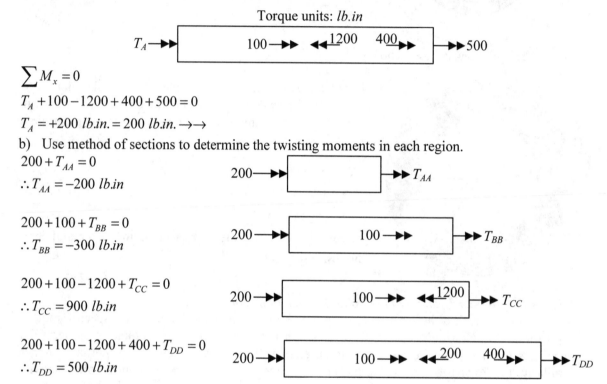

$$\sum M_x = 0$$

$$T_A + 100 - 1200 + 400 + 500 = 0$$

$$T_A = +200 \ lb.in. = 200 \ lb.in. \rightarrow\rightarrow$$

b)   Use method of sections to determine the twisting moments in each region.

$$200 + T_{AA} = 0$$

$$\therefore T_{AA} = -200 \ lb.in$$

$$200 + 100 + T_{BB} = 0$$

$$\therefore T_{BB} = -300 \ lb.in$$

$$200 + 100 - 1200 + T_{CC} = 0$$

$$\therefore T_{CC} = 900 \ lb.in$$

$$200 + 100 - 1200 + 400 + T_{DD} = 0$$

$$\therefore T_{DD} = 500 \ lb.in$$

Final Twisting Moment Diagram

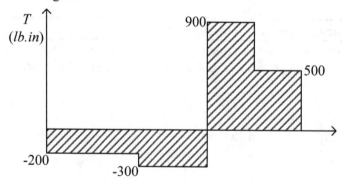

Step 2: Determine the Polar Moment of Inertia of the shaft and determine the shear stress in each region using equation 5.1

Polar Moment of Inertia $J = \dfrac{\pi c^4}{2} = \dfrac{\pi (2)^4}{2} = 25.13 \ in^4$

$$\tau = \frac{Tc}{J}$$

$$\tau_{AA} = \frac{T_{AA}c}{J} = \frac{(-200 \; lb.in.)(2 \; in.)}{25.13 in^4} = -15.91 \; psi$$

$$\tau_{BB} = \frac{T_{BB}c}{J} = \frac{(-300 \; lb.in.)(2 \; in.)}{25.13 \; in^4} = -23.87 \; psi$$

$$\tau_{CC} = \frac{T_{CC}c}{J} = \frac{(900 \; lb.in.)(2 \; in.)}{25.13 \; in^4} = 71.6 \; psi$$

$$\tau_{DD} = \frac{T_{DD}c}{J} = \frac{(500 \; lb.in.)(2 \; in.)}{25.13 \; in^4} = 39.8 \; psi$$

Note: The maximum shear stress is the maximum absolute value of the shear stress values. Hence, the maximum shear stress in the shaft is 71.6 *psi*.

A positive sign indicated that the right section is experiencing a shear stress in the counterclockwise direction while a negative value indicates that the shear stress is in the clockwise section. In most cases the direction of the shear stress in not relevant, unlike those in axial forces where a change in direction (tension or compression) represents a completely different behavior and consequently a different design procedure.

5.2.2 Shear stresses on a hollow circular cross-section

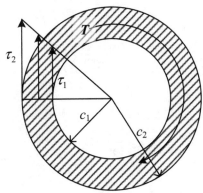

Figure 5.8: Hollow circular shaft

Consider a shaft made of a circular hollow cross-section as shown in Figure 5.8 with an inner radius of c_1 and an outer radius c_2, subjected to a twisting moment T. The shear stress distribution across the cross-section due to the twisting moment is also shown in the figure. The magnitude of the shear stress increases from a value τ_1 to a value of τ_2 and is given as

$$\tau_1 = \frac{T}{J_{hollow}}c_1$$

$$\tau_2 = \frac{T}{J_{hollow}}c_2$$

Eqn (5.4)

where, J_{hollow} is the polar moment of inertia in the Equation 5.3.

Example 5.2: Shear stresses in hollow tubes subjected to torsion

Determine and draw the shear stress distribution across the section of a hollow tube with an outer diameter of 1 *in.* and an inner diameter of 0.9 *in.* The tube is subjected to a torque of 400 *lb.in.*

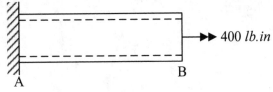

Required: To determine the maximum shear stress in the shaft cross-section and draw the shear stress distribution.

Solution:

Step 1: Determine the torque in the shaft. Since the shaft is subjected to a single torque and is fixed at end A, the reaction at A is equal and opposite of the torque at B and is equal to

$T_A = -400 \ lb.in. = 400 \ lb.in. \rightarrow\rightarrow$.

Hence, the shaft is subjected to a uniform positive torque of 400 *lb.in.*

Step 2: Determine the Polar Moment of Inertia of the shaft and determine the shear stress in each region using equation 5.4

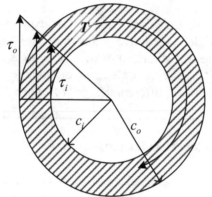

Polar Moment of Inertia

$$J = \frac{\pi(c_o^4 - c_i^4)}{2} = \frac{\pi(0.5^4 - 0.45^4)}{2} = 0.0337 \ in^4$$

$$\tau = \frac{Tc}{J}$$

$$\tau_{outer} = \frac{Tc_o}{J} = \frac{(400 \ lb.in.)(0.5 \ in.)}{0.0337 \ in^4} = 5,934.7 \ psi$$

$$\tau_{inner} = \frac{Tc_i}{J} = \frac{(400 \ lb.in.)(0.45 \ in.)}{0.0337 \ in^4} = 5,341.25 \ psi$$

The shear stress distribution across the cross-section, which gives the magnitudes at different radii, is shown in the figure.

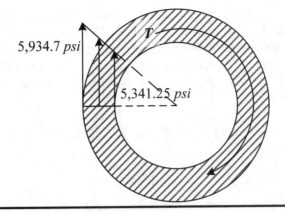

5.3   Shear Strain and Angle of Twist

The deformation behavior of a solid shaft subjected to a torque is addressed in this section. It is observed in section 5.2 that a torque causes shear stresses on the circular cross-section of the shaft. From chapter 4 it is seen that shear stresses causes shear strains. However, shear strain are not a very convenient measure of deformation in shafts. This section introduces an objective deformation mode, namely the *angle of twist*. The possible deformations are geometrically described which is then followed by the relationship between them.

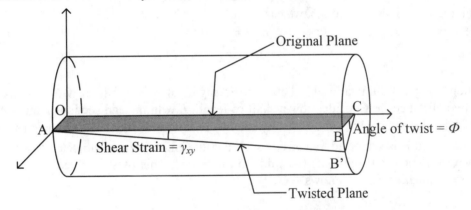

Figure 5.9: Definitions of angle of twist and shear strain

Consider a circular shaft, as shown in Figure 5.9, which is fixed at one end and is subjected to a torque T at the other end. This represents a solid shaft subjected to a uniform twisting moment at all points along the length. In this shaft, a plane OABC represents a horizontal plane in which line OA lies on the fixed side. Line OC is also the longitudinal axis of the shaft – the axis about which the torque is applied. After the section is twisted, under small elastic deformations, the point B is the only point that moves down to B'. Hence, the plane OABC deforms to plane OAB'C after deformation. Based on this deformation pattern two definitions follow.

Angle of Twist: The angle of twist φ is defined on the circular cross section. It is defined as the angle, in radians, by which line CB rotates. In other words, the angle of twist is defined as the angle between CB and CB'.

Shear Strain: The shear strain is the angle (in radians) along the longitudinal axis at the outer surface. From Figure 5.9, it can be seen that the line AB now becomes AB' after the twist. The shear strain γ is defined as the angle between line AB and AB'.

Relationship between Angle of Twist and Shear Strain: The geometric relationship between the angle of twist and the shear strain is now derived. Consider the shaft of radius c and having a length dx along the longitudinal axis. Since we are considering an incremental length we designate the angle of twist in this section to be $d\varphi$. Keep in mind that this angle of twist is relative to the rotation of the other cross-section. In other words, the cross section is assumed to be fixed at the back section.

Consider the circular cross section as shown in Figure 5.9. The angle of twist can be geometrically expressed as

$$\tan(d\phi) = \frac{BB'}{CB}$$

For small angle of twists the above expression can be written as

$$d\phi \approx \tan(d\phi) = \frac{BB'}{CB} = \frac{BB'}{c} \qquad \text{Eqn (5.5)}$$

$$BB' = c\,d\phi$$

From the longitudinal section at the outermost surface the expression for shear strain can now be written geometrically as

$$\gamma_{max} \approx \tan(\gamma) = \frac{BB'}{AB} = \frac{BB'}{dx} \qquad \text{Eqn (5.6)}$$

$$BB' = \gamma_{max}\,dx$$

Combining Equations, 5.5and 5.6, we can write

$$c\,d\phi = \gamma_{max}\,dx$$

$$\frac{d\phi}{dx} = \frac{\gamma_{max}}{c} \qquad \text{Eqn (5.7)}$$

Equation 5.7 gives the relationship between the angles of twist between two sections which are apart by a distance dx. Consider now a shaft of length L with the end sections named A and B. If end A twists by an angle ϕ_A, end B also twists by the same amount. This is known as a rigid body rotation. If end B is subjected to a torque such that the entire shaft is subjected to a torque T, end B now experiences an additional twist due to the torque. This twist is given in general form by integrating equation 5.7 as follows

$$d\phi = \frac{\gamma_{max}}{c}\,dx$$

$$\phi = \int_A^B \frac{\gamma_{max}}{c}\,dx$$

$$\phi_B = \int \frac{\gamma_{max}}{c}\,dx + \phi_A \qquad \text{Eqn (5.8)}$$

Equation 5.8 now gives a general expression to compute the angle of twist. However, it is noted that the expression still contains γ the shear strain. We now seek an expression to compute the angle of twist given the geometry and the torque. To this effect two concepts, which have been discussed before, are used. The first concept is the Hooke's law relating the shear stress to the shear strain in the elastic region given as

$$\tau = G\gamma$$

where, G is the shear modulus and τ is the shear stress due to the torque. Using the expression for the shear stress experienced by a cross-section of a solid uniform shaft subjected to a uniform torque we get

$$\gamma = \frac{\tau}{G} = \left(\frac{Tr}{J}\right)\frac{1}{G}$$

It has been seen earlier that the shear stress increases with the radius and has the maximum value at the outermost point at the shaft. Consequently, the shear strain at the outermost point is given as

$$\gamma_{max} = \frac{Tc}{GJ}$$
Eqn (5.9)

Substituting for the shear strain at the outer most point in the cross-section in the equation for the angle of twist, the expression can be written as

$$\phi_B = \int \frac{T c}{GJ}\frac{1}{c}dx + \phi_A$$
Eqn (5.10)

For a shaft of uniform cross-section (J = constant) make of the same material (G = constant) the expression in Equation 5.10 can be integrated as follows

$$\phi_B = \frac{Tx}{GJ}\Big|_0^L + \phi_A$$

$$= \frac{TL}{GJ} + \phi_A$$

The relative angle of twist between two sections can now be given as

$$\phi_B - \phi_A = \frac{TL}{GJ}$$
Eqn (5.11)

Example 5.3: Angle of twist due to torsion

Problem Statement: A solid shaft of diameter 4 *in.*, as described in example 5.1, is subjected to a set of four torques, as shown in the figure. Draw the Twisting Moment Diagram (TMD) and determine the total twist at E. Assume $G = 11,200$ *psi.*

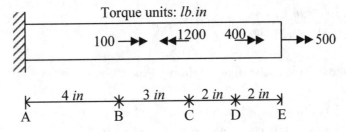

Required: To determine the total twist at E?

Solution:

Step 1: Draw the Twisting Moment Diagram (TMD). This step is the same as step 1 in example 5.1 and is not repeated here. The final Twisting Moment Diagram is shown below

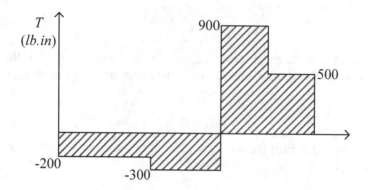

From the TMD it can be seen the torsion in each region is as follows
$T_{AB} = -200 \; lb.in; \; T_{BC} = -300 \; lb.in; \; T_{CD} = 900 \; lb.in; \; T_{DE} = 500 \; lb.in.$

Step 2: Determine the relative angle of twist in each region

Polar Moment of Inertia $J = \dfrac{\pi c^4}{2} = \dfrac{\pi 2^4}{2} = 25.13 \; in^4$

$$\phi = \dfrac{TL}{GJ}$$

$$\phi_{AB} = \dfrac{T_{AB}L_{AB}}{GJ} = \dfrac{(-200 \; lb.in.)(48 \; in.)}{(11,200 \; psi)(25.13 \; in^4)} = -0.0341 \; rads$$

$$\phi_{BC} = \dfrac{T_{BC}L_{BC}}{GJ} = \dfrac{(-300 \; lb.in.)(36 \; in.)}{(11,200 \; psi)(25.13 \; in^4)} = -0.0384 \; rads$$

$$\phi_{CD} = \dfrac{T_{CD}L_{CD}}{GJ} = \dfrac{(900 \; lb.in.)(24 \; in.)}{(11,200 \; psi)(25.13 \; in^4)} = 0.0767 \; rads$$

$$\phi_{DE} = \dfrac{T_{DE}L_{DE}}{GJ} = \dfrac{(500 \; lb.in.)(24 \; in.)}{(11,200 \; psi)(25.13 \; in^4)} = 0.0426 \; rads$$

Step 3: Determine the twist at each point as follows. Since, point A is fixed there is no twist at point A hence $\phi_A = 0$.

$\phi_B = \phi_{AB} + \phi_A = -0.0341 + 0 = -0.0341 \; rads$

$\phi_C = \phi_{BC} + \phi_B = -0.0384 + (-0.0341) = -0.0725 \; rads$

$\phi_D = \phi_{CD} + \phi_C = 0.0767 + (-0.0725) = 0.0042 \; rads$

$\phi_E = \phi_{DE} + \phi_D = 0.0042 + 0.0426 = 0.0466 \; rads$

Hence, the total twist at point E $= 0.0468 \; rads = 0.0468 \times \dfrac{180}{\pi} = 2.68°$

A positive sign indicates that, looking into the shaft at E, the twist in a counterclockwise direction.

Alternate Flexibility method to calculate the relative twists in each section: The flexibility of a section of shaft is given as $f = \dfrac{L}{GJ}$ and the relative twist in each section is given as $\phi = fT$

where T is the torque in the section. The total twist at E can be expressed as the sum of individual twists as follows $\phi_E = \phi_A + f_{AB}T_{AB} + f_{BC}T_{BC} + f_{CD}T_{CD} + f_{DE}T_{DE}$ where;

$$f_{AB} = \left(\frac{L}{GJ}\right)_{AB} = \left(\frac{48\ in.}{(11,200\ psi)(25.13\ in^4)}\right) = 1.705 \times 10^{-4}\ rads/lb.in$$

$$f_{BC} = \left(\frac{L}{GJ}\right)_{BC} = \left(\frac{36\ in.}{(11,200\ psi)(25.13\ in^4)}\right) = 1.28 \times 10^{-4}\ rads/lb.in$$

$$f_{CD} = \left(\frac{L}{GJ}\right)_{CD} = \left(\frac{24\ in.}{(11,200\ psi)(25.13\ in^4)}\right) = 0.852 \times 10^{-4}\ rads/lb.in$$

$$f_{DE} = \left(\frac{L}{GJ}\right)_{DE} = \left(\frac{24\ in.}{(11,200\ psi)(25.13\ in^4)}\right) = 0.852 \times 10^{-4}\ rads/lb.in$$

Hence, the total twist is given as

$$\phi_E = 0 + (1.704 \times 10^{-4}\ rads/lb.in)(-200\ lb.in) + (1.28 \times 10^{-4}\ rads/lb.in)(-300\ lb.in) +$$
$$(0.852 \times 10^{-4}\ rads/lb.in)(900\ lb.in) + (0.852 \times 10^{-4}\ rads/lb.in)(500\ lb.in)$$
$$= 0.0468\ rads.$$

5.4 Statically Indeterminate Torsion Problems

We dealt with statically indeterminate axial force problems in chapter 4. The basic principles, which govern the definition of static indeterminacy, are the same. In a problem where the reactions or unknown forces are to be determined, if the equilibrium equations alone are not sufficient, the problem is said to be statically indeterminate. Additional equations are sought by converting the physical condition that is responsible for the indeterminacy into a usable geometric condition, hence giving additional equations. Three basic principles are used, namely
1. Equilibrium equations based on the overall free body diagram
2. Force-deformation relationships, particularly in torsion problems – the relationship between the applied torque and the angle of twist it causes
3. Geometric compatibility condition, which usually is applied in the form of a constraint imposed on twist at a certain location.

Two kinds of problems are described and illustrated in the following sections. These are problems where the number of unknown reactions is more than the available equations of equilibrium and secondly composite shafts which are made of two materials that are tightly fit.

5.4.1 Indeterminate Reactions

The method and technique for solving problems involving two or more unknown reactions while only one equation of equilibrium (the moment about the longitudinal axis) is best illustrated using an example as outlined below.

Example 5.5: Statically Indeterminate Shafts

Problem Statement: A solid shaft is made of two materials, aluminum and steel, and is joined rigidly at C such that they act as one unit. The aluminum portion of the shaft has a diameter of 50 mm while the steel portion has a diameter of 25 mm. A torque of $200\pi\ N.m.$ is acting as shown in the figure.

Assume: $G_{Steel} = 84 \; GPa$ and $G_{Al.} = 28 \; GPa$.

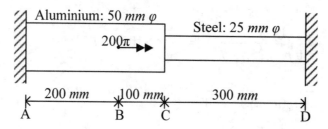

Required: Determine the following
1. The resisting torques at A and C
2. The angle of twist at C
3. Maximum shear stress in the aluminum and steel shafts.

Solution:

Note: A consistent choice of units is critical to solving the problem correctly. The following choice for units is made. Force units::N, length units::mm. This choice requires the following conversion for consistency.

$G_{St.} = 84 \; GPa = 84 \times 10^3 \; MPa = 84 \times 10^3 \; N/mm^2$

$G_{Al.} = 28 \; GPa = 28 \times 10^3 \; MPa = 28 \times 10^3 \; N/mm^2$

Torque $:: 200\pi \; N.m. = 200,000\pi \; N.mm.$

Step 1: The equilibrium equation from the overall free body diagram forms the first equation required to solve for the unknown reactions.

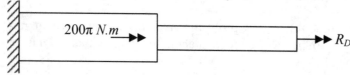

$\sum M_x = 0 : R_A + 200000\pi + R_D = 0$

$\therefore R_A + R_D = -200,000\pi$

It can be seen that the static equilibrium equation has two unknowns in it and is thus a statically indeterminate problem (one equation and two unknowns).

Step 2: The second equation required to solve the problem comes from the geometric condition at D. The fact that D is rigidly fixed and consequently has a zero twist is now utilized.

Step 2a: Release end D of the original structure and replace it with an unknown reaction as shown in the figure below. This structure is now statically determinate.

The torsional flexibilities are now determined for the three regions AB, BC and CD. First the polar moment of inertias of each shaft are found as follows.

$$J_{Al.} = J_{AB} = J_{BC} = \frac{\pi(50)^4}{32} = 613,592 \ mm^4$$

$$J_{St.} = J_{CD} = \frac{\pi(25)^4}{32} = 38,349 \ mm^4$$

$$f_{AB} = \left(\frac{L}{GJ}\right)_{AB} = \left(\frac{200 \ mm}{28\times10^3 \ N/mm^2 \times 613,592 \ mm^4}\right) = 1.164\times10^{-8} \ rads/N.mm$$

$$f_{BC} = \left(\frac{L}{EA}\right)_{BC} = \left(\frac{100mm}{28\times10^3 \ N/mm^2 \times 613,592mm^4}\right) = 0.582\times10^{-8} \ rads/N.mm$$

$$f_{CD} = \left(\frac{L}{EA}\right)_{CD} = \left(\frac{300mm}{84\times10^3 \ N/mm^2 \times 38,349mm^4}\right) = 9.313\times10^{-8} \ rads/N.mm$$

Step 2b: Determine the twist at D (ϕ_{D1}) on the released structure due to applied torques. The reaction and the resulting axial force diagram is also shown.

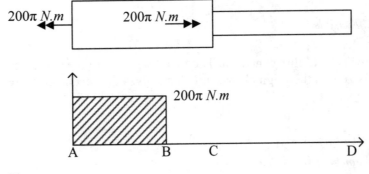

$$T_{AB} = +200,000\pi \ N.mm$$

$$T_{BC} = 0$$

$$T_{CD} = 0$$

$$\therefore \phi_{D1} = \phi_A + \phi_{AB} + \phi_{BC} + \phi_{CD}$$

$$\phi_{D1} = 0 + f_{AB}T_{AB} + f_{BC}T_{BC} + f_{CD}T_{CD}$$

$$\phi_{D1} = 0 + (1.164\times10^{-8} \ \frac{rads}{N.mm})(200,000\pi \ N.mm) + 0 + 0$$

$$\phi_{D1} = 0 + 0.0073 = 0.0073 \ rads.$$

Step 2c: Determine the twist at D (ϕ_{D2}) on the released structure due to unknown reaction torque R_D. The reaction at A due to this torque is also R_D acting in the opposite direction as shown. The resulting torque moment diagram is also shown.

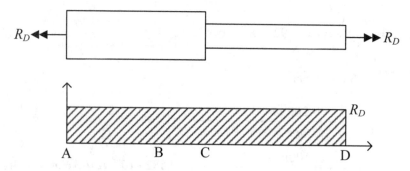

$T_{AB} = R_D \ N.mm$

$T_{BC} = R_D \ N.mm$

$T_{CD} = R_D \ N.mm$

$\therefore \ \phi_{D2} = \phi_A + \phi_{AB} + \phi_{BC} + \phi_{CD}$

$\phi_{D2} = 0 + f_{AB}T_{AB} + f_{BC}T_{BC} + f_{CD}t_{CD}$

$\phi_{D1} = 0 + (1.164 \times 10^{-8} \ \dfrac{rads}{N.mm})(R_D) + (0.582 \times 10^{-8} \ \dfrac{rads}{N.mm})(R_D) + (9.313 \times 10^{-8} \ \dfrac{rads}{N.mm})(R_D)$

$\phi_{D1} = 1.106 \times 10^{-7} \ R_D \ rads.$

Step 3: Apply the compatibility condition. The total twist, due to the two cases described in steps 2b and 2c, at D is zero in the original structure. This gives the second equation (the first was the equilibrium equation).

$\phi_{D1} + \phi_{D2} = 0$

$0.0073 + 1.106 \times 10^{-7} R_D = 0$

$R_D = -66,000 \ N.mm = 21,010\pi \ N.mm. \leftarrow$

From the overall equilibrium equation from step 1, the other reaction at A can be determined.

$\sum M_X = 0: \ R_A + R_D + 200,000\pi = 0$

or

$R_A = -200,000\pi - R_D = -200,000\pi - (-21,010)\pi$

$\therefore \ R_A = -178990\pi = 178,990\pi \ N.mm \leftarrow$

Step 4: Draw the Final Torque Moment Diagram and determine the maximum shear stress in each bar from this diagram.

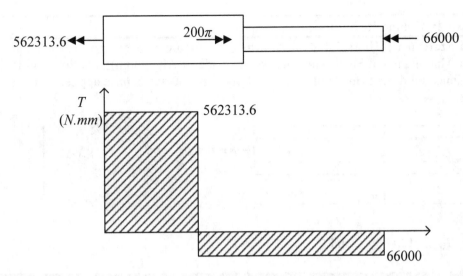

$T_{AB} = 562,313.6 \; N.mm$

$\therefore \tau_{AB} = \dfrac{T_{AB}c}{J_{AB}} = \dfrac{(562,313.6 \; N.mm.)(12.5 \; mm)}{613,592 \; mm^4} = +11.455 \; \dfrac{N}{mm^2}(MPa)$

$T_{BC} = -66,000 \; N.mm$

$\therefore \tau_{BC} = \dfrac{T_{BC}c}{J_{BC}} = \dfrac{(-66,000 \; N.mm.)(12.5 \; mm)}{613,592 \; mm^4} = -1.345 \; \dfrac{N}{mm^2}(MPa)$

$T_{CD} = -66,000 \; N.mm$

$\therefore \tau_{CD} = \dfrac{T_{CD}c}{J_{CD}} = \dfrac{(-66,000 \; N.mm.)(6.25 \; mm)}{38,349 \; mm^4} = -10.76 \; \dfrac{N}{mm^2}(MPa)$

Step 5: Determine the total twist at the junction

$\phi_{AB} = f_{AB}T_{AB} = (1.162 \times 10^{-8} \; rads/N.mm)(562,313.6 \; N.mm) = 0.0065 \; rads.$

$\phi_{BC} = f_{BC}T_{BC} = (0.582 \times 10^{-8} \; rads/N.mm)(-66,000 \; N.mm) = -0.00038 \; rads$

$\therefore$

$\phi_{A} = 0$

$\phi_{B} = \phi_{A} + \phi_{AB} = 0.0065 \; rads.$

$\phi_{C} = \phi_{B} + \phi_{BC} = 0.0065 + (-0.00038) = 0.00612 \; rads.$

5.4.2   Composite Shafts

Composite shafts are made of two different materials bonded together to form a tight fit such that there is no relative slip between the two materials at the interface. Such problems can however be deceiving at the first step. This is because there is one unknown reaction which can be directly determined from the equilibrium equation. The basic principle is that a certain portion of the torque is resisted by one material and the other material takes up the rest. This gives rise to the static indeterminacy, since there is one known applied torque and two unknown components. The second equation is determined from the geometric compatibility condition the total twist at any point is the same for both the materials.

Example 5.4: Composite Shafts

Problem Statement: The solid shaft shown in the figure is a composite shaft made of two materials Aluminum and Steel. The outer shaft (made of Aluminum) is hollow and is tightly fit over the inner solid shaft (made of steel). A. torque $T = 6000\pi$ $lb.in.$ is applied to the free end of the shaft.

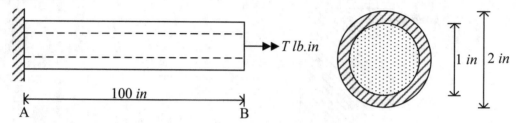

Assume: $G_{Steel} = 12,000$ ksi and $G_{Al.} = 4000$ ksi

Required: Determine the following
1. The resisting torques in each shaft
2. The angle of twist at the free end.
3. Maximum shear stress in the aluminum and steel shafts.

Solution:

Step 1: Determine the torque acting in the shaft. It can be seen that the reactions are statically determinate. Hence, the total torque acting at any point can be found as before.

$$\sum T_x = 0; \quad R_A + 6000\pi = 0$$

$$\therefore R_A = -6000\pi = 6000\pi \leftarrow lb.in.$$

Since the shaft is subjected to a uniform torque the torque experienced at any section is also equal to 6000π $lb.in.$

Step 2: The static indeterminacy in this problem arises from the equilibrium equation that arises from the splitting of the total torque (T) taken up by the steel ($T_{St.}$) and aluminum ($T_{Al.}$) portions.

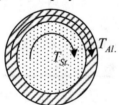

$$T = T_{Al.} + T_{St.}$$

$$6000\pi = T_{Al.} + T_{St.}$$

It can be seen that there are two unknowns and only one equilibrium equation. Hence, it can be classified as a statically indeterminate shaft.

Step 3: Geometric compatibility equation; as in all statically indeterminate problems, the extra equation required to solve the problem is sought in some form of geometric compatibility. In this problem, it is stated that the two materials are in a tight fit – this implies that *the two sections undergo the same twist.*

$$\phi = \phi_{Al.} = \phi_{St.}$$

$$\frac{T_{Al.}L_{Al.}}{G_{Al.}J_{Al.}} = \frac{T_{St.}L_{St.}}{G_{St.}J_{St.}}$$

The two materials can be thought of as an outer hollow aluminum shaft and an inner solid steel shaft. Hence, the polar moments of inertia can be expressed as follows

$$J_{Al.} = \frac{\pi(d_o^4 - d_i^4)}{32} = \frac{\pi(2^4 - 1^4)}{32} = \frac{15\pi}{32} \ in^4$$

$$J_{St.} = \frac{\pi d_i^4}{32} = \frac{\pi 1^4}{32} = \frac{\pi}{32} \ in^4$$

Hence, the compatibility equation can be rewritten as follows

$$\frac{T_{Al.}(100 \ in.)}{(4000 \ ksi)(15\pi/32 \ in^4)} = \frac{T_{st.}(100 \ in.)}{(12000 \ ksi)(\pi/32 \ in^4)}$$

or $T_{Al.} = 5T_{St.}$

Step 4: Solve for the individual torques using the compatibility and equilibrium equations

$$T_{Al.} + T_{St.} = 6000\pi$$

$$5T_{St.} + T_{St.} = 6000\pi$$

$$\therefore T_{St.} = 1000\pi \ lb.in.$$

$$T_{Al.} + 1000\pi = 6000\pi$$

$$\therefore T_{Al.} = 5000\pi \ lb.in$$

Step 5: Determine the angle of twist at the free end.

$$\phi = \frac{T_{St.}L_{St.}}{G_{St.}J_{St.}} = \frac{T_{Al.}L_{Al.}}{G_{Al.}J_{Al.}}$$

$$\phi_{AB} = \frac{(1.0\pi \ k.in.)(100 \ in.)}{(12,000 \ ksi)(\pi/32 \ in^4)} = 0.267 \ rads$$

Step 6: Maximum stresses in aluminum and steel portions
Aluminum portion:

$$c_o = 1 \ in.$$

$$c_i = 0.5 \ in$$

$$\tau_o = \frac{T_{Al.}c_o}{J_{Al.}} = \frac{(5000\pi \ lb.in.)(1 \ in.)}{(15\pi/32 \ in^4)} = 10,667 \ psi$$

$$\tau_i = \frac{T_{Al.}c_i}{J_{Al.}} = \frac{(5000\pi \ lb.in.)(0.5 \ in.)}{(15\pi/32 \ in^4)} = 5,333 \ psi$$

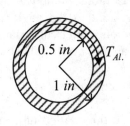

Steel portion:
$c = 0.5$ in.

$$\tau_{max} = \tau_o = \frac{T_{St.}c}{J_{St.}}$$

$$= \frac{(1000\pi \ lb.in.)(0.5 \ in.)}{(\pi/32 \ in.^4)} = 16,600 \ psi.$$

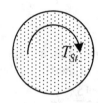

The overall shear stress distribution, in the cross section, can now be drawn as follows.

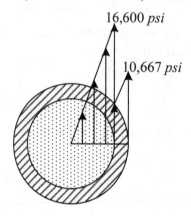

16,600 psi

10,667 psi

5.5 Torsion in shafts made of non-circular cross sections

In engineering practice, often one uses equations developed based on certain simplifying principles and assumptions. Consequently, a student of engineering must be acutely aware of the assumptions underlying those equations. Embodying this concept, the theory and numerical examples described in this chapter, up to this point, are applicable to prismatic circular sections.

Q: Why is the theory and applications described so far applicable only to circular cross sections?
A: There were two major assumptions made in developing the equations for stresses and angle of twists in bars subjected to torsion. A linear variation of stresses, starting from zero at the center to a maximum at the outermost radius point, was assumed. Also, it was assumed that the shear strain in the shaft is directly related to the angle of twist in a linear fashion. These simplifying assumptions are applicable only to circular shafts in the elastic region of behavior – small strain region. Such assumptions are not even applicable to shafts made of rectangular cross-sections.

5.6 Thin walled cross-section

Consider a closed prismatic thin walled tube subjected to a torque. The shear stresses and the angle of twist experienced by this cross-section do not follow the simplifying assumptions made earlier. A full analysis would, in general, require advanced techniques. However, a simple technique developed in the late 19th century by a German engineer named Bredt. This methodology is now described.

5.6.1 Shear Stresses in the shaft

For simplicity consider a thin shaft of made of a circular cross-section, as shown in Figure 5.10, having a small thickness $t = c_2 - c_1$ compared to the radius. From the theory of circular cross-sections described earlier in the chapter it can be seen that the variation of shear stress across the cross-section due to an applied torque is as shown in Figure 5.10.

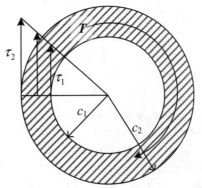

Figure 5.10: Thin shaft of circular cross-section

Implication of Small thickness assumption: The implication of assuming a small thickness of the wall is that the stresses at the inner and outer radii τ_1 and τ_2 are approximately equal. Consequently, it will be assumed that the shear stress across the cross-section remains constant. The shear stress $\tau \cong \tau_{avg.} = (\tau_2 + \tau_1)/2$ in the thickness will be considered at the center of the thickness, a point at a distance $c = (c_2 + c_1)/2$. Although, this scenario has been described for a circular cross section, it is reasonable to assume that in the elastic range this assumption is valid for non-circular thin walled shafts as well.

5.6.2 Shear flow

The concept of shear flow q, is now described. Consider a thin walled shaft with a small but varying thickness, as shown in Figure 5.11. The shear stress experience by the cross-section is as shown. A small three-dimensional element is now considered. In the longitudinal direction the element has a dimension dx. The thickness of the element at one end is t_2 and the thickness at the other end is t_1.

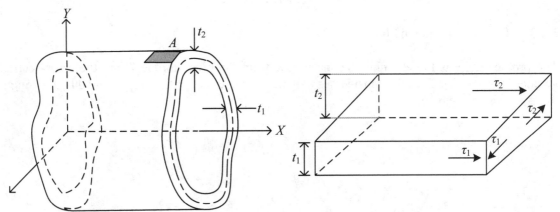

Figure 5.11: Cross-section and element from a thin walled section

It was seen earlier that the shear stress in the shaft could be considered as the average of the shear stresses at the inner and outer radii points. Hence, it can be assumed that the magnitude of the shear stress in the shaft changes with thickness. Let the shear stress at thickness t_1 be τ_1 and the thickness t_2 be τ_2, as shown in Figure 5.11. The equilibrium of the shaft is now considered. Since only forces can be in equilibrium we consider the equilibrium of forces in the longitudinal direction. This can be expressed as follows

$$\sum F_x = 0: \ F_2 - F_1 = 0$$
$$\tau_2 dA_2 - \tau_1 dA_1 = 0$$
$$\tau_2(dxt_2) - \tau_1(dxt_1) = 0$$

or

$$\tau_2 t_2 - \tau_1 t_1 = 0$$

The expression derived above describes an important concept, namely the product of the shear stress and the thickness is a constant. This product, called the *shear flow*, can be written as

$$q = \tau t \quad (psi)(in) \Rightarrow lb/in.$$

Shear flow has the units of force/distance. The term shear flow is derived from its analogy to fluid flow. Consider a closed pipe, as shown in Figure 5.12, with an arbitrary varying cross-section carrying a constant flow of $Q \ m^3/s$, where $Q = vA$ is the product of the velocity at any point and the area of cross-section there. It can be seen that in regions where the area is small the velocity is high, while the greater area regions have a smaller velocity. The shear flow is analogous to the flow rate, while the velocity and area are analogous to the shear stress and the thickness of the section.

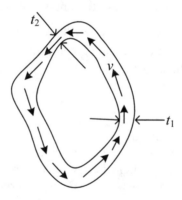

Figure 5.12: Fluid Flow Analogy

5.6.3 Torque and Shear Flow

The problem now is to determine the shear flow from the given torque T and the cross-section geometric properties. For this, consider a small area of the cross section, represented by the length *ds,* as shown in Figure 5.13

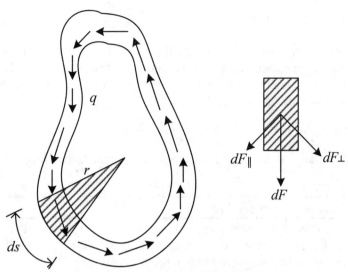

Figure 5.13: Shear flow and torque

The torque due to the shear force in this incremental segment is now derived.

1. Force in the segment ds: $dF = qds$

2. Torque due to this force: $dT = dF_\perp r$

   where, $dF_\perp$ is the component perpendicular to the line from the center to that point r. The parallel component of the force does not cause any torque.

3. Total torque over the entire shaft can be now expressed as a line integral

$$T = \int dT = \int rdF = \int rqds$$

4. Since, the shear flow is constant at any point in the cross section, it comes out of the line integral. Hence, the total torque reduces to the evaluation of the line integral as follows.

$$T = q\int rds$$

5. For the evaluation of the line integral, consider the physical area of the triangle, shaded as shown in figure 5.13, given as

$$dA = rds/2$$

The total area enclosed by the perimeter of the line through the centerline of the thickness is

$$2dA = rds$$

$$2\int dA = \int rds = \int rds$$

$$2A = \int rds$$

6. Hence, the relationship between the torque and the shear flow can now be expressed as

$$T = q(2A)$$

$$q = \frac{T}{2A}$$

$$\tau = \frac{q}{t} = \frac{T}{2At}$$

where, A is the area enclosed by the perimeter formed by the line passing through the center of the thickness of the shaft.

5.6.4 Angle of twist and Torque

The expression for the twist experienced by the thin shaft is derived using principles of energy stored in the shaft due to the applied torque and assuming a linear behavior. The derivation is not shown here, as principles of energy have not yet been introduced. However, the final expression for the angle of twist is also given as a line integral, as follow.

$$\phi = \frac{TL}{4A^2G}\int\frac{ds}{t}$$

An example to demonstrate the usage of the equations in order to determine the shear stress and the angle of twist follows.

Example 5.5: Thin walled hollow section

Problem Statement: A shaft 100 *mm* long is made of a 5 *mm* thin walled hollow section as shown in the figure. If it is subjected to a torque of 0.75 *kN m*, determine the maximum shear stress in the cross section and the angle of twist at the free end.

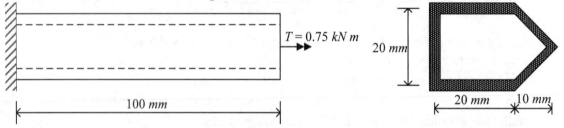

Required: Determine the maximum shear stress in the cross section and the angle of twist at the free end.

Solution:

Step 1: Determine the area enclosed by the centerline of the thin walled cross section.

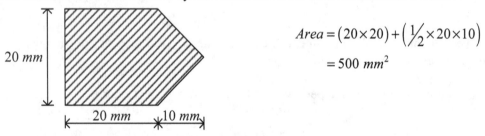

$$Area = (20\times20)+\left(\frac{1}{2}\times20\times10\right)$$
$$= 500 \ mm^2$$

Step 2: Determine the shear stress in the shaft cross section

$$\tau = \frac{T}{2At} = \frac{0.75\times1000000}{2\times500\times5}$$
$$= 150 \ N/mm^2$$
$$= 150 \ MPa$$

Step 3: Determine the angle of twist at the free end. For aluminum $G = 26 \ GPa = 26000 \ MPa$

The angle of twist is determined by a line integral equation. For straight line sections, the formula is applied as shown below.

$$\phi = \frac{TL}{4A^2G}\int\frac{ds}{t} = \frac{TL}{4A^2G}\sum\frac{L_i}{t_i}$$

where, L_i and t_i are the length and thickness of the individual segments. In this example they are as follows.

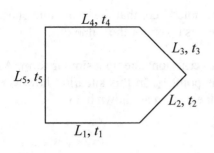

$$L_1 = L_4 = L_5 = 20 \ mm$$

$$L_2 = L_3 = \sqrt{10^2 + 10^2} = 14.14 \ mm$$

$$t_1 = t_2 = t_3 = t_4 = t_5 = 5mm$$

$$\therefore \phi = \frac{T}{4A^2G}\left[\frac{L_1}{t_1} + \frac{L_2}{t_2} + \frac{L_3}{t_3} + \frac{L_4}{t_4} + \frac{L_5}{t_5}\right]$$

$$= \frac{750000}{4(500)^2 \times 26000}\left[\frac{20}{5} + \frac{14.14}{5} + \frac{14.14}{5} + \frac{20}{5} + \frac{20}{5}\right]$$

$$= \frac{750000}{4(500)^2 \times 26000}\left[\frac{60}{5} + \frac{28.28}{5}\right]$$

$$= 5.09 \times 10^{-4} \ rads$$

$$= 0.29 \ degrees$$

5.7   Design of shafts

The design of circular shafts, either to resist a given torque or to find the torque capacity of a shaft of a given geometry, is outlined in this section. The design of shafts, or any other member in general, should satisfy two criteria, namely;

1. **Strength Criterion:** In this criterion, the main objective is to ensure that the actual maximum shear stress in the shaft does not exceed the allowable shear stress. This can be expressed in equation form as follows

$$\tau_{act.} \leq \tau_{all.}$$

   where, $\tau_{all.}$ is the allowable shear stress. This value is a well defined material property which is determined from experimental observations and a pre-specified factor of safety. The actual maximum shear stress in the shaft is determined from the equations given earlier in this chapter.

2. **Stiffness Criterion:** This is a deformation related criterion and ensures that the angle of twist at any point is less than a specified limit. The specified limit is usually a tolerance limit or comfort limit and is not a material property.

Design of shaft diameter: The design of shafts to resist an applied design torque involves the determination of the size of the shaft cross-section, satisfying both the strength and the stiffness criterion.

For circular shafts, the design for strength criterion typically involves the rearrangement of the stress equation to group all geometry terms on one side as follows

$$\frac{T}{\tau_{all.}} = \frac{J}{c}$$

$$= \frac{\pi c^4 / 2}{c}$$

$$= \frac{\pi c^3}{2}$$

from which, the radius of the shaft c can be found. It is to be noted here that the maximum shear stress for a circular shaft occurs at the outermost point; hence c is taken for the value of r.

For hollow circular sections, the design equations for strength criterion take up a similar form. As before, the maximum shear stress occurs at the outer radius point c_2. In this situation however, there are two geometric unknowns c_2 and c_1, and one strength equation as shown below

$$\frac{T}{\tau_{all.}} = \frac{J}{c}$$

$$= \frac{\pi(c_2^4 - c_1^4)/2}{c_2}$$

Hence, one has to make an assumption on the thickness or refer to some standard tables that give commercially available tube section sizes in order to get the geometric parameters required for checking the design.

Transmission Shafts

One of the main applications of the design of circular shafts is in transmission shafts of automobile and other similar applications, where the torque generated by the engine is to be transferred to the drive wheels. There are two requirements in the design of drive shafts, namely the power to be transmitted P at a certain speed, which is specified as rounds per minute N (or radians per second ω). The design of the shaft typically involves the selection of the diameter of the rod, such that the shear stresses in the material do not exceed the allowable shear stress.

The relationship between torque T, power P and the frequency f in rotations per second (Hertz, Hz) (or ω) is given as follows

$$P = T\omega = T(2\pi f)$$

In US Customary units, power is often specified in horse-power (hp) units. One horse power is equivalent to 550 $ft.lbs/s$. Hence, if the power required is specified in hp units and the speed at which it is to be delivered is specified in rotations per minute, then the required torque is given as follows

$$P = (P\ hp)(550\ \frac{ft.lb}{s.hp})(12\ in/lb) = 6600P\ in.lb/s$$

$$N(rpm) = N(\frac{rounds}{minute})2\pi\ \frac{rads}{round}\frac{1}{60}\ \frac{m}{s} = \frac{2\pi N}{60}\ rads/s$$

$$\therefore \omega = \frac{2\pi N}{60}\ rads/s$$

$$T = \frac{P}{\omega} = \frac{6600P}{2\pi N/60} = 63,024\frac{P}{N}\ in.lb$$

Where, P is given in hp units and N is given in rounds per minute (RMP) units. For example, the torque generated by a 3 hp motor delivering the power at 1000 RPM is

$$T = 63,024\frac{3}{1000} = 189\ lb.in.$$

5.8   Summary

This chapter discusses the topics related to members subjected to a torque. Torsion causes both shear stresses and shear strains in the material. However, the angle of twist is a practical measurable quantity. The chapter dealt with circular sections and hollow thin walled sections subjected to torsion. Both statically determinate and indeterminate problems were considered. The keywords introduced in this chapter are as follows.

1. **Angle of Twist:** The angle of twist ϕ is defined on the circular cross section. It is defined as the angle, in radians, by which the cross section rotates due to the torque.

2. **Positive Twisting Moment:** A set of two torques acting at the two ends of the shaft such that they cause a counter clock wise twist of the cross section at each end.

3. **Shear Strain:** The shear strain, also defined as an angle, is the angle (in radians) along the longitudinal axis at the outer surface.

4. **Shear Flow:** The product of the shear stress and the thickness, in a thin walled cross section, is a constant and is called the shear flow.

5. **Stiffness Criterion for Design:** This is a deformation related criterion and ensures that the angle of twist at any point is less than a specified limit.

6. **Strength Criterion for Design:** In this criterion, the main objective is to ensure that the actual maximum shear stress in the shaft does not exceed the allowable shear stress.

7. **Torsional Flexibility:** The flexibility of a section of shaft is given as $f = \dfrac{L}{GJ}$.

5.9 Problems

5.1 Draw the free body diagram of a circular shaft in a state of pure torsion.

5.2 Draw a diagram showing the stress distribution on a circular cross section of a shaft experiencing torsion. Show the variation in the stress magnitude.

5.3 Draw a diagram which explains the relationship between the angle of twist (ϕ) and the shear strain (γ).

For problems 5.4, 5.5, 5.6, 5.7, 5.8 & 5.9 refer the figure below:

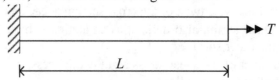

5.4 A circular shaft, as shown in the figure, has a diameter of ¾ *in* and is subjected to a torque of 10 *ft.k.*
   a. Draw the torque moment diagram
   b. Draw the shear stress magnitude variation in the cross section
   c. What is the maximum shear stress in the cross section? Draw an element clearly showing the element representation of the stress.

5.5 Redo problem 5.4 assuming that the cross section is made of a hollow circular shaft. The outer and inner diameters are 1 *in* and ¾ *in* respectively.

5.6 If the shaft in problem 5.4 has a length of *L*=10 *in* and is made of aluminum, determine the a) angle of twist at the free end, b) maximum shear strain in the bar. Draw a diagram showing the shear strain and the angle of twist geometrically. (G_{Al}= 4000 *ksi*)

5.7 Repeat problem 5.6 assuming now that the torque is applied at midspan. What is the maximum angle of twist?

5.8 Redo problem 5.6 for a hollow circular shaft of 1 *in* outer diameter and ¾ *in* inner diameter.

5.9 Solve problem 5.8 assuming that the torque is applied at midspan.

5.10 A solid shaft of diameter 1.5 *in.*, as described in example 5.1, is subjected to a set of four torque and is shown in the figure below. Draw the Twisting Moment Diagram (TMD) and determine the maximum shear stress in the shaft. Find the angle of twist at the free end.

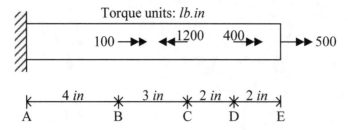

Assume *G* =11,200 *ksi*

5.11 A solid shaft of diameter 0.5 *m*., as described in example 5.1, is subjected to a set of four torque and is shown in the figure below. Draw the Twisting Moment Diagram (TMD) and determine the maximum shear stress in the shaft. Find the angle of twist at the free end. Assume G =130 *GPa*.

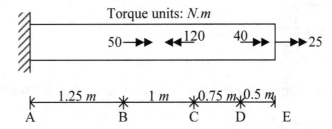

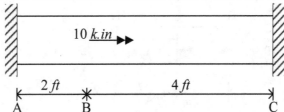

5.12 A statically indeterminate solid shaft, fixed at both ends, of diameter 1 *in*, is subjected to twisting moment of 10 *in.k* as shown in the figure. Draw the Twisting Moment Diagram (TMD) and determine the maximum shear stress in the shaft. Find the angle of twist at B.

5.13 Using the flexibility approach, for the statically indeterminate shaft as shown in the figure above having diameter 1 *in* determine a) the resisting torques at A and C, b) the angle of twist at B and c) maximum shear strain in the torque. Given that E =29,000 *ksi* and v =0.33.

5.14 The rod shown in the figures below is subjected to a twisting moment of 20 *k.in* and is fixed at both ends. For each of the figures shown,
   a. Determine the resisting torques at the ends
   b. Draw the torque moment diagram
   c. Find the maximum shear stress in the rod
   Use the values in the following table if not given in the figures

	Suffix 1	Suffix 2
E	30,000 *ksi*	29, 000 *ksi*
v	0.3	0.33
L	4 *ft*	3 *ft*
d	2 *in*	1 *in*

i.

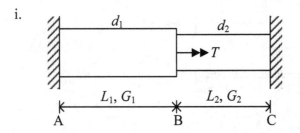

ii.

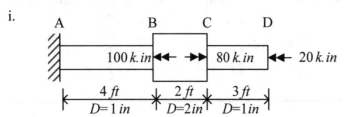

5.15 If the material in the figures shown below is made of steel (E =29,000 ksi / 210 GPa and v =0.33) determine
   a. Twist at the free end
   b. Maximum twist in the rods
   c. Maximum shear stress in the rods
   d. Draw the Torque Moment Diagram

i.

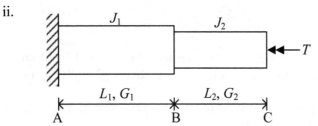

ii.

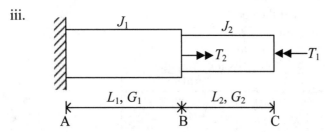

iii.

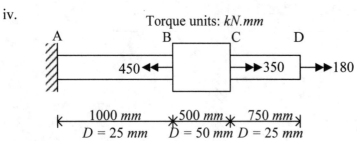

iv.

Torque units: $kN.mm$

v.

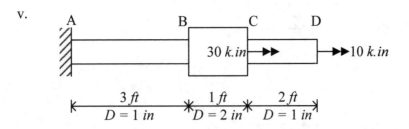

5.16 In the figure shown below, given that the material is steel ($E =29,000$ ksi, allowable stress $\sigma_{all.}=24$ ksi), determine the minimum diameter of the bar.

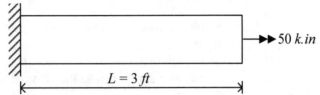

5.17 If the bar in problem 5.15 is also subjected to the stiffness criterion in which the twist at the free end is limited to 0.001 rad., determine the bar diameter which would satisfy both the strength and stiffness criterion

5.18 Determine the axial stiffness and flexibility of the rod shown below

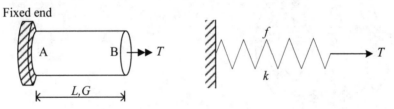

   a. $E = 29,000$ ksi , $d = 2$ in, $L = 3$ ft, $v= 0.3$.
   b. $E = 29,000$ ksi, $d = 1$ in, $L = 6$ ft, $v= 0.3$.
   c. $E = 210$ GPa, $d = 25$ mm, $L = 2$ m, $v= 0.3$.
   d. $E = 210$ GPa, $d = 50$ mm, $L = 4$m, $v= 0.3$.

5.19 For the thin walled sections shown in the figures below, determine
   a. The maximum shear stress in the shaft
   b. The twist per unit length of the shaft

   i.

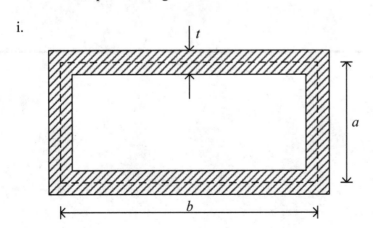

ii.

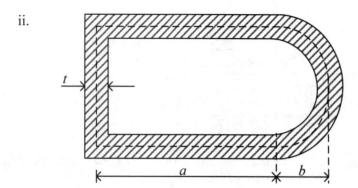

5.20 The rod shown in the figure below is made of composite cross section as shown below. For each of the cross sections determine
   a.   The maximum shear stress in each material
   b.   Draw the shear stress distribution diagram across the cross section
   c.   The angle of twist at the free end

i.

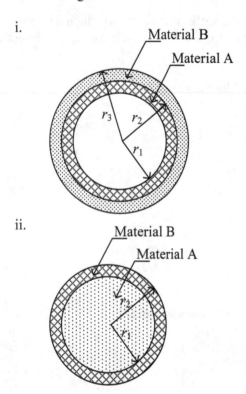

ii.

Chapter 6

Shear Force and Bending Moment Diagrams

Goals: The learning objectives in this chapter are as follows:

1. Define the physical phenomenon of being moment and shear force
2. Define and determine the internal shear force and bending moment in beams
3. Introduce the concept of internal hinges in beams
4. Draw shear force and bending moment diagram by Method of Sections
5. Draw shear force and bending moment diagram by Summation Method

6   Shear Force and Bending Moment Diagrams

6.1   Introduction

In earlier chapters, we studied the idea of representing the variation of internal axial forces and torque along the length of the member, in a representation known as axial force diagrams (AFD) and torsion moment diagrams (TMD). In this chapter, we learn to represent the variation of two more types of internal quantities namely, the bending moment and shear force in terms of bending moment diagram and shear force diagram.

6.2   Definitions of Bending Moment and Shear Force

In a structural element such as a two-dimensional beam subjected to external loads has a smooth deformation pattern, as shown in Figure 6.1. The beam deforms with a smooth curvature, as shown, with the concave face upwards.

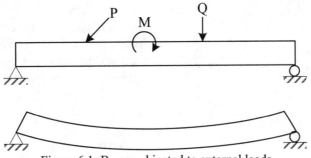

Figure 6.1: Beam subjected to external loads

The external forces P, Q and the moment M applied to this beam are resisted internally by three sets of forces and moments, namely the axial force, bending moment and a shear force. In order to physically define these internal forces, consider section A-A of the beam shown in Figure 6.2, which splits the beam into two parts. The left half of the beam, along with the forces and the reactions at its supports and a set of internal forces are referred to as the *left section free body diagram*. Similarly, the right section can be represented, as shown in Figure 6.2, by the *right section free body diagram*.

A set of internal forces is shown in Figure 6.2. Two types of forces, one parallel to the surface called the *shear force* (V) and one perpendicular to the surface called the *axial force* (P), transfers the forces between the two sections. The third internal quantity, shown by a circular arrow and called the *bending moment* (M) is responsible for transferring the moment between the two sections. It can be seen that the internal forces are shown as equal in magnitude and opposite in directions in the two sections of the free body diagrams.

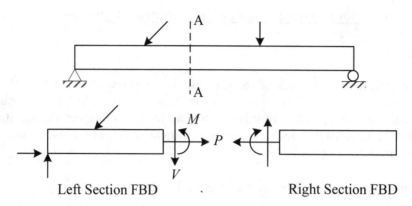

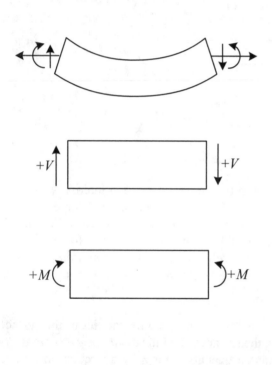

Left Section FBD   Right Section FBD

Figure 6.2: Section free body diagrams

Sign Convention: It has been seen that the internal forces and moments are shown as equal and opposite forces on the two section free body diagrams. We now define the *positive sign convention* for these forces and moments. Figure 6.3 describes the sign convention schematically.

The first part of Figure 6.3 shows the internal forces on the left and right face of an internal section, cut from the beam. Each of the three figures shown below the top figure depicts the individual positive force directions in each face.

Positive Shear (+V): A positive shear force is defined by an upward force on the left face of the section and a downward force on the right face of the section.

Positive Bending Moment (+M): A positive bending moment is defined by a clockwise moment on the left face and a counter clockwise moment on the right face of the section. A positive bending moment causes a *smiling face* or a concave face upwards action physically.

Positive Axial Force (+P): A positive axial force is as shown in Figure 6.3 represented by a force to the left on the left face and force to the right on the right face (forces away from the faces). A positive axial force represents the object in tension physically.

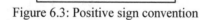

Figure 6.3: Positive sign convention

The difference between a positive force and positive moment from a positive axial force and positive bending moment must be carefully noted. A positive force or a positive moment depends only on the direction in which they are acting. For example a counterclockwise moment in considered as positive while a clockwise moment is given a negative sign. In contrast, the positive sign convention of the three internal forces are based on a physical action; tension in body in the case of axial force, upward curvature in the case of a bending moment and a shearing action in the case of a positive shear force. In order to cause a positive axial force or bending moment, two equal and opposite forces and moments are required.

6.3   Method of Sections

It was seen in earlier chapters on axial force and torsion that the first step towards the finding of the axial and shear stresses they cause, is the determination of the internal forces by the method of sections. The determination of the three internal forces acting in a beam, namely the axial force (P), shear force (V) and the bending moment (M) follow a general process outlined below.

1. Determine the external reaction forces caused due to the loading on the structure by drawing a free body diagram of the *entire structure,* writing equations of Statics and solving the resulting set of linear equations for unknown reaction magnitudes.

2. Cut or section the beam at the point, along the span of the beam, where the internal forces are to be determined and draw the free body diagram of the section, the left section or the right section. The *Section Free Body Diagram* should clearly show the internal forces and moment at the cut point drawn as per the guidelines outlined earlier in this chapter.

3. Determine the *magnitudes* and *types* of internal forces P, V and M by writing and solving equations of equilibrium for that section free body diagram.

4. Interpret the signs of the internal forces: Unlike reactions, where a negative sign simply implies that the actual direction of the reaction is opposite to what one has assumed, the signs of P, V and M as determined in step 3 have a physical interpretation. A negative P would imply that the section is in compression; a negative M implies that the beam bends with a downward curvature and a negative V implies that the beam shears in an opposite direction.

6.3.1   Shear and Moment Diagrams

The goal of many engineering problems is to design a structure or a structural element, for example, the main members of a building frame are beams and columns. Beams are the horizontal members and columns are the vertical members.

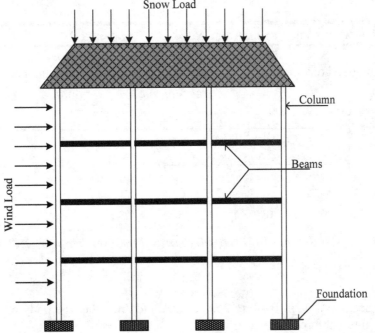

Figure 6.4: Schematic representation of a building subjected to different loading.

Due to the application of structural loads, as shown in Figure 6.4, the beams and columns are subjected to axial forces, shear forces and bending moments. In order to design the sizes for the beams, columns and other structural members, a designer has to clearly understand and quantify the axial forces, shear forces and bending moments and follows the sequence of steps as shown below

1. Determine the loads on the structure
2. Analyze the structure and study the axial, shear and moment behavior by drawing what are called as Axial Force Diagrams (AFD), Shear Force Diagrams (SFD) and Bending Moment Diagrams (BMD).

The process of determination of these diagrams involves the determination of the internal forces (P, V and M) using the method of sections. There are two purposes for using the method of sections in determining the internal forces, namely

1. Determination P, V and M at a specific known point along the span
2. Determination of P, V and M at any general point along the span, which is represented by a variable x. The equations of equilibrium resulting from the section diagrams result in analytical expressions for $P(x)$, $V(x)$ and $M(x)$, which are now functions of x. Shear Force Diagram (SFD) and Bending Moment Diagrams (BMD) are graphical representations of these equations over the entire span and give a quick understanding of the overall behavior of the entire beam. Examples of these two cases are presented next.

Example 6-1: Equations for Axial Force, Shear Force and Bending Moment

Problem Statement: Determine the axial force; shear force and bending moment in the beam shown, at a point 12 *inches* to the right of support A?

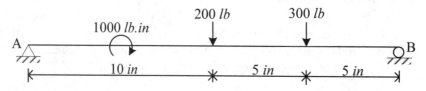

Required: P, V and M at a point 12 *in* from A.

Solution:

Step 1: Draw the free body diagram of the *overall* structure and determine the reactions

$$\sum F_x = 0 : A_x + 0 = 0; \quad \therefore A_x = 0$$

$$\sum F_y = 0 : A_y + B_y - 200 - 300 = 0; \quad \therefore A_y + B_y = 500$$

$$\sum M_A = 0 : B_y(20 \ in) - (200 \ lbs)(10 \ in) - (300 \ lbs)(15 \ in) - 1000 \ lb.in. = 0; \quad \therefore B_y = 375 \ lbs. \uparrow$$

$$\therefore A_y = 500 - 375 = 125 \ lbs. \uparrow$$

Step 2: Pass a section through B-B at 12 *in* from A and draw the free body of the left (or right) section with the internal forces drawn appropriately

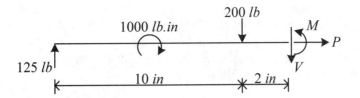

Step 3: Write the equations of equilibrium and interpret the signs of the internal forces

$$\sum F_x = 0: P + 0 = 0; \quad \therefore P = 0$$

$$\sum F_y = 0: 125 - V - 200 = 0; \quad \therefore V = -75 \; lbs; \quad \therefore V = 75 \; lb \uparrow$$

$$\sum M_{@12 \; in} = 0: M - 125(12) - 1000 + 200(2) = 0; \quad \therefore M = 2100 \; lb.in.$$

A negative V implies that shear forces in each section are in the direction opposite to that originally assumed. A positive M implies that the beam is bending with an upward curvature.

Example 6-2: Equations for Axial Force, Shear Force and Bending Moment

Problem Statement: Determine a general expression for the axial force; shear force and bending moment in the beam.

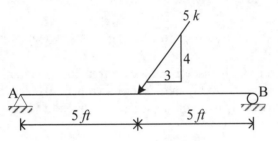

Required: P, V and M at point distance x from support A.

Solution:

Step 1: Draw the free body diagram of the *overall* structure and determine the reactions

$$\sum F_x = 0: A_x - 3 = 0; \quad \therefore A_x = 3 \; k \rightarrow$$

$$\sum F_y = 0: A_y + B_y - 4 = 0; \quad \therefore A_y + B_y = 4$$

$$\sum M_A = 0: B_y(10 \; ft) - (4 \; k)(5 \; ft) = 0; \quad \therefore B_y = 2 \; k \uparrow$$

$$\therefore A_y = 2 \; k \uparrow$$

Concept: The first determination to be made is - how many sections are needed in order to represent the variation of P, V and M over the entire span. Let us first consider a section to the left of the concentrated load, at a distance of x from support A. In this region AC ($0 < x < 5 \; ft$) it can be seen that the free body diagram does not change except for a change in x. As x goes beyond the concentrated load in region CB the free body diagram changes since a concentrated load now appears in it. Hence, a new section is needed for this region (5<x<10 ft.).

Details of the two section free bodies, the resulting equilibrium equations and the expressions of *P, V* and *M* derived from them are now illustrated.

Step 2a: Pass a section through B-B at a distance less than 5 ft from A and draw the free body of the left (or right) section with the internal forces drawn appropriately

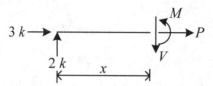

Step 2b: Write the equations of equilibrium for the left section free body diagram

$$\sum F_x = 0 : P + 3 = 0; \quad \therefore P = -3\ k$$

$$\sum F_y = 0 : 2 - V = 0; \quad \therefore V = 2\ k \qquad \text{For } 0 < x < 5$$

$$\sum M_x = 0 : M - 2x = 0; \quad \therefore M = 2x\ k.ft$$

Step 3a: Section in region CB at *x* (>5 ft.) from point A. The *x* value in this region varies from 5 ft. to 10 ft.

Important: A frequent error that is made is to draw a free body diagram starting from point C. A correct free body diagram cuts the body into exactly two parts. Hence, if a section is cut beyond C, then the left section free body diagram must include the entire beam from A to that point, as shown below.

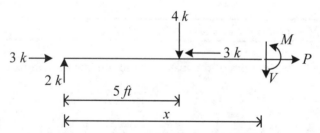

Step 3b: Write the equation of equilibrium for the left section free body diagram

$$\sum F_x = 0 : P + 3 - 3 = 0; \quad \therefore P = 0$$

$$\sum F_y = 0 : 2 - 4 - V = 0; \quad \therefore V = -2\ k \qquad \text{For } 5 < x < 10$$

$$\sum M_x = 0 : M - 2x + 4(x - 5) = 0; \quad \therefore M = 20 - 2x\ k.ft$$

A negative *V* implies that shear forces in each section are opposite in the direction originally assumed.

A positive *M* implies that the beam is bending with an upward curvature.

Alternative choice of origin for *x*: In many cases it might be easier to redefine the choice of the origin for *x*. The option is to move it to the starting point of the region in which the shear and moment equations are being determined. There are two things to keep in mind

➤ The actual physical body to be included in the section diagram would include everything to the left of the section

➤ The origin and the limits of x and the mathematical representations of the distances of the forces to the section point changes as shown. In this case the origin is now at the point C. So the limits of the variable x now become 0 to 5 (since the origin is at C and the distance between C and B is 5 *inches*).

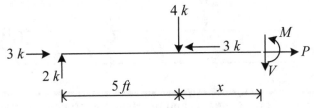

$$\sum F_x = 0 : P + 3 - 3 = 0; \quad \therefore P = 0$$

$$\sum F_y = 0 : 2 - 4 - V = 0; \quad \therefore V = -2 \ k$$

$$\sum M_x = 0 : M - 2(x+5) + 4(x) = 0; \quad \therefore M = 10 - 2x \ k.ft$$

Step 4: The equations of P, V and M are now summarized below and sketched in a graph to draw what are called as Axial Force Diagram (AFD), Shear Force Diagram (SFD) and the Bending Moment Diagram (BMD)

AFD: $0 < x < 5$ $P = -3 \ k$
       $5 < x < 10$ $P = 0$

SFD: $0 < x < 5$ $V = +2 \ k$
       $5 < x < 10$ $V = -2 \ k$

BMD: $0 < x < 5$ $M = 2x \ k.ft$
       $5 < x < 10$ $M = (20 - 2x) \ k.ft$

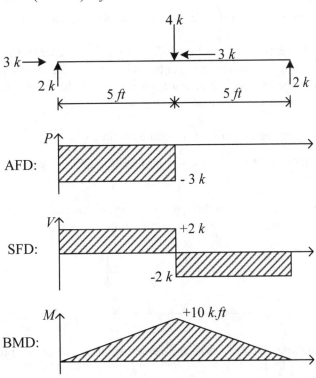

Example 6-3: Equations for Axial Force, Shear Force and Bending Moment

Problem Statement: Determine a general expression for the axial force; shear force and bending moment in the beam.

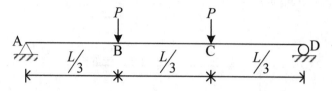

Required: Axial and Shear force diagrams and the Bending moment diagram

Solution:

Step 1: Draw the free body diagram of the *overall* structure and determine the reactions

$$\sum F_x = 0: A_x + 0 = 0; \quad \therefore A_x = 0$$

$$\sum F_y = 0: A_y + D_y - 2P = 0; \quad \therefore A_y + D_y = 2P$$

$$\sum M_A = 0: D_y(L) - P\left(\frac{L}{3}\right) - P\left(\frac{2L}{3}\right) = 0; \quad \therefore D_y = P \uparrow$$

$$\therefore A_y = P \uparrow$$

Q: How many sections are needed in order to represent the variation of *P, V* and *M* over the entire span?

It can be seen that three sections would be needed in this case representing regions AB, BC and CD. As we go from left to right and cut in region AB it can be seen that nothing changes in the diagram (except the distance *x*). At B a new load is introduced hence a new section is required in region BC. A similar argument can be made for region CD.

The values of *x* in the three regions are (keeping the origin fixed at A):

Region AB: $0 < x < \dfrac{L}{3}$, Region BC: $\dfrac{L}{3} < x < \dfrac{2L}{3}$ and Region CD: $\dfrac{2L}{3} < x < L$

Step 2: Pass a section through A-A in the region within AB and draw the free body of the left (or right) section with the internal forces drawn appropriately

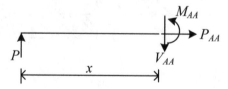

Step 3: Write the equations of equilibrium for the left section free body diagram

$\sum F_x = 0 : P_{AA} = 0; \quad \therefore P_{AA} = 0 \ k$

$\sum F_y = 0 : P - V_{AA} = 0; \quad \therefore V_{AA} = +P \qquad\qquad 0 < x < \dfrac{L}{3}$

$\sum M_x = 0 : M_{AA} - P(x) = 0; \quad \therefore M_{AA} = +Px$

Step 4: Section in region BC at x from point A. The x value in this region varies from $L/3$ to $2L/3$

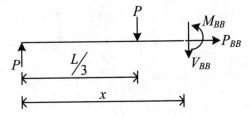

Step 5: Write the equation of equilibrium for the left section free body diagram

$\sum F_x = 0 : P_{BB} = 0; \quad \therefore P_{BB} = 0$

$\sum F_y = 0 : P - P - V_{BB} = 0; \quad \therefore V_{BB} = 0 \qquad\qquad$ For $\dfrac{L}{3} < x < \dfrac{2L}{3}$

$\sum M_x = 0 : M_{BB} - P(x) + P\left(x - \dfrac{L}{3}\right) = 0; \quad \therefore M_{BB} = +\dfrac{PL}{3}$

Step 6: Section in region CD at x from point A. The x value in this region varies from $L/3$ to $2L/3$

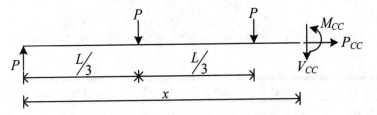

Step 7: Write the equation of equilibrium for the left section free body diagram in region CD

$\sum F_x = 0 : P_{CC} = 0; \quad \therefore P_{CC} = 0k$

$\sum F_y = 0 : P - P - P - V_{CC} = 0; \quad \therefore V_{CC} = -P \qquad\qquad$ For $\dfrac{2L}{3} < x < L$

$\sum M_x = 0 : M_{CC} - P(x) + P\left(x - \dfrac{L}{3}\right) + P\left(x - \dfrac{2L}{3}\right) = 0; \quad \therefore M_{CC} = +PL - Px$

Step 8: The equations of P, V and M are now summarized below and the Shear Force Diagram (SFD) and the Bending Moment Diagram (BMD) sketches are also shown

SFD: $\qquad 0 < x < \dfrac{L}{3} \qquad V = P$

$\qquad\qquad \dfrac{L}{3} < x < \dfrac{2L}{3} \qquad V = 0$

$\qquad\qquad \dfrac{2L}{3} < x < L \qquad V = -P$

BMD:

$$0 < x < \frac{L}{3} \qquad M = Px$$

$$\frac{L}{3} < x < \frac{2L}{3} \qquad M = \frac{PL}{3}$$

$$\frac{2L}{3} < x < L \qquad M = PL - Px$$

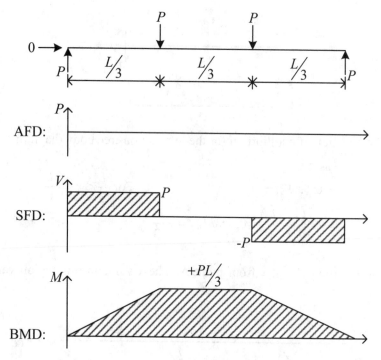

AFD:

SFD:

BMD:

Example 6-4: Axial Force, Shear Force and Bending Moment -Uniformly Distributed Load

Problem Statement: Determine a general expression for the axial force; shear force and bending moment in the beam.

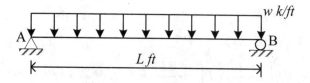

Required: Axial and Shear force diagrams and Bending moment diagram.

Solution:

Step 1: Draw the free body diagram of the *overall* structure and determine the reactions

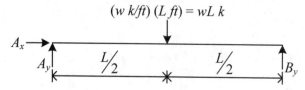

$$\sum F_x = 0 : A_x + 0 = 0; \quad \therefore A_x = 0$$

$$\sum F_y = 0 : A_y + B_y - wL = 0; \quad \therefore A_y + B_y = wL$$

$$\sum M_A = 0 : B_y(L) - wL\left(\frac{L}{2}\right) = 0; \quad \therefore B_y = \frac{wL}{2} \uparrow$$

$$\therefore A_y = \frac{wL}{2} \uparrow$$

It can be seen that only one section would be needed in this case representing the region AB. As we go from left to right and cut in region AB it can be seen that nothing changes in the diagram (except the distance x).

Step 2: Pass a section through A-A at a distance x from A and draw the free body of the left (or right) section with the internal forces drawn appropriately. Two important points must be kept in mind while drawing the section free body diagram

➢ From the original diagram given in the problem, draw a section diagram showing the left section of the body, the part of the distributed load that is applied on the section and the reactions and the internal forces

➢ *Do not* use the free body diagram drawn to determine the reactions in the earlier step for finding internal forces in this section.

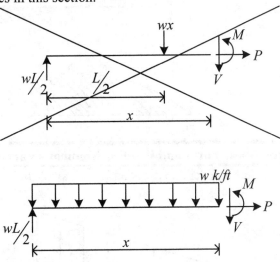

Step 3: Write the equations of equilibrium for the left section free body diagram

$$\sum F_x = 0 : P = 0; \quad \therefore P = 0$$

$$\sum F_y = 0 : \frac{wL}{2} - wx - V = 0; \quad \therefore V = w\left(\frac{L}{2} - x\right) \qquad 0 < x < L$$

$$\sum M_x = 0 : M - \frac{wL}{2}(x) + wx\left(\frac{x}{2}\right) = 0; \quad \therefore M = +\frac{wL}{2}x - \frac{wx^2}{2}$$

Step 4: Determine the values of shear and moment at certain important locations such as the center of the beam and the ends and draw the shear and moment diagrams

$x = 0 \qquad V = \dfrac{wL}{2} \qquad\qquad M = 0$

$x = \dfrac{L}{2} \qquad V = \dfrac{wL}{2} - \dfrac{wL}{2} = 0 \qquad M = \dfrac{wL^2}{4} - \dfrac{wL^2}{8} = \dfrac{wL^2}{8}$

$x = L \qquad V = -\dfrac{wL}{2} \qquad\qquad M = 0$

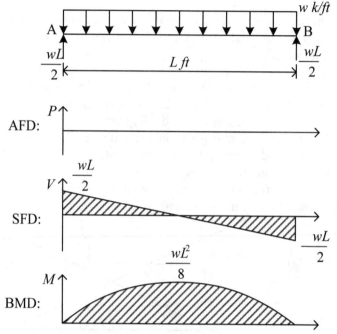

Example 6-5: Axial Force, Shear Force and Bending Moment - Varying Distributed Load

Problem Statement: Determine a general expression for the axial force; shear force and bending moment in the beam.

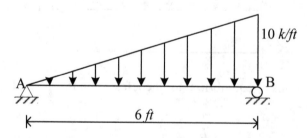

Required: Axial and Shear force diagrams and the Bending moment diagram.

Solution:

Step 1: Draw the free body diagram of the *overall* structure and determine the reactions

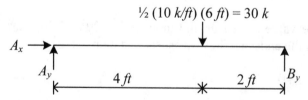

$$\sum F_x = 0 : A_x + 0 = 0; \quad \therefore A_x = 0$$

$$\sum F_y = 0 : A_y + B_y - (10\,k/ft)(6\,ft)/2 = 0; \quad \therefore A_y + B_y = 30\,k$$

$$\sum M_A = 0 : B_y(6\,ft) - (30\,k)(4\,ft) = 0; \quad \therefore B_y = 20\,k\uparrow$$

$$\therefore A_y = 10\,k\uparrow$$

It can be seen that only one section would be needed in this case representing the region AB. As we go from left to right and cut in region AB it can be seen that nothing changes in the diagram (except the distance x).

Step 2: In a varying distributed load, the loading function w is first determined.

$$w = ax + b$$

$$x = 0 \Rightarrow w = 0; \quad \therefore 0 = a(0) + b; \quad \therefore b = 0$$

$$x = 10 \Rightarrow w = 10; \quad \therefore 10 = a(6) + 0; \quad \therefore a = 10/6$$

The Loading function: $w = \left(\dfrac{10}{6}\right)x \quad k/ft$

The loading function represents the height of the distributed load at the point where the section is taken, as seen in the diagram below. The magnitude of the portion of the distributed load within the left section and its location is determined as shown below.

Step 3: Draw a Section Diagram: Pass a section through A-A at a distance x from A and draw the free body of the left (or right) section with the internal forces drawn appropriately. Write the equations of equilibrium for the left section free body diagram to find these internal forces.

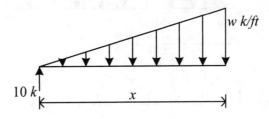

$$\sum F_x = 0 : P = 0; \quad \therefore P = 0$$

$$\sum F_y = 0 : 10 - \frac{5x^2}{6} - V = 0; \quad \therefore V = 10 - \frac{5x^2}{6} \qquad 0 < x < 6$$

$$\sum M_x = 0 : M - 10(x) + \left(\frac{5x^2}{6}\right)\left(\frac{x}{3}\right) = 0; \quad \therefore M = +10x - \frac{5x^3}{18}$$

Step 4: Determine the values of shear and moment at certain important locations such as the center of the beam and the ends and draw the shear and moment diagrams. To find the location x of the maximum shear force and bending moment, the derivatives of shear and moment equations are equated to zero.

$$\frac{dV}{dx} = -\frac{10x}{6} = 0; \quad \therefore x = 0$$

$$\therefore V_{max}(x=0) = 10 - 0 = 10 \ k$$

$$\frac{dM}{dx} = 10 - \frac{15x^2}{18} = 0; \quad \therefore x = \sqrt{12} \ ft$$

$$M_{max}\left(x = \sqrt{12}\right) = 10\sqrt{12} - \frac{5 \times \left(\sqrt{12}\right)^3}{18} = 23.09 \ k.ft$$

$x = 0 \qquad V = V_{max} = 10 \ k \qquad\qquad M = 0$

$x = \sqrt{12} \qquad V = 10 - \dfrac{5\left(\sqrt{12}\right)^2}{6} = 0 \qquad M = M_{max} = 23.09 \ k.ft$

$x = 6 \qquad V = 10 - \dfrac{5(6)^2}{6} = -20 \ k \qquad M = 10(6) - \dfrac{5(6)^3}{18} = 0$

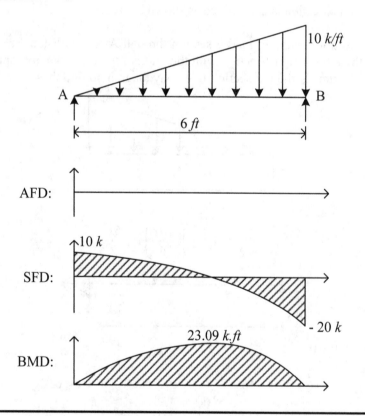

6.4 Method of Integration

It can be seen from the above examples that while the method of sections is based on fundamentals and depends on a clear understanding of the concept of free body diagrams, it is a tedious method. Even for a one span beam, with multiple loads on it the determination of equations that represent the shear and moment functions can take a very long time. This leads to the motivation for solving the problem by using alternate methods. The methods based on integration of the load and shear equations represents one such technique.

Loading function $w(x)$: The loading function represents the variation of the magnitude of the distributed load over the span. Its magnitude is expressed in force/length units, for example *kips/ft* (*klf* – kips per linear foot) or *kN/m*. This function is an algebraic representation of the curve that represents the top of load function. Some examples of loading functions are given below. It is to be noted that the functional form of the loading function is dependent on the choice of the origin of *x*. A positive sign indicates that the direction of the load is the positive *y* direction (upwards) and a negative sign represents a downward acting distributed load

a) Uniformly distributed load function

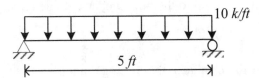

$w = ax + b$
$x = 0 \Rightarrow w = -10; \quad \therefore -10 = a(0) + b; \quad \therefore b = -10$
$x = 5 \Rightarrow w = -10; \quad \therefore -10 = a(5) + 10; \quad \therefore a = 0$
The Loading function: $w(x) = -10 \ k/ft$

b) Triangular load function

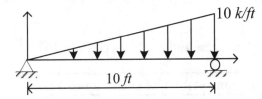

$w = ax + b$
$x = 0 \Rightarrow w = 0; \quad \therefore 0 = a(0) + b; \quad \therefore b = 0$
$x = 5 \Rightarrow w = -10; \quad \therefore -10 = a(5) + 0; \quad \therefore a = -2$
The Loading function: $w(x) = -x \ k/ft$

c) Trapezoidal load function

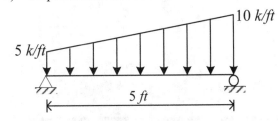

$w = ax + b$
$x = 0 \Rightarrow w = -5; \quad \therefore -5 = a(0) + b; \quad \therefore b = -5$
$x = 5 \Rightarrow w = -10; \quad \therefore -10 = a(5) + 5; \quad \therefore a = -1$
The Loading function: $w(x) = (-x - 5) \ k/ft$

d) Parabolic load function

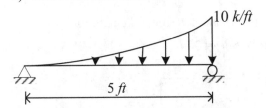

The Loading function: $w(x) = -2x^2 \ k/ft.$

e) Partially loaded distributed load in a span (origin at the left end)

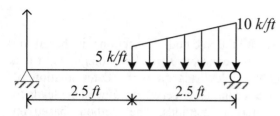

$$w = ax + b$$
$$x = 2.5 \Rightarrow w = -5; \quad \therefore -5 = a(2.5) + b$$
$$x = 5 \Rightarrow w = -10; \quad \therefore -10 = a(5) + b$$
The Loading function: $w(x) = (-2.5x + 2.5) \ k/ft$

f) Partially loaded distributed load in a span (origin at the starting point of the distributed load)

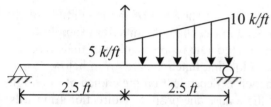

$$w = ax + b$$
$$x = 0 \Rightarrow w = -5; \quad \therefore -5 = a(0) + b; \quad \therefore b = -5$$
$$x = 2.5 \Rightarrow w = 10; \quad \therefore -10 = a(2.5) - 5; \quad \therefore a = -6$$
The Loading function: $w(x) = (-6x - 5) \ k/ft$

Representation of Shear Force: The shear force can now be represented mathematically as the integral of the loading function. From a physical standpoint, integration represents a summation and hence the shear force is the sum of all the vertical forces up to the point under consideration, in the beam.

$$V(x) = \int w(x) + C$$

where C, a constant of integration, represents the shear force value at the starting point ($x=0$).

Representation of Bending Moment: The bending moment is physically the sum of the shear force over the span under consideration. It can be represented mathematically as follows

$$M(x) = \int V(x) + C_1$$

where C_1, a constant of integration, represents the moment value at the starting point ($x=0$).

Example 6-6: Axial Force, Shear Force and Bending Moment - Varying Distributed Load

Problem Statement: Determine a general expression for the axial force; shear force and bending moment in the beam.

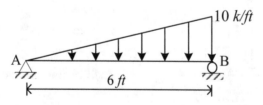

Required: Axial force, Shear force and Bending Moment Equations

Solution:

Step 1: Draw the free body diagram of the *overall* structure and determine the reactions.

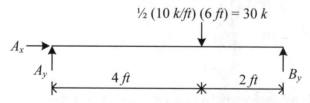

$$\sum F_x = 0 : A_x + 0 = 0; \quad \therefore A_x = 0$$

$$\sum F_y = 0 : A_y + B_y - (10\ k/ft)(6\ ft)/2 = 0; \quad \therefore A_y + B_y = 30\ k$$

$$\sum M_A = 0 : B_y(6\ ft) - (30\ k)(4\ ft) = 0; \quad \therefore B_y = 20\ k \uparrow$$

$$\therefore A_y = 10\ k \uparrow$$

Step 2: In a varying distributed load, the loading function w is first determined.

$$w = ax + b$$

$$x = 0 \Rightarrow w = 0; \quad \therefore 0 = a(0) + b; \quad \therefore b = 0$$

$$x = 6 \Rightarrow w = -10; \quad \therefore -10 = a(6) + 0; \quad \therefore a = -\frac{10}{6}$$

The Loading function: $w(x) = \left(-\dfrac{10}{6}\right) x\ k/ft$

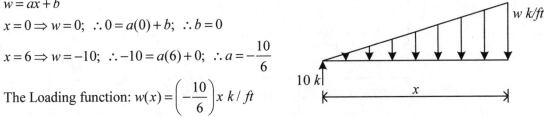

Step 3: Determine the shear force function using the integration method

$$V(x) = \int_0^6 w(x)dx = \int_0^6 \frac{-10x}{6}dx = -\frac{5x^2}{6} + V(0)$$

$$V(x) = -\frac{5x^2}{6} + A_y = -\frac{5x^2}{6} + 10 \qquad\qquad 0 < x < 6$$

$$M(x) = \int_0^6 V(x)dx = \int_0^6 \frac{-5x^2}{6}dx = -\frac{5x^3}{18} + M(0)$$

$$M(x) = -\frac{5x^3}{18} + M_A = -\frac{5x^3}{18} + 0 = -\frac{5x^3}{18}$$

6.5   Summation Method

The summation method represents a direct form of the integration method and is highly suitable for many practical and simpler problems. Shear force and bending moment diagrams are nothing but graphical representation of the equations. Also the primary interest in drawing these diagrams is the determination of the magnitude and location of the maximum values. The motivation of this method can be explained as follows. Consider any arbitrary curve as shown in Figure 6.5. In order to draw the general shape of the curve the following two quantities are needed

1.   The magnitudes (y_A and y_B) at the two ends
2.   The slope values at the two ends

Knowing these the general shape of the curve in between, assuming that it is continuous, can be sketched by drawing a continuous line between the two points with the slope values at the two ends. Figure 6.5 illustrates this point.

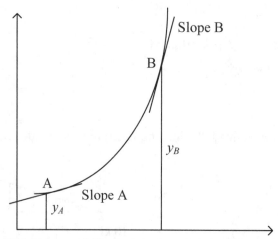

Figure 6.5: Curve with the magnitude and slope of the end points.

SFD by Summation Method:

With the above idea in mind the shear force diagram for a beam can be constructed by the applying the concept as follows. Consider a section of a beam, shown in Figure 6.7, in which the shear and moment at the left hand side is V_L and M_L and the values on the right is given by V_R and M_R. Any arbitrary distributed load $w(x)$ is applied on the section.

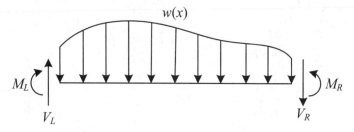

Figure 6.6: Beam loaded with arbitrary distributed load

The information needed to draw the shear force diagram is as follows;

a) Shear Magnitude at left end - V_L

b) Shear Magnitude at right end - V_R

c) Slope of SFD at left end is $Slope_L = \dfrac{dV}{dx}\Big|_L = w(x=0)$ which represents the *magnitude of the distributed load at the left end.*

d) Slope of SFD at right end is $Slope_R = \dfrac{dV}{dx}\Big|_R = w(x=a)$ which represents the *magnitude of the distributed load at the right end.*

Using the four pieces of information shown above, the shear force diagram can be draw as shown below

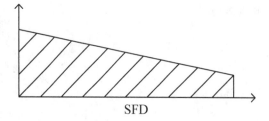

SFD

Figure 6.7: SFD of the beam shown above

BMD by Summation Method:

In the beam shown in Figure 6.6, the information needed to draw the bending moment diagram is as follows;

a) Moment Magnitude at left end - M_L

b) Moment Magnitude at right end - M_R

c) Slope of BMD at left end is $Slope_L = \dfrac{dM}{dx}\bigg|_L = V_L$ which represents the *magnitude of the shear force at the left end.*

d) Slope of BMD at right end is $Slope_R = \dfrac{dM}{dx}\bigg|_R = V_R$ which represents the *magnitude of the shear force at the right end.*

The bending moment diagram can now be drawn as shown below

BMD

Figure 6.8: BMD of the beam shown above

Concentrated Forces and Moments: The treatment of concentrated forces and concentrated moments with the summation method is done in the following manner. Consider the section of a beam, as shown in Figure 6.9(a) and Figure 6.9(b), which shows the free body diagram of the small portion containing the concentrated force and moment respectively. In this illustration a downward concentrated force and a clockwise concentrated bending moment is considered.

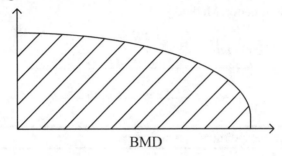

(a) Section with concentrated load

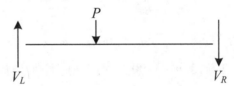

(b) Section with Moment

Figure 6.9: Small section of a beam

The equilibrium equations of the free body diagram can now be written as

$$V_L - P - V_R = 0$$

$$-M_L - M + M_R = 0$$

From the equilibrium equation the shear force and bending moment on the right hand side can be expressed as

$$V_R = V_L - P$$

$$M_R = M_L + M$$

Eqn (6.1)

The significance of the equations 6.1 is as follows;
a) For a concentrated force acting *downwards* – the shear to the right is the shear force at the left *minus* the concentrated force. This implies a *downward jump* in the shear force diagram of a magnitude equal to the *magnitude of the concentrated force*.
b) A *clockwise concentrated* moment results in an increase *(upward jump)* in the bending moment in the BMD. Alternatively, a *counterclockwise concentrated* moment results in a *downward jump* in the bending moment diagram.

The examples outlined earlier in this chapter are now recast in the summation method, in order to illustrate the ease of usage of this method.

Example 6-7: Shear Force and Bending Moment by the summation method

Problem Statement: Draw the shear force and bending moment diagram for the beam loaded as shown below, using the Summation Method.

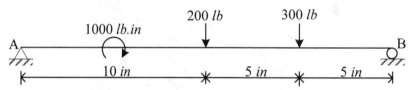

Required: Shear Force and Bending Moment Diagram

Solution:

Step 1: Draw the free body diagram of the *overall* structure and determine the reactions

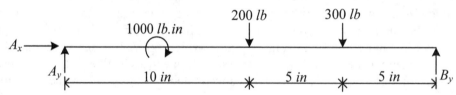

$$\sum F_x = 0: A_x + 0 = 0; \quad \therefore A_x = 0$$

$$\sum F_y = 0: A_y - 200 - 300 + B_y = 0; \quad \therefore A_y + B_y = 500 \; lbs.$$

$$\sum M_A = 0: B_y(20 \; in) - (200 \; lbs)(10 \; in) - (300 \; lbs)(15 \; in) - 1000 \; lb.in. = 0; \quad \therefore B_y = 375 \; lbs. \uparrow$$

$$\therefore A_y = 125 \; lbs \uparrow$$

Step 2: Develop the shear force diagram using the summation method.
a) The determination of the values is started from the left end where the shear force is equal to the reaction at A (a concentrated force). In this example the distributed load is zero. The right end is the location of the 200 *lbs.* force.

$$V_L = A_y = 125$$

$$V_R = V_L + \text{Area under the distributed load}$$

$$= 125 + 0 = 125$$

$$Slope_L = 0; \; Slope_R = 0$$

b) The concentrated force, acting downwards, causes a jump down in the SFD. Hence the new shear force value (just to the right of the concentrated force) is $125 - 200 = -75 \; lbs$
c) In the region between the 200 and 300 *lbs.* forces the values can be computed as follows

$$V_L = -75$$

$$V_R = -75 + 0 = -75$$

$$Slope_L = Slope_R = 0$$

d) At the 300 *lbs.* concentrated force location, the shear force to the right of the force is $-75 - 300 = -375$ *lbs*

e) Then in the region between the 300 *lbs.* force and the end reaction at B the values can be computed as follows

$$V_L = -375$$

$$V_R = -375 + 0 = -375$$

$$Slope_L = Slope_R = 0$$

f) Finally at the end, the end reaction of 375 *lbs.* upwards results in the SFD jumping up back to zero.

For ease of depiction the above steps can be shown in tabular form as follows

	Region AC		Region CD		Region DB	
Area under DL	0		0		0	
Shear force value	+125	+125	-75	-75	-375	-375
Slope Value	0	0	0	0	0	0

Slope value equating to zero at the two ends indicates a horizontal line. The SFD can now be drawn as follows using the tabulated values shown above.

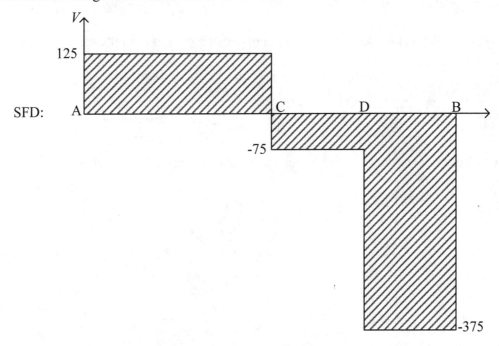

Step 3: The bending moment diagram using the summation method is illustrated below

a) At the left end the bending moment is equal to zero. The region AD calculations can be expressed as follows

$M_L = 0$

$M_R = M_L +$ Area under the shear force diagram

$= 0 + (125lb. \times 5in.) = 625 \ lb.in.$

$Slope_L = 125; \ Slope_R = 125$

b) The concentrated moment, acting clockwise, causes a jump up in the BMD. Hence the new bending moment value (just to the right of the concentrated moment) is $625 + 1000 = 1625 \ lbs$

c) In the region between the moment and 200 *lbs.* force

$M_L = 1625 \ lb.in$

$M_R = 1625 + (125lb. \times 5in.) = 2250 \ lb.in.$

$Slope_L = 125; \ Slope_R = 125$

d) In the region between the 200 and 300 *lbs.* forces the values can be computed as follows

$M_L = 2250 \ lb.in$

$M_R = 2250 - (75 \times 5) = 1875 \ lb.in$

$Slope_L = Slope_R = -75$

e) Then in the region between the 300 *lbs.* force and the end reaction B the values can be computed as follows

$M_L = 1875 \ lb.in$

$M_R = 1875 - (375 \times 5) = 0$

$Slope_L = Slope_R = -375$

For ease of depiction the above steps can be shown in tabular form as follows

	Region AC		Region CD		Region DE		Region EB	
Area under SFD	$125 \times 5 = 625$		$125 \times 5 = 625$		$-75 \times 5 = -375$		$-375 \times 5 = -1875$	
Bending Moment	0	625	1625	2250	2250	1875	1875	0
Slope Value	125	125	125	125	-75	-75	-375	-375

The BMD can now be drawn as follows using the tabulated values shown above.

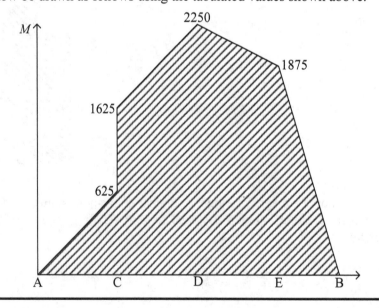

Example 6-8: Shear Force and Bending Moment diagram by the summation method

Problem Statement: Draw the shear force and bending moment diagram for the beam loaded as shown below, using the Summation Method.

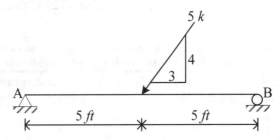

Required: Shear Force and Bending Moment Diagram

Solution:

Step 1: Draw the free body diagram of the *overall* structure and determine the reactions.

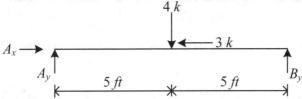

$$\sum F_x = 0 : A_x - 3 = 0; \quad \therefore A_x = 3\,k \rightarrow$$

$$\sum F_y = 0 : A_y + B_y - 4 = 0; \quad \therefore A_y + B_y = 4$$

$$\sum M_A = 0 : B_y(10\ in) - (4\,k)(5\ in) = 0; \quad \therefore B_y = 2\,k \uparrow$$

$$\therefore A_y = 2\,k \uparrow$$

Step 2: Develop the shear force diagram using the summation method.

For the determination of SFD and BMD we consider two regions; Region AC and Region CB.

	Region AC		Region CB	
Area under DL	0		0	
Shear force value	+2	+2	-2	-2
Slope Value	0	0	0	0

SFD: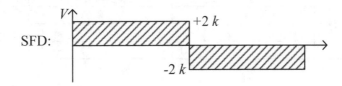

Step 3: Develop the bending moment diagram using summation method.

	Region AC		Region CB	
Area under SFD	$2 \times 5 = 10$		$-2 \times 5 = -10$	
Bending Moment	0	10	10	0
Slope Value	+2	+2	-2	-2

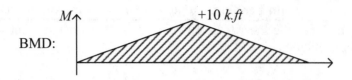

BMD:

M +10 k.ft

Example 6-9: Shear Force and Bending Moment diagram by the summation method

Problem Statement: Draw the shear force and bending moment diagram for the beam loaded as shown below, using the Summation Method.

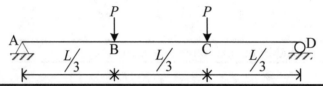

Required: Shear force and Bending Moment diagrams

Solution:

Step 1: Draw the free body diagram of the *overall* structure and determine the reactions.

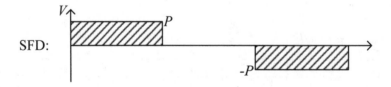

$$\sum F_x = 0: A_x + 0 = 0; \quad \therefore A_x = 0$$

$$\sum F_y = 0: A_y + D_y - 2P = 0; \quad \therefore A_y + D_y = 2P$$

$$\sum M_A = 0: D_y(L) - P\left(\frac{L}{3}\right) - P\left(\frac{2L}{3}\right) = 0; \quad \therefore D_y = P \uparrow$$

$$\therefore A_y = P \uparrow$$

Step 2: Develop the shear force diagram using the summation method.
For the determination of SFD and BMD we consider three regions; Region AB, Region BC and Region CD.

	Region AB		Region BC		Region CD	
Area under DL	0		0		0	
Shear force value	+P	+P	0	0	-P	-P
Slope Value	0	0	0	0	0	0

SFD:

V P $-P$

Step 3: Develop the bending moment diagram using summation method.

	Region AB	Region BC	Region CD
Area under SFD	$P \times \dfrac{L}{3} = \dfrac{PL}{3}$	0	$-P \times \dfrac{L}{3} = -\dfrac{PL}{3}$
Bending Moment	0 $\quad\quad\quad \dfrac{PL}{3}$	$\dfrac{PL}{3} \quad\quad\quad \dfrac{PL}{3}$	$\dfrac{PL}{3} \quad\quad\quad$ 0
Slope Value	$P \quad\quad\quad\quad P$	0 $\quad\quad\quad\quad$ 0	$-P \quad\quad\quad\quad -P$

BMD:

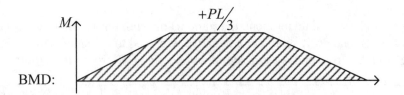

Example 6-10: Shear Force and Bending Moment diagram by the summation method

Problem Statement: Draw the shear force and bending moment diagram for the beam loaded as shown below, using the Summation Method.

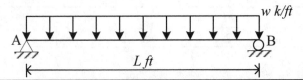

Required: Shear force and Bending Moment diagrams

Solution:

Step 1: Draw the free body diagram of the *overall* structure and determine the reactions

$$\sum F_x = 0 : A_x + 0 = 0; \ \therefore A_x = 0$$

$$\sum F_y = 0 : A_y + B_y - wL = 0; \ \therefore A_y + B_y = wL$$

$$\sum M_A = 0 : B_y(L) - wL\left(\frac{L}{2}\right) = 0; \ \therefore B_y = \frac{wL}{2} \uparrow$$

$$\therefore A_y = \frac{wL}{2} \uparrow$$

Step 2: Develop the shear force diagram using the summation method. Since the beam is loaded uniformly without any point load, the entire beam is considered as a section for drawing the SFD.

	Region AB	
Area under DL	$-w \times L = -wL$	
Shear force value	$\dfrac{wL}{2}$	$-\dfrac{wL}{2}$
Slope Value	w	w

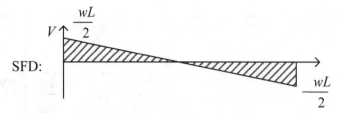

SFD:

It can be seen that the Shear force value at the two ends are equal in magnitude and opposite in direction. Hence the shear force value is zero at the midpoint.

Step 3: Develop the bending moment diagram using summation method. Since the SFD is divided in two parts; one positive and one negative, we need to consider two sections for drawing the BMD. Section AC from end A to midpoint and Section CB, from midpoint to the end B.

	Region AC		Region CB	
Area under SFD	$\frac{1}{2} \times \left(\frac{wL}{2} \right) \times \frac{L}{2} = \frac{wL^2}{8}$		$\frac{1}{2} \times \left(-\frac{wL}{2} \right) \times \frac{L}{2} = -\frac{wL^2}{8}$	
Bending Moment	0	$\frac{wL^2}{8}$	$\frac{wL^2}{8}$	0
Slope Value	$\frac{wL}{2}$	0	0	$-\frac{wL}{2}$

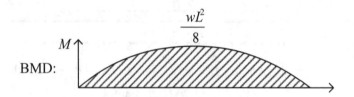

BMD:

Example 6-11: Shear Force and Bending Moment by the summation method and method of sections

Problem Statement: Draw the shear force and bending moment diagram for the beam loaded as shown below, using the Summation Method. Use the method of sections if necessary.

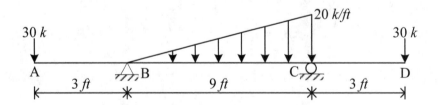

Required: Shear Force and Bending Moment Diagram

Solution:

Step 1: Draw the free body diagram of the *overall* structure and determine the reactions

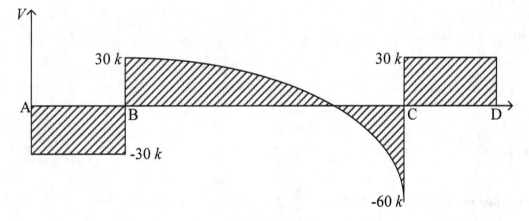

$$30\,k \qquad \frac{1}{2}(20k\,/\,ft)(9\,ft) = 90k \qquad 30\,k$$

A B_x B_y 9 ft C_y 3 ft   D

3 ft

$$\sum F_x = 0 : B_x + 0 = 0 \quad B_x = 0$$

$$\sum F_y = 0 : B_y - 30 - 0.5 \times (20\ k\,/\,ft.) \times (9\ ft.) + C_y - 30 = 0$$

$$\sum M_A = 0 : (30\ k) \times (3\ ft.) - (90\ k) \times (6\ ft.) + C_y \times (9\ ft.) - (30\ k) \times (12\ ft.) = 0$$

$$C_y = 90\ k \uparrow; B_y = 60\ k \uparrow$$

Step 2: Develop the shear force diagram using the summation method. The steps are be shown in tabular form as follows

	Region AB		Region BC		Region CD	
Area under DL	0		$0.5(-20\ k\,/\,ft)(9\ ft) = -90\ k$		0	
Shear force value	-30	-30	+30	-60	30	30
Slope Value	0	0	0	-20	0	0

The slopes at the two ends indicates a horizontal line. The SFD can now be drawn as follows using the tabulated values shown above. The slope of the curve in the central region changes from 0 to -20 and can be drawn a shown below.

Step 3: The bending moment diagram using the summation method is illustrated below in a tabular manner.

	Region AB		Region BC			Region CD	
Area under SFD	−90					90	
Bending Moment	0	-90	-90	x	x	-90	-90	0
Slope Value	-30	-30	30	0	0	-60	30	30

One of the disadvantages of the summation method, as shown, is that for complex quadratic shear curves the areas under the curve cannot be determined. One possible solution to overcome this problem is to use the method of sections in those regions.

In this example, since the moments cannot be determined in region CD only, the method of sections is used for the region, as shown below.

Section Diagram:

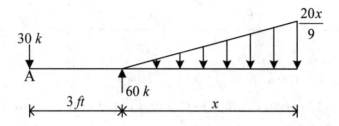

Section Free Body Diagram

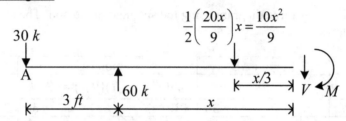

$\sum F_y = 0$:

$$-30 + 60 - \frac{1}{2}\left(\frac{20x}{9}\right) \times x - V = 0$$

$\sum M_A = 0$:

$$+30 \times (x+3) - 60x + \left(\frac{10x^2}{9}\right) \times \frac{x}{3} + M = 0$$

$$V(x) = -\left(\frac{10x^2}{9}\right) + 30$$

$$\qquad\qquad 0 < x < 9\, ft.$$

$$M(x) = -\left(\frac{10x^3}{27}\right) + 30x - 90$$

Maximum moment occurs at $(V=0)$:

$$V = 0 = -\left(\frac{10x^2}{9}\right) + 30 \Rightarrow x = \sqrt{27} = 5.2\ ft.$$

$$M_{max.} = M(5.2) = -\left(\frac{10 \times 5.2^3}{27}\right) + 30 \times 5.2 - 90 = 13.9\ k.ft.$$

$$M(0) = -\left(\frac{10 \times 0^3}{27}\right) + 30 \times 0 - 90 = -90\ k.ft.$$

$$M(9) = -\left(\frac{10 \times 9^3}{27}\right) + 30 \times 9 - 90 = -90\ k.ft.$$

The BMD can now be drawn as follows using the tabulated values shown above.

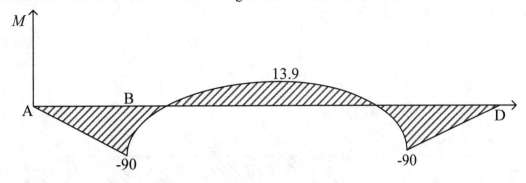

Example 6-12: Shear Force and Bending Moment by the summation method

Problem Statement: Draw the shear force and bending moment diagram for the beam loaded as shown below, using the Summation Method. Please note that there is an internal hinge at C.

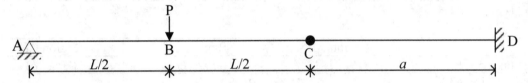

Required: Shear Force and Bending Moment Diagram

Solution:

Step 1: Draw the free body diagram of the *each segment* structure and determine the reactions

$$\sum F_x = 0 : A_x + C_x = 0$$

$$\sum F_y = 0 : A_y - P + C_y = 0$$

$$\sum M_A = 0 : C_y \times L - P \times \frac{L}{2} = 0$$

$$C_y = \frac{P}{2} \uparrow ; A_y = \frac{P}{2} \uparrow$$

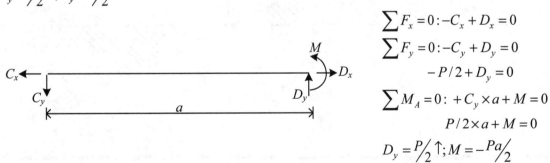

$$\sum F_x = 0 : -C_x + D_x = 0$$

$$\sum F_y = 0 : -C_y + D_y = 0$$

$$-P/2 + D_y = 0$$

$$\sum M_A = 0 : +C_y \times a + M = 0$$

$$P/2 \times a + M = 0$$

$$D_y = \frac{P}{2} \uparrow ; M = -\frac{Pa}{2}$$

Step 2: Develop the shear force diagram using the summation method. The steps are be shown in tabular form as follows

	Region AB		Region BC		Region CD	
Area under DL	0		0		0	
Shear force value	$+\frac{P}{2}$	$+\frac{P}{2}$	$-\frac{P}{2}$	$-\frac{P}{2}$	$-\frac{P}{2}$	$-\frac{P}{2}$
Slope Value	0	0	0	0	0	0

The slope at the two ends indicates a horizontal line. The SFD can now be drawn as follows using the tabulated values shown above.

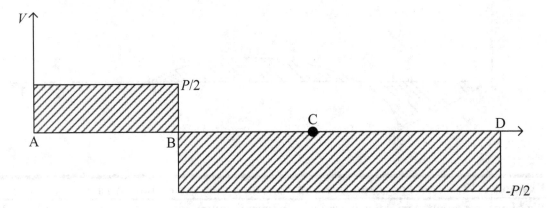

Step 3: The bending moment diagram using the summation method is illustrated below in a tabular manner.

	Region AB		Region BC		Region CD	
Area under SFD	$(P/2)(L/2)$		$(-P/2)(L/2)$		$(-P/2)(a)$	
Bending Moment	0	$PL/4$	$PL/4$	0	0	$-Pa/2$
Slope Value	$+P/2$	$+P/2$	$-P/2$	$-P/2$	$-P/2$	$-P/2$

The BMD can now be drawn as follows using the tabulated values shown above.

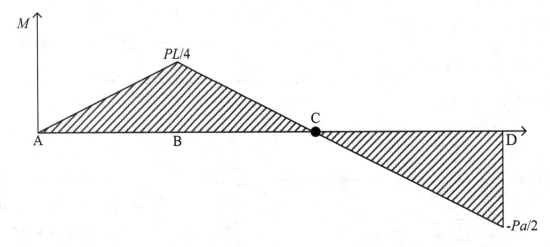

Example 6.13: SFD and BMD for beam with internal hinge

Problem Statement: Draw SFD and BMD for the beam with the loading as shown below.

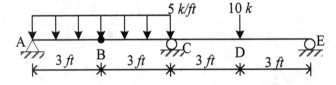

Required: Shear force and bending moment diagram

Solution:

Step 1: Draw free body diagram of the entire section and find reactions.

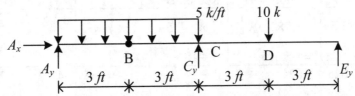

It can be seen that there are four unknown reactions and only three equilibrium equations available. There is an additional equilibrium condition due to the presence of internal hinge. The equilibrium condition states that the moment at the internal hinge is zero. To apply this equilibrium condition, the entire beam is divided in two parts on either side of the internal hinge. The moment of the loading on each of these parts about the internal hinge is then equated to zero. For the section AB;

$$\sum M_B = 0 : A_y(3) - \frac{5(3)^2}{2} = 0; \quad \therefore A_y = 7.5 \ k$$

For the section BE;

$$\sum M_B = 0 : \frac{5(3)^2}{2} - C_y(3) + 10(6) - E_y(9) = 0; \quad \therefore 3C_y + 9E_y = 82.5 \ k \Rightarrow (1)$$

Applying the equilibrium equations to the entire beam;

$$\sum F_x = 0 : A_x + 0 = 0; \quad \therefore A_x = 0$$

$$\sum F_y = 0 : 7.5 - 5(6) + C_y - 10 + E_y = 0; \quad \therefore C_y + E_y = 32.5 \ k \Rightarrow (2)$$

Solving equations (1) and (2) simultaneously, we get

$$E_y = -2.5 \ k$$

$$C_y = 35 \ k$$

Step 2: Develop the shear force diagram using the summation method.

For the determination of SFD, the beam is divided in four regions; Region AB, Region BC, Region CD and Region DE.

	Region AB		Region BC		Region CD		Region DE	
Area under DL	$-5 \times 3 = -15$		$-5 \times 3 = -15$		0		0	
Shear force value	+7.5	-7.5	-7.5	-22.5	+12.5	+12.5	+2.5	+2.5
Slope Value	5	5	5	5	0	0	0	0

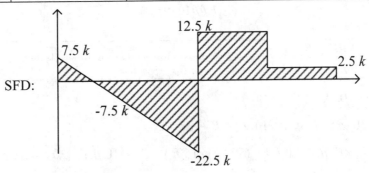

SFD:

Step 2: Develop the bending moment diagram using the summation method.

The region AB is now divided in two parts; Region AB' and B'B, where B' is the point where the shear force is zero between point A and B. This zero shear force occurs at 1.5 ft from A.

	Region AB'	Region B'B	Region BC	Region CD	Region DE
Area under SFD	$\frac{1}{2} \times 7.5 \times 1.5$ $= 5.625$	$-7.5 \times 1.5 \times \frac{1}{2}$ $= -5.625$	$\frac{1}{2} \times \left(-7.5 + (-22.5)\right) \times 3$ $= -45$	$12.5 \times 3 = 37.5$	$2.5 \times 3 = 7.5$
Bending Moment	0 5.625	5.625 0	0 -45	-45 -7.5	-7.5 0
Slope Value	7.5 0	0 -7.5	-7.5 -22.5	12.5 12.5	2.5 2.5

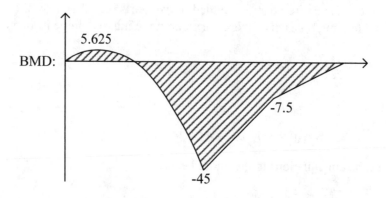

BMD:
5.625
-7.5
-45

Example 6-14: Shear Force and Bending Moment by the summation method

Problem Statement: Draw the shear force and bending moment diagram for the beam loaded as shown below, using the Summation Method.

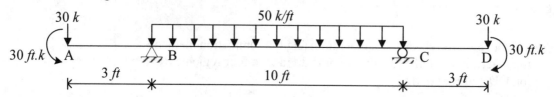

Required: Shear Force and Bending Moment Diagram

Solution:

Step 1: Draw the free body diagram of the *overall* structure and determine the reactions

$$\sum F_x = 0: C_x + 0 = 0 \quad C_x = 0$$

$$\sum F_y = 0: C_y - 30 - (50 \ k/ft.) \times (10 \ ft.) + B_y - 30 = 0$$

$$\sum M_B = 0: (30 \ k) \times (3 \ ft.) + 30 \ ft.k - (500 \ k) \times (5 \ ft.) + C_y \times (10 \ ft.) - (30 \ k) \times (3 \ ft.) - 30 \ ft.k = 0$$

$$B_y = 280 \ k \uparrow; C_y = 280 \ k \uparrow$$

Step 2: Develop the shear force diagram using the summation method.

a) The determination of the values is started from the left end where the shear force is equal to a concentrated force. There is no distributed load in this region

$$V_L = -30k$$

$$V_R = V_L + \text{Area under the distributed load} = -30 + 0 = -30$$

$$Slope_L = 0; \; Slope_R = 0$$

b) The concentrated reaction B_y force, acting upwards, causes a jump up in the SFD. Hence the new shear force value (just to the right of the concentrated force) is -30+280=250k

c) In the region between the supports there is a distributed force.

$$V_L = 250 \; k$$

$$V_R = V_L + \text{Area under the distributed load}$$

$$V_R = -250 \; k - (50 \; k/ft) \times (10 \; ft.) = -250 \; k$$

$$Slope_L = Slope_R = -50 \; k/ft$$

d) The concentrated reaction C_y force, acting upwards, causes a jump up in the SFD. Hence the new shear force value (just to the right of the concentrated force) is -250+280=30 k.

e) Then in the region between the C_y and the end D the values can be computed as follows

$$V_L = 30k$$

$$V_R = V_L + \text{Area under the distributed load} = 30 + 0 = 30 \; k$$

$$Slope_L = 0; \; Slope_R = 0$$

f) Finally at the end, the end concentrated force of 30 k downwards results in the SFD jumping up back to zero.

For ease of depiction the above steps can be shown in tabular form as follows

	Region AB		Region BC		Region CD	
Area under DL	0		-50(k/ft.)(10 ft.) = -500 k		0	
Shear force value	-30	-30	+250	-250	30	30
Slope Value	0	0	0	0	0	0

Two slope at the two ends indicates a horizontal line. The SFD can now be drawn as follows using the tabulated values shown above.

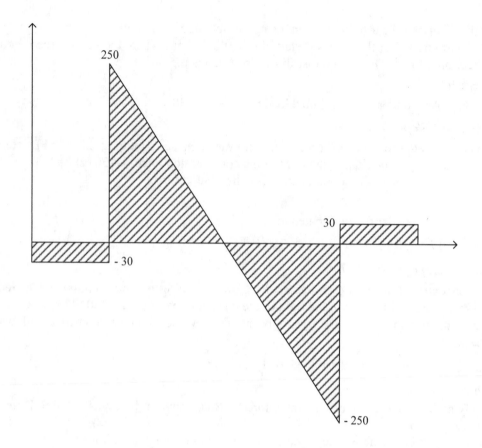

Step 3: The bending moment diagram using the summation method is illustrated below.

a) At the left end the bending moment is equal to concentrated moment. The region AB calculations can be expressed as follows

$M_L = -30$

$M_R = M_L +$ Area under the shear force diagram

$\quad = -30 + (-30\,k \times 3\,ft.) = -120\,k.ft.$

$Slope_L = -30\,k;\ Slope_R = -30\,k$

b) Region BC has to be separated into 2 regions as the shear force changes in sign. The point where $V=0$ can be found from geometry of similar triangles as $\dfrac{x}{250} = \dfrac{10-x}{250}$ or $x = 5\,ft.$ The moments and slopes in the two regions is shown below

$M_L = -120\quad M_R = -120 + (0.5 \times +250 \times 5) = 505$

$Slope_L = V_L = 250\,k;\ Slope_R = V_R = -0$

$M_L = 505\quad M_R = 505 + (0.5 \times -250 \times 5) = -120$

$Slope_L = V_L = 0;\ Slope_R = V_R = -250\,k$

c) The region CD is similar to region AB as shown in step (a) with a reversed sign and is not rewritten here. It should be noted that the moment at D is clockwise in direction and hence is an additive moment, resulting in an upward jump in the BMD at that point.

For ease of depiction the above steps can be shown in tabular form as follows

	Region AB		Region BC		Region CD	
Area under SFD	$-30 \times 3 = -90$		$0.5 \times 250 \times 5$ $= 625$	$0.5 \times -250 \times 5$ $= -625$	$30 \times 3 = 90$	
Bending Moment	-30	-120	-120	505	505	-120	-120	-30
Slope Value	-30	-30	250	0	0	-250	30	30

The BMD can now be drawn as follows using the tabulated values shown above.

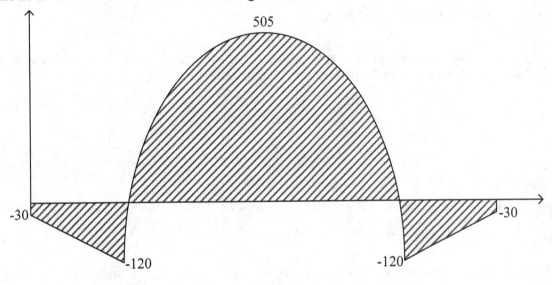

6.6   Shear Force and Bending Moment Diagrams for Cantilever Beams

So far in the chapter we have studied three different approaches to draw shear force and bending moment diagram for a hinged and roller supported beams. In this section shear force and bending moment for cantilever type of beams are studied. As seen in earlier chapters, cantilever beams are those beams which are support only at one end by a rigid support. This rigid support allows no linear or rotational movement resulting in a force reaction, both in vertical and horizontal direction and a moment reaction. The other end of the cantilever beam that is the unsupported end is known as *free end*.

The SFD and BMD of the examples given below are drawn using Method of Sections.

Example 6.15: Axial and Shear force diagrams and Bending moment diagram.

Problem Statement: Draw the axial force, shear force and bending moment diagram for the cantilever beam shown below.

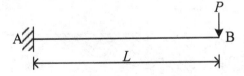

Required: Axial and Shear force diagrams and Bending moment diagram.

Solution:
Step 1: Draw the free body diagram of the *overall* structure and determine the reactions.

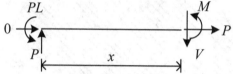

$$\sum F_x = 0 : A_x + 0 = 0; \quad \therefore A_x = 0$$

$$\sum F_y = 0 : A_y - P = 0; \quad \therefore A_y = P \uparrow$$

$$\sum M_A = 0 : M_A - P(L) = 0; \quad \therefore M_A = PL$$

Step 2: Pass a section through A-A at an arbitrary distance x from A and draw the free body of the left (or right) section with the internal forces drawn appropriately.

$$\sum F_x = 0 : P + 0 = 0; \quad \therefore P = 0$$

$$\sum F_y = 0 : P - V = 0; \quad \therefore V = +P \uparrow \qquad 0 < x < L$$

$$\sum M_x = 0 : M - Px + PL = 0; \quad \therefore M = Px - PL$$

Step 3: Determine the values of shear and moment at certain important locations such as the ends and draw the shear and moment diagrams

$x = 0 \qquad V = +P \qquad M = -PL$

$x = L \qquad V = +P \qquad M = P(L) - PL; \quad \therefore M = 0$

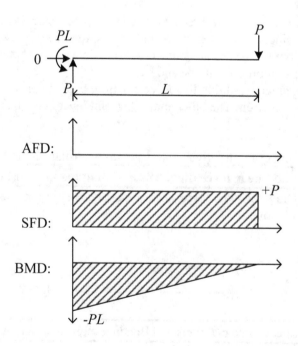

Example 6-16: Axial Force, Shear Force and Bending Moment-Uniformly Distributed Load

Problem Statement: Determine a general expression for the axial force; shear force and bending moment in the beam and the draw the diagram for the same.

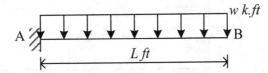

Required: Axial and Shear force diagrams and Bending moment diagram.

Solution:

Step 1: Draw the free body diagram of the overall structure and determine the reactions.

$$\sum F_x = 0 : A_x + 0 = 0; \quad \therefore A_x = 0$$

$$\sum F_y = 0 : A_y - wL = 0; \quad \therefore A_y = wL \uparrow$$

$$\sum M_A = 0 : M_A - wL\left(\frac{L}{2}\right) = 0; \quad \therefore M_A = \frac{wL^2}{2}$$

Step 2: Pass a section through A-A at an arbitrary distance x from A and draw the free body of the left (or right) section with the internal forces drawn appropriately.

Start from the original diagram to draw the section diagram and the section free body diagram

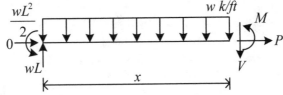

$$\sum F_x = 0 : P = 0; \quad \therefore P = 0$$

$$\sum F_y = 0 : wL - wx - V = 0; \quad \therefore V = w(L - x)$$

$$\sum M_x = 0 : M - wL(x) + \frac{wL^2}{2} + wx\left(\frac{x}{2}\right) = 0; \quad \therefore M = + wLx - \frac{wx^2}{2} - \frac{wL^2}{2}$$

Step 3: Determine the values of shear and moment at certain important locations such as the ends and draw the shear and moment diagrams

$$x = 0 \quad V = +wL \quad M = -\frac{wL^2}{2}$$

$$x = L \quad V = 0 \quad M = wL^2 - \frac{wL^2}{2} - \frac{wL^2}{2}; \quad \therefore M = 0$$

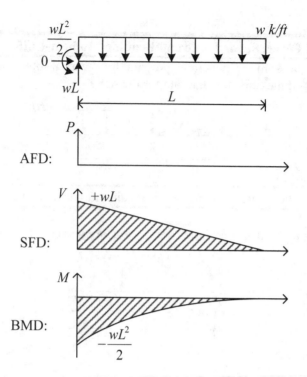

AFD:

SFD:

BMD:

The AFD, SFD and BMD of the cantilever beam shown earlier were drawn using method of sections. The summation method approach for drawing SFD and BMD for cantilever beams is outlined now, in order to illustrate the ease of usage of this method.

Example 6.17: Axial and Shear force diagrams and Bending moment diagram.

Problem Statement: Draw the axial force; shear force and bending moment diagram for the cantilever beam shown below.

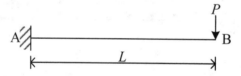

Required: Axial and Shear force diagrams and Bending moment diagram.

Solution:

Step 1: Draw the free body diagram of the *overall* structure and determine the reactions.

$$\sum F_x = 0 : A_x + 0 = 0; \quad \therefore A_x = 0$$
$$\sum F_y = 0 : A_y - P = 0; \quad \therefore A_y = P \uparrow$$
$$\sum M_A = 0 : M_A - P(L) = 0; \quad \therefore M_A = PL$$

Step 2: Develop the shear force diagram using the summation method.

Since there is just a single point load at the end of the beam, we consider the entire beam as one section.

	Region AB	
Area under DL	0	
Shear force value	$+P$	$+P$
Slope Value	0	0

SFD:

Step 3: Develop the bending moment diagram using summation method.

	Region AB	
Area under SFD	$P \times L = PL$	
Bending Moment	$-PL$	0
Slope Value	$+P$	$+P$

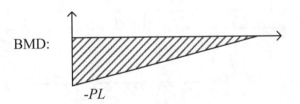

BMD:

$-PL$

Example 6-18: Axial Force, Shear Force and Bending Moment-Uniformly Distributed Load

Problem Statement: Determine a general expression for the axial force; shear force and bending moment in the beam and the draw the diagram for the same.

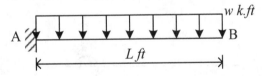

Required: Axial and Shear force diagrams and Bending moment diagram.

Solution:

Step 1: Draw the free body diagram of the overall structure and determine the reactions.

$$\sum F_x = 0 : A_x + 0 = 0; \ \therefore A_x = 0$$

$$\sum F_y = 0 : A_y - wL = 0; \ \therefore A_y = wL \uparrow$$

$$\sum M_A = 0 : M_A - wL\left(\frac{L}{2}\right) = 0; \ \therefore M_A = \frac{wL^2}{2}$$

Step 2: Develop the shear force diagram using the summation method.
Since there the entire beam is loading uniformly, we consider the entire beam as one section.

	Region AB	
Area under DL	$-w \times L = -wL$	
Shear force value	$+wL$	0
Slope Value	$-w$	$-w$

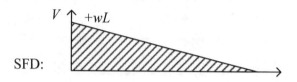

SFD:

Step 3: Develop the bending moment diagram using summation method.

	Region AB	
Area under SFD	$\dfrac{1}{2} \times wL \times L = \dfrac{wL^2}{2}$	
Bending Moment	$-\dfrac{wL^2}{2}$	0
Slope Value	$+wL$	0

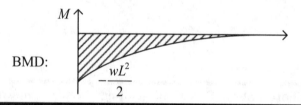

BMD:

Example 6.19: SFD and BMD for cantilever beam with multi loading

Problem Statement: Draw the shear force and bending moment diagram for the beam loaded as shown below, using the Summation Method.

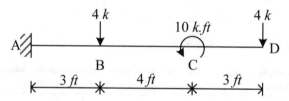

Required: Shear force and bending moment diagram.

Solution:

Step 1: Draw the free body diagram of the overall structure and find the reactions.

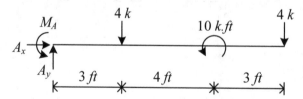

$$\sum F_x = 0: A_x + 0 = 0; \quad \therefore A_x = 0$$

$$\sum F_y = 0: A_y - 4 - 4 = 0; \quad \therefore A_y = 8k \uparrow$$

$$\sum M_A = 0: M_A - 4(3) + 10 - 4(10) = 0; \quad \therefore M_A = 42 \ k.ft$$

Step 2: Develop the shear force diagram using the summation method.

For the determination of SFD and BMD we consider three regions; Region AB, Region BC and Region CD.

	Region AB		Region BC		Region CD	
Area under DL	0		0		0	
Shear force value	+8	+8	+4	+4	+4	+4
Slope Value	0	0	0	0	0	0

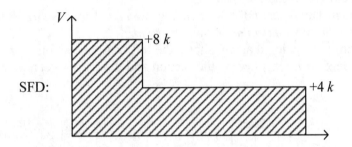

SFD:

Step 3: Develop the bending moment diagram using summation method.

	Region AB		Region BC		Region CD	
Area under SFD	$8 \times 3 = 24$		$4 \times 4 = 16$		$4 \times 3 = 12$	
Bending Moment	-42	-18	-18	-2	-12	0
Slope Value	8	8	4	4	4	4

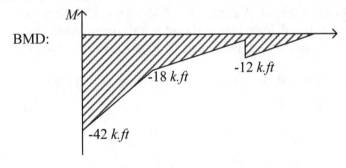

BMD:

6.7   Summary

In this chapter we learnt to represent the variation of two more types of internal quantities namely, the bending moment and shear force in terms of bending moment and shear force diagrams. The keywords introduced in this chapter are as follows.

1. **Internal Shear Force (V):** The internal force parallel to the surface called the shear force (V)
2. **Internal Bending Moment (M):** The bending moment (M) is responsible for transferring the moment between the two sections.
3. **Loading function $w(x)$:** The load function represents the variation of the magnitude of the distributed load over the span. Its magnitude is expressed in force/length units, for example *kips/foot* (*klf* – kips per linear foot) or *kN/m*.
4. **Shear Force Diagram (SFD):** Shear Force Diagram (SFD) is the graphical representation of the shear equation over the entire span.
5. **Bending Moment Diagrams (BMD):** *Bending Moment Diagrams (BMD) is the graphical representation of the moment equation over the span.*
6. **Section Diagram:** A section diagram shows the left or right section of the body, the part of the distributed load that is applied on the section and the reactions and the internal forces in that section.

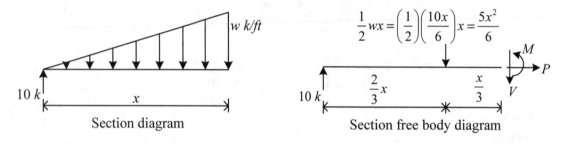

Section diagram   Section free body diagram

7. **Section Free Body Diagram:** A section free body diagram is based on the section diagram in which all the distributed loads are replaced with concentrated loads with their locations clearly shown. All dimensions must also be clearly shown. An example is shown in the diagram above.
8. **Elastic Curve:** The elastic curve is an approximate deflection shape due to the applied loads.

6.8   Problems:

6.1   Determine the axial force, shear force and bending moment for the problems shown below at section A-A. Use the method of sections.

a.

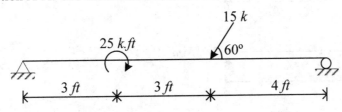

b.

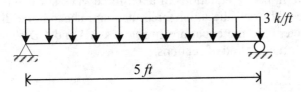

c.

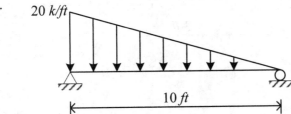

d.

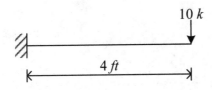

e.

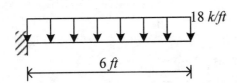

f.

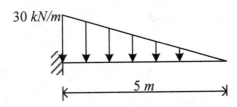

g.

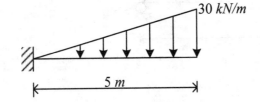

h.

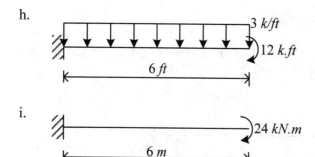

3 k/ft

12 k.ft

6 ft

i.

24 kN.m

6 m

6.2   For the following figures, determine the equations of axial force $P(x)$, shear force $V(x)$ and bending moment $M(x)$ in the and draw the axial force diagram, shear force diagram and bending moment diagram. Determine the equations in regions AB and CD separately, but draw a combined diagram. Use the method of sections.

a.

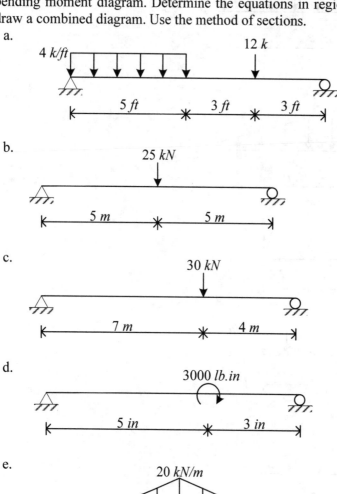

4 k/ft

12 k

5 ft   3 ft   3 ft

b.

25 kN

5 m   5 m

c.

30 kN

7 m   4 m

d.

3000 lb.in

5 in   3 in

e.

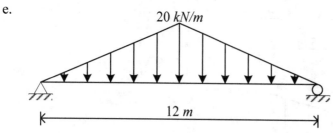

20 kN/m

12 m

f.

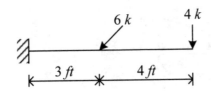

g.

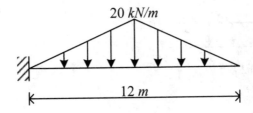

h.

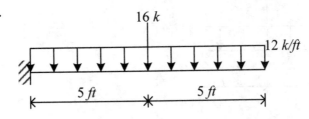

i.

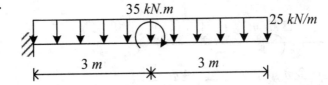

6.3   For the following figures determine the equations of axial force $P(x)$, shear force $V(x)$ and bending moment $M(x)$ in the and draw the axial force diagram, shear force diagram and bending moment diagram. Use the method of sections. Clearly show the section diagram and the section free body diagrams.

a.

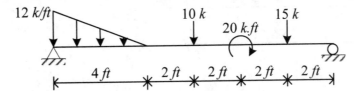

b.

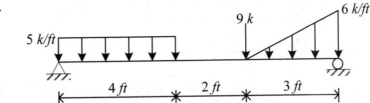

c.

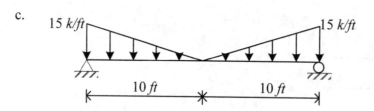

d.

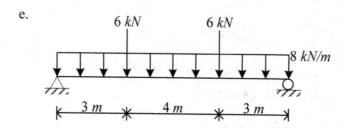

e.

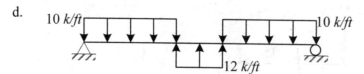

f.

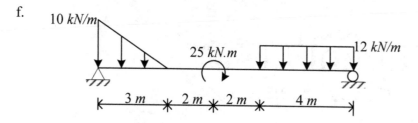

g.

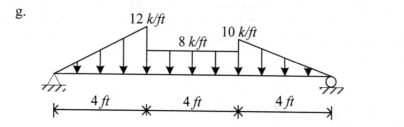

h.

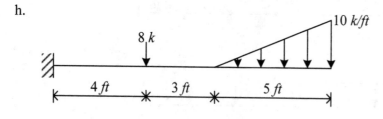

6.4 For the following problems draw the axial force diagram, shear force diagram and bending moment diagram using the summation method.

a.

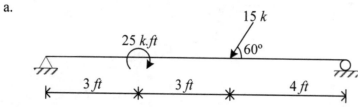

b.

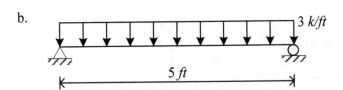

3 k/ft

5 ft

c.

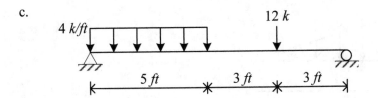

4 k/ft

12 k

5 ft   3 ft   3 ft

d.

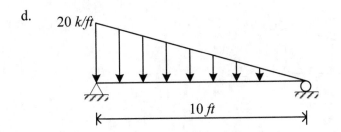

20 k/ft

10 ft

e.

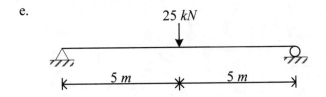

25 kN

5 m   5 m

f.

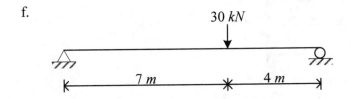

30 kN

7 m   4 m

g.

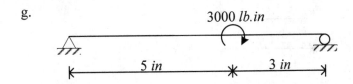

3000 lb.in

5 in   3 in

h.

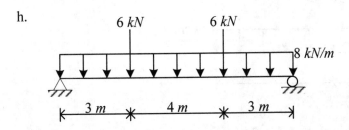

6 kN   6 kN

8 kN/m

3 m   4 m   3 m

i.

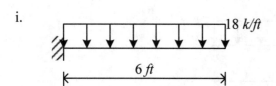

18 *k/ft*

6 *ft*

j.

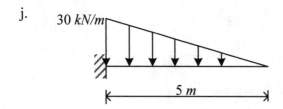

30 *kN/m*

5 *m*

k.

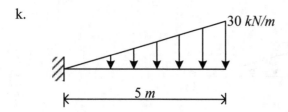

30 *kN/m*

5 *m*

l.

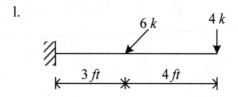

6 *k*

4 *k*

3 *ft*

4 *ft*

m.

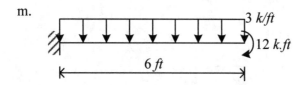

3 *k/ft*

12 *k.ft*

6 *ft*

n.

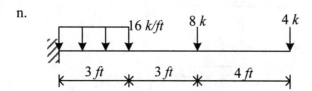

16 *k/ft*

8 *k*

4 *k*

3 *ft*

3 *ft*

4 *ft*

o.

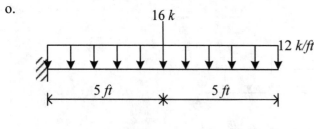

16 *k*

12 *k/ft*

5 *ft*

5 *ft*

p.

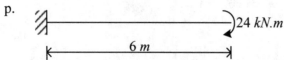

24 *kN.m*

6 *m*

6.5　For the following problems draw the axial force diagram, shear force diagram and bending moment diagram using the summation method.

a.

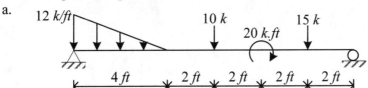

b.

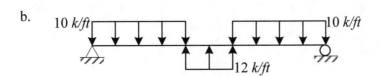

c.

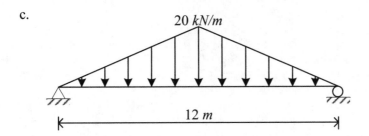

d.

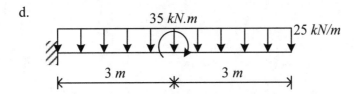

6.6　For the following problems draw the axial force diagram, shear force diagram and bending moment diagram using the summation method.

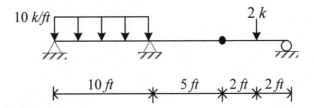

Chapter 7

Bending (Flexural) Stresses in Beams

Goals: The learning objectives of this chapter are as follows:

1. Introduce bending stresses in prismatic beam
2. Outline the concept and steps to calculate bending/flexural stress
3. Discuss the phenomenon of forces associated with bending stress
4. Apply the concept of bending stress to composite beams

7   Bending (Flexural) Stresses in Beams

7.1   Introduction

A common exercise that a person does routinely is the bending exercise, where the back is bent forward and down in order to touch the toes with the tip of the fingers. During this exercise, one can feel two things; the back bone and the muscles in the area are stretched while the stomach muscles feel compressed. The same concept of bending is applicable to any other object undergoing a similar deformation pattern.

Figure 7.1 shows a beam bent at the two ends. Such a beam is said to experience a bending moment. The phenomenon of bending moment and how to numerically calculate it was outlined in Chapter 6. From Figure 7.1 it can be seen that the top of the beam is in compression while the bottom fibers of the beam experience tension. The compressive stresses at the top and the tensile stresses at the bottom are also termed as *flexural stresses*. This chapter outlines the nature of bending in prismatic beams, the concepts and steps involved in the calculation of bending/flexural stresses and the phenomenon of forces associated with bending stresses. Some applications of the bending stresses such as composite sections are finally outlined.

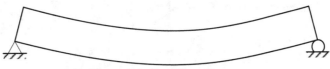

Figure 7.1: Bending of beams

7.2   Phenomenon of Bending

Some of the basic definitions which are universally recognized and used are defined first. A prismatic beam is a beam with a prismatic cross-section. Figure 7.2 shows a prismatic beam and its cross section.

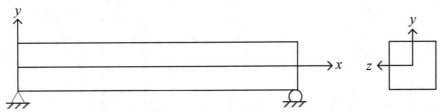

Figure 7.2: Beam shown along with its cross section

The axes used are defined as follows.
Longitudinal Axis: The *x*-axis of the beam, as shown in Figure 7.2, is the longitudinal axis. It has an origin at the left end of the beam, runs along the span of the beam and passes through the centroid of the cross section at the two ends. The significance of the centroid will be explained in a later section.

Transverse/Lateral Axes: Figure 7.2 also shows the origin at the centroid of the cross section and the cross section lies in the plane of the transverse or lateral axes, the *y-z* axes. For consistency it will be assumed that the vertical axis in the upward direction is the *y*-axis and the *z*-axis points to the left, in order to maintain the right handed axis system. In other words the *z*-axis is perpendicular to the plane of the paper and pointing out of the plane of the paper.

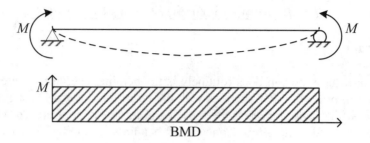

Figure 7.3: Beam subjected to pure bending and geometry of deformation

Pure Bending: The beam shown in Figure 7.3 is considered to be subjected to pure bending. Pure bending is said to occur when the bending moment at the two ends of the beam are equal in magnitude. In such a case it can be seen that the shear in the beam is zero, hence the term pure bending (remember that $V = \dfrac{dM}{dx} = 0$ if $dM=0$, constant moment in the beam). Such a scenario is considered in order to isolate the effects of bending moment. Hence, the two important aspects of a beam subjected to pure bending are

a)   The shear in the beam is zero ($V=0$)
b)   The axial force in the beam is zero ($P=0$)

7.2.1   Kinematics of bending

The term kinematics is used commonly in engineering to represent the deformation characteristics. It generally deals with the displacement, deformation and strains and the interrelationships between these quantities. The kinematics of bending is now examined. Figure 7.3 shows the geometry of the beam subjected to pure bending. All the theoretical development outlined below is based on a very important assumption, namely *plane sections remain plane after bending*. This statement is also known as the *plane section hypothesis*.

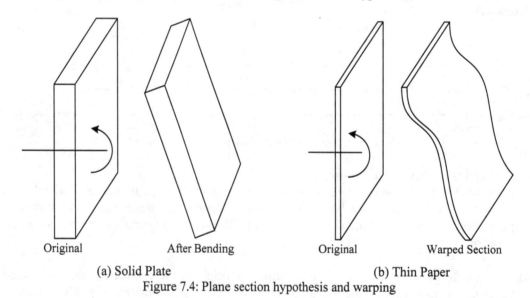

(a) Solid Plate   (b) Thin Paper
Figure 7.4: Plane section hypothesis and warping

Figure 7.4 shows the physical significance of the plane section hypothesis. Plane section hypothesis implies that all points in the plane of the cross section remain in the same plane after bending. For example, consider a solid vertical plate bent as shown in Figure 7.4. It can be seen that although the plane of the plate is now inclined all the points are still on the same inclined plane.

If plane sections do not remain plane after bending the section is said to be *warping*. Instead of the solid vertical plate consider a thin vertical paper and try to bend it. As seen in Figure 7.4, the plane of the paper is no longer plane after bending. Such a cross section is considered to have warped. As mentioned earlier, all the equations developed in this chapter are valid only for plane section hypothesis as in solid beams undergoing very small deformations, in the elastic regime.

Consider the beam to be a set of lines parallel to the longitudinal axis. It can be easily visualized that when the beam is subjected to a positive bending moment, the lines at the top will shorten (compress) while the lines at the bottom will extend (tension). It naturally leads to the idea that there is one line, in between, which experiences no change in length. This line is called the *neutral axis* (along the longitudinal direction).

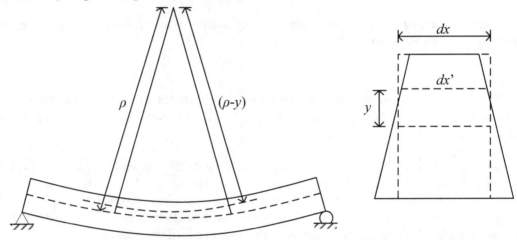

Figure 7.5: Curvature of the beam and elemental deformation

Consider a small element of length dx as shown in Figure 7.5. The beam bends in a circular/parabolic manner as shown. The radius of the neutral axis is called the *radius of curvature* ρ of the beam. The angle subtended by the two ends of the elemental length dx at the center of the parabola is $d\theta$, as shown in Figure 7.5. The equation which expresses the relationship between the element length dx, the radius of curvature and the angle subtended can be written as

$$dx = \rho d\theta \qquad \text{Eqn (7.1)}$$

Now consider a short segment dx above the neutral axis which experiences compression. It must be kept in mind that the region above the neutral axis is in the $+y$ region. This line decreases in length to dx'. Hence, the compressive strain experienced by this line can be expressed as

$$\varepsilon_x = \frac{dl}{l} = \frac{dx' - dx}{dx} \qquad \text{Eqn (7.2)}$$

From Figure 7.5, the location of the line dx' is $+y$ above the neutral (z) axis. Hence, from geometry the length of the line can be expressed as

$$dx' = (\rho - y)d\theta \qquad \text{Eqn (7.3)}$$

Hence, the axial strain can now be expressed as

$$\varepsilon_x = \frac{(\rho - y)d\theta - \rho d\theta}{\rho d\theta} = -\frac{y}{\rho} \qquad \text{Eqn (7.4)}$$

Once again, the physical significance of the equation must be kept in mind. The expression for axial strain has a negative sign, which indicated that in the $+y$ region the strain value becomes negative and hence represents the compression region. In the negative y ($-y$) region, below the neutral axis the strain becomes positive $\varepsilon_x = -\dfrac{-y}{\rho} = \dfrac{y}{\rho}$. Hence, this region is in tension.

7.2.2 Connecting Kinematics to Material Behavior

The kinematic behavior is now combined with the material behavior. It is considered that for small deformations to occur the material behavior elastically. For a beam subjected to pure bending it is reasonable to assume that the axial stresses in the y and z directions are zero. Hence, the generalized equation of stresses and strain for elastic behavior can be reduced as follows

$$\varepsilon_x = \frac{1}{E}\left[\sigma_x - v(\sigma_y + \sigma_z)\right] = \frac{\sigma_x}{E} \qquad \text{Eqn (7.5)}$$

which represents a uniaxial behavior. Combining equations 7.4 and 7.5 the equation for bending stress can be written as follows

$$\sigma_x = E\varepsilon_x = -\frac{Ey}{\rho} \qquad \text{Eqn (7.6)}$$

So far two concepts, namely the kinematic (geometric) behavior and the material behavior (using the elastic modulus) have been connected in order to get an expression for the flexural (axial) stress.

It can also be seen that axial stress varies linearly with the distance from the neutral axis (y). The same linear variation is valid for axial strains as well. Figure 7.6 depicts the variation of the flexural stress and strain along the cross section depth. It should be noted that the origin of the y-z axis is at an assumed neutral point. Its exact location will be derived in the next section. The z-axis, about which the applied bending moment acts, is also called the *neutral axis*.

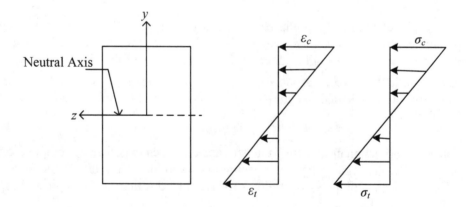

Figure 7.6: Variation of the axial strain and axial stress across the depth of the cross section

7.2.3 Relating the Bending Moment to the Axial Stress

It is much more meaningful to relate the applied bending moment directly to the axial stress. Consider a free body diagram of a segment of the beam undergoing pure bending. The net axial force experienced by the cross section is zero ($P = 0$).

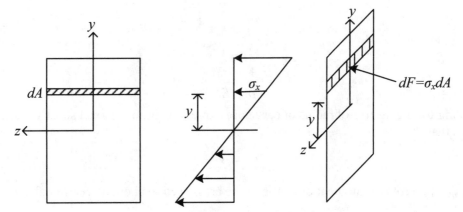

Figure 7.7: Stresses on a small element dA

Neutral (Centroidal) Axis: As seen in Figure 7.6 the stress is not constant across the depth. In order to calculate the total axial force due to bending stress, a small area dA is considered, as shown in Figure 7.7, which is at a distance y from the z-axis and over which the stress σ_x remains constant. Hence, the total axial force in the cross section can be expressed as follows

$$P = \int dF = \int \sigma_x dA = 0$$

$$P = \int -\frac{Ey}{\rho} dA = -\frac{E}{\rho} \int y dA = 0$$

Eqn (7.7)

Since, E and the radius of curvature ρ are constant they are removed from the integral. This leads to a familiar equation from statics

$$Q = \int y dA = \bar{y} A = 0$$

or

$$\bar{y} = 0$$

Eqn (7.8)

Equation 7.8 is the mathematical representation of the engineering meaning - the z-axis, which represents the neutral axis, is the centroidal axis as well. The derivation shown above leads to one of the most significant conclusion for elastic bending that; *the centroidal axis of the cross section is its neutral axis.*

The relationship between the internal axial stresses and the bending moment is now derived. In Figure 7.7, consider the force $\sigma_x dA$ acting on the incremental area dA. By taking the moment of this force about the z-axis, integrating over the entire y-axis range and equating it to the applied moment as follows

$$M + \int y(\sigma_x dA) = M + \int y\left(-\frac{Ey}{\rho}\right) dA = 0$$

$$M = \frac{E}{\rho} \int y^2 dA$$

Once again, from Statics it is known that the expression in the integral represents the *Moment of Inertia* of the cross section, about the z-axis which is also the neutral axis. Hence, the above expression can be written as

$$M = \frac{EI_{NA}}{\rho}$$

or

$$\frac{1}{\rho} = \frac{M}{EI_{NA}}$$

Substituting for the inverse of radius of curvature expression in to the axial stress equation it can be shown that

$$\sigma_x = -\frac{My}{I_{NA}}$$

Eqn (7.9)

where, I_{NA} represents the moment of inertia of the cross section about its centroidal axis.

7.2.4   Summary of equations

The basic equations of flexure can now be summarized as follows. The following three items are the inputs required in order to determine the quantities related to flexure.
1. From a structural analysis, the bending moment diagram is drawn in order to determine the location and the type (positive or negative) maximum moment M.
2. The geometry in the form of the cross sectional details forms the second input. The information required from the cross section are;
    a. The location of the centroid of the area, which is the neutral axis and
    b. The centroidal moment of inertia I_{NA}.
3. The third input is the type of material. Since, elastic behavior is being considered only the elastic modulus of the material E is required.

The summary of the equations, derived in this chapter are;
1. **Radius of curvature of the beam**

$$\frac{1}{\rho} = \frac{M}{EI_{NA}}$$

2. **Axial or flexural strain**

$$\varepsilon_x = -\frac{y}{\rho} = -\frac{My}{EI_{NA}}$$

3. **Axial or flexural stress:** It must be kept in mind that y is measured with the origin at the centroid / neutral axis of the cross section and y is positive in the upward direction. Hence, a positive moment will cause compression (negative flexural stress) in the positive y region.

$$\sigma_x = -\frac{My}{I_{NA}}$$

4. **Combined or general form of the equation**

$$\frac{\sigma_x}{y} = \frac{E}{\rho} = -\frac{M}{I_{NA}}$$

Problem 7.1: Centroidal Moment of Inertia

Problem Statement: Find the Centroidal moment of inertia for the section show.

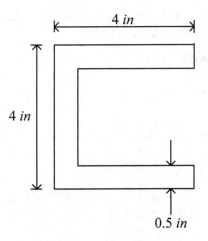

Required: a) Find the Centroidal axis

b) Find moment of inertia about this Centroidal axis.

Solution:

Step 1: Divide the area into well defined sub areas (such as triangles, rectangles, circles, semi-circles etc.). Draw these areas with respect to common axes of reference.

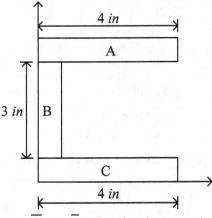

Step 2: Determine the coordinates $\bar{x}_i$ and $\bar{y}_i$ of each sub area and apply the centroid equation as shown in the following table.

Shape	A (in^2)	$\bar{x}_i$ (in)	$\bar{y}_i$ (in)	$A\bar{x}_i$ (in^3)	$A\bar{y}_i$ (in^3)
Rectangle A	2	2	3.75	4	7.5
Rectangle B	1.5	0.25	2	0.375	3
Rectangle C	2	2	0.25	4	0.5
	$\sum A_i = 5.5$			$\sum \bar{x}_i A_i = 8.375$	$\sum \bar{y}_i A_i = 11$

$$\bar{x} = \frac{\sum \bar{x}_i A_i}{\sum A_i} = \frac{8.375}{5.5} = 1.522 \ in.$$

$$\bar{y} = \frac{\sum \bar{y}_i A_i}{\sum A_i} = \frac{11}{5.5} = 2 \ in.$$

Step 3: Determine the centroidal moments of inertia of each shape. This is the moment of inertia about the axis passing through the centroid of each area.

$$(\bar{I}_x)_A = \frac{1}{12}bh^3 = \frac{1}{12} \times 4 \times 0.5^3 = 0.0416 \; in^4$$

$$(\bar{I}_x)_B = \frac{1}{12}bh^3 = \frac{1}{12} \times 0.5 \times 3^3 = 1.125 \; in^4$$

$$(\bar{I}_x)_C = \frac{1}{12}bh^3 = \frac{1}{12} \times 4 \times 0.5^3 = 0.0416 \; in^4$$

$$(\bar{I}_y)_A = \frac{1}{12}bh^3 = \frac{1}{12} \times 0.5 \times 4^3 = 2.667 \; in^4$$

$$(\bar{I}_y)_B = \frac{1}{12}bh^3 = \frac{1}{12} \times 3 \times 0.5^3 = 0.03125 \; in^4$$

$$(\bar{I}_y)_C = \frac{1}{12}bh^3 = \frac{1}{12} \times 0.5 \times 4^3 = 2.667 \; in^4$$

$$I_X = [(\bar{I}_x)_A + A_A \times d_{Ay}^2] + [(\bar{I}_x)_B + A_B \times d_{Bx}^2] + [(\bar{I}_y)_C + A_C \times d_{Cx}^2]$$

where

$d_{Ay} = x$ distance between centroid of the sub area and the centroid of the entire area

$\qquad = 2 - 1.522 = 0.478 \; in.$

$d_{By} = 1.522 - 0.5 = 1.022 \; in.$

$d_{Cy} = 2 - 1.522 = 0.478 \; in.$

giving

$$I_X = (0.0416 + 2 \times 0.478^2) + (1.1.25 + 1.5 \times 1.022^2) + (0.0416 + 2 \times 0.478^2) = 3.689 \; in^4$$

$$I_Y = [(\bar{I}_y)_A + A_A \times d_{Ax}^2] + (\bar{I}_y)_B + [(\bar{I}_y)_C + A_C \times d_{Cx}^2]$$

where

$d_{Ax} = x$ distance between the centroid of the subarea and the centroid of the entire area

$\qquad = 3.75 - 2 = 1.75 \; in$

$d_{Cx} = 2 - 0.25 = 1.75 \; in.$

giving

$$I_Y = (2.667 + 2 \times 1.75^2) + (0.03125) + (2.667 + 2 \times 1.75^2) = 17.62 \; in^4$$

Hence we have,

$$I_X = 3.689 \; in^4$$

$$I_Y = 17.62 \; in^4$$

7.3　Steps for the determination of maximum bending stress in a beam

The steps to determine the bending stresses in a beam subjected to any combination of loads and boundary conditions are shown below.

1. Determine the reactions in the beam and draw the shear force and bending moment diagram. From the bending moment diagram, determine the maximum positive (*M*) and negative bending moment values (-*M*)

2. From the geometry, determine the centroid of the cross section, hence the origin for the y-axis and the neutral axis. Using principles of statics, determine the centroidal moment of inertia.
3. Using the equations, given in section 7.2, determine the required quantities.

7.4 Forces due to flexural stresses

The physical manner in which a bending moment is resisted by a cross section is by bending stresses. For a positive bending moment, the cross section area above the neutral axis is in compression and that below the neutral axis is in tension. It has also been seen that the variation of the stresses across the depth is linear, with the maximum values at the extreme ends while the stress value is zero at the neutral axis.

The bending stresses across the cross section can be visualized as a net compressive force (C) on the area above the neutral axis and a net tensile force (T) below the cross section. If the net external axial force in the section is zero then these forces are equal. These two forces form a couple, which has a value of the couple moment equal to the bending moment that the cross section experiences.

7.4.1 Basic Idea of Force Computation

Consider a simple case, as shown in Figure 7.8, which shows a rectangular cross section with the area in compression and tension experiencing uniform stress (hence the rectangular distribution). In a later course, it will be shown that this case can occur for steel cross sections subjected to full plastification. For a rectangular cross section the neutral axis is at the center.

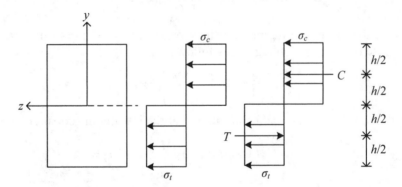

Figure 7.8: Rectangular cross section subjected to equal compressive and tensile stress

Since the entire area is subjected to equal stresses the following observations can be made
1. The tensile force is equal to the stress value multiplied by the area in tension and the compressive force is equal to the stress value multiplied by the area in compression. So $C = \sigma_C \left(\dfrac{bh}{2} \right)$ & $T = \sigma_T \left(\dfrac{bh}{2} \right)$. Since the stresses are equal, $C=T$.
2. The location of the tensile force and the compressive force is at the center of the respective areas. Hence, the distance or the lever arm between them is equal to $h/2$.
3. The moment that the cross section is subjected to is thus

$$M = T \times \frac{h}{2} = C \times \frac{h}{2}$$

Eqn (7.10)

It must be kept in mind that the reason the force equation was taken to be stress multiplied by the area, is that the stress is constant in the area.

7.4.2   Force due to bending stress

Since the stress value in a cross section subjected to a bending moment varies linearly with depth, the concept of the force being equal to the stress multiplied by the area can not be directly applied. In order the compute the total compressive or tensile force, a small area $dA = b'\ dy$ is considered, as shown in Figure 7.9 at a distance y from the neutral axis.

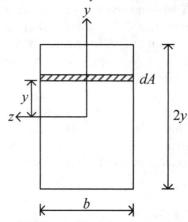

Figure 7.9: Incremental force and total force

Over this incremental area the stress value can be considered as constant, hence the incremental force can be written as

$$dF = \sigma \times dA = -\left(\frac{My}{I_{NA}}\right)(b \times dy)$$

The total force in the respective regions can now be found by taking an integral over the total height of the tensile or compression region, as follows

$$C = \int dF = \int_{0}^{y_c} -\left(\frac{My}{I_{NA}}\right)(b \times dy)$$

By taking out all the values that remain constant out of the integral the equation now reduces to

$$C = \int dF = -\left(\frac{M}{I_{NA}}\right)\int_{0}^{y_c}(y \times bdy) = -\left(\frac{M}{I_{NA}}\right)\int_{0}^{y_c}(ydA) = -\left(\frac{M}{I_{NA}}\right)Q_{NA}$$

Eqn (7.11)

$$\text{where } Q_{NA} = \int_{0}^{y_c}(ydA)$$

The term inside the integral, from Statics, is the first moment of area in compression about the neutral axis. It can be rewritten as follows

$$Q_{NA} = \int_{0}^{y_c}(y \times b \times dy) = \bar{y}A_C$$

where, $\bar{y}$ is the distance of the centroid of the area in compression A_c from the neutral axis. The tensile force can also be found in a similar manner.

7.4.3   Location of the Compressive or Tensile force

The location of the force can now be derived using the concept of the moment of force about the neutral axis. In Figure 7.9, the moment due to compressive forces can be found by taking the moment of the incremental force dF and integrating it over the height of the compression area The equations can be written as follow.

$$\int dM = \int dF \times y = -\left(\frac{M}{I_{NA}}\right) \int_{0}^{y_c} (y \times dA) \times y$$

$$M_C = \int dM = -\left(\frac{M}{I_{NA}}\right) \int_{0}^{y_c} (y^2 \times dA)$$

$$M_C = -\left(\frac{M}{I_{NA}}\right) I_c$$

where, I_c is the moment of inertia of the compression area about the neutral axis. By equating the total compressive force C multiplied by the location of the compressive force y_c the location can be now found as follows.

$$M_C = C \times y_c$$

$$-\left(\frac{M}{I_{NA}}\right) I_c = -\left(\frac{M \times Q_{NA}}{I_{NA}}\right) y_c$$

$$y_c = \frac{I_c}{Q_{NA}}$$

7.4.4   Summary of Equations

The equations pertaining to the force and location calculations can now be summarized as follows.
1. The **compressive or the tensile force** in the respective areas can now be written in general as

$$F = -\left(\frac{M \times Q_{NA}}{I_{NA}}\right)$$

2. **The location of the force** is

$$y_c = \frac{I_c}{\left(Q_{NA}\right)_{\text{compression region}}}$$

$$y_t = \frac{I_t}{\left(Q_{NA}\right)_{\text{tension region}}}$$

3. **The bending moment** in the cross section can be written as

$$M = C(y_c + y_t)$$

Example 7-2: Bending stress and forces due to bending stresses

Problem Statement: A cantilever beam is fixed at A and is loaded at B by a 50 *lbs.* force as shown. Its cross section is rectangular with a width of 5 *in* and depth of 10 *in*. Determine the magnitude and location of the maximum bending stress. Draw the bending stress distribution at the support and determine the forces in the cross section due to bending stresses.

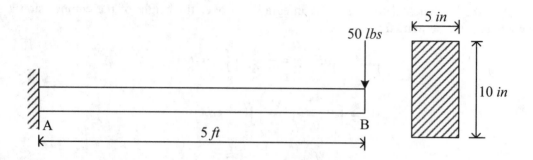

Required: a) Magnitude and location of maximum bending stress
b) Bending stress distribution at the support
c) Forces in the cross section due to bending stresses

Solution:

Step 1: Determine the reactions

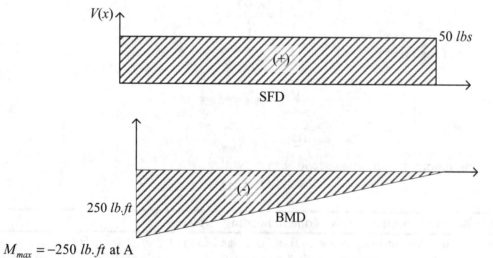

$$\sum F_X = 0 : A_X + 0 = 0 \therefore A_X = 0$$

$$\sum F_Y = 0 : V_A - 50 \; lb = 0 \therefore V_A = 50 \; lb \uparrow$$

$$\sum M_A = 0 : M_A - (50 \; lb)(5 \; ft) = 0 \therefore M_A = 250 \; lb.ft$$

Step 2: Draw the shear force and bending moment diagrams.

$M_{max} = -250 \; lb.ft$ at A

Since the moment is negative it results in tension at the top and compression at the bottom

Step 3: Determine the centroidal moment of inertia and bending stresses

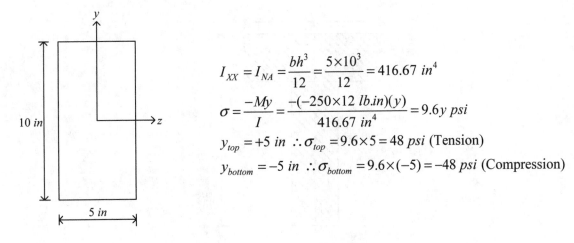

$$I_{XX} = I_{NA} = \frac{bh^3}{12} = \frac{5 \times 10^3}{12} = 416.67 \ in^4$$

$$\sigma = \frac{-My}{I} = \frac{-(-250 \times 12 \ lb.in)(y)}{416.67 \ in^4} = 9.6y \ psi$$

$$y_{top} = +5 \ in \ \therefore \sigma_{top} = 9.6 \times 5 = 48 \ psi \ \text{(Tension)}$$

$$y_{bottom} = -5 \ in \ \therefore \sigma_{bottom} = 9.6 \times (-5) = -48 \ psi \ \text{(Compression)}$$

Step 4: Determine the forces in the compression and tension region

$$F = \frac{-MQ}{I_{NA}} = \frac{-M(A\bar{y})}{I_{NA}} = \frac{(-3000 \ lb.in)Q}{416.67 \ in^4}$$

$$Q = A\bar{y} = (5 \ in \times 5 \ in)(2.5 \ in) = 62.5 \ in^3$$

$$F = \frac{(-3000 \ lb.in)(62.5 \ in^3)}{416.67 \ in^4} = -450 \ lb \ \text{(Compression)}$$

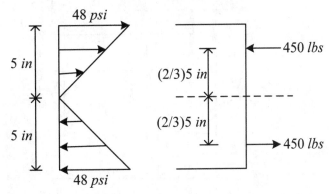

Example 7-3: Determination of Flexural forces and stresses

Problem Statement: A T beam as shown in figure is subjected to moment of 136 $k.in$. Determine the magnitude of the maximum bending stress. Draw the bending stress distribution and determine the forces in the cross section due to bending stresses.

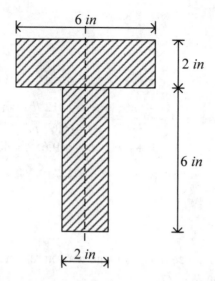

Required: a) Magnitude of bending stresses.
b) Forces in the cross section due to bending stresses

Solution:

Step 1: Determine the centroid of the cross section

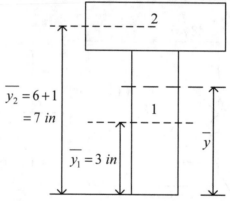

$$A\overline{y} = A_1\overline{y}_1 + A_2\overline{y}_2 = (12\ in^2)(3\ in) + (12\ in^2)(6\ in + 1\ in) = 120\ in^3$$

$$\overline{y} = \frac{120\ in^3}{(12\ in^2 + 12\ in^2)} = 5\ in\ \text{(from bottom)}$$

Hence, the neutral axis is located at 5 *in* from the bottom

Step 2: Determine the composite section centroidal moment of inertia

$$I_{composite} = \sum(\overline{I} + Ad^2)$$

$$= (\overline{I}_1 + A_1 d_1^2) + (\overline{I}_2 + A_2 d_2^2)$$

$$\overline{I}_1 = \frac{2 \times 6^3}{12} = 36\ in^4;\ A_1 = 12\ in^2;\ d_1 = (5-3)\ in = 2\ in.$$

$$\overline{I}_2 = \frac{6 \times 2^3}{12} = 4\ in^4;\ A_2 = 12\ in^2;\ d_2 = (5-7)\ in = -2\ in.$$

$$\overline{I}_{composite} = (36 + 12 \times 2^2) + (4 + 12 \times 2^2) = 136\ in^4$$

Step 3: Determine the bending stress distribution across the cross section

$$\sigma = -\frac{My}{I_{NA}} = \frac{-(136,000\ lb.in)(y)}{136\ in^4} = -1000y\ psi$$

At top fiber

$$y = +3\ in.;\ \therefore \sigma = -(1000 \times 3) = -3000\ psi$$

At bottom fiber

$$y = -5\ in.;\ \therefore \sigma = -(1000 \times (-5)) = 5000\ psi$$

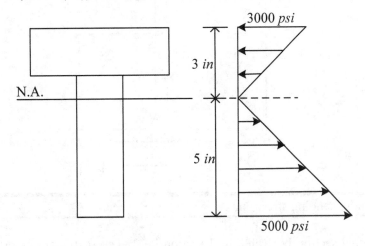

Step 4: Determine the forces in the compression and tension region

$$F = -\frac{MQ}{I_{NA}} = -\frac{(-136,000\ lb.in)(Q)}{136\ in^4}$$

$$Q_{bottom} = A\bar{y} = (5\ in \times 2\ in)(2.5\ in.) = 25\ in^3$$

$$F_{bottom} = -\frac{(-136,000\ lb.in.)(25\ in^3)}{136\ in^4} = 25,000\ lb.\ \text{(tension)}$$

$$F_{top} = -F_{bottom} = -25,000\ lb.\ \text{(compression)}$$

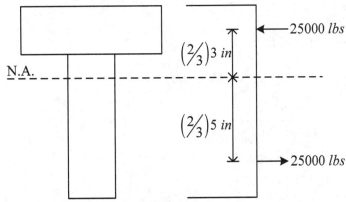

Example 7-4: Application of bending stress determination to rolled steel section

Problem Statement: Determine the maximum flexural stress in the beam made of two rolled sections (S12 x 31.8 and a channel section) and combined as shown. The beam is simply supported and is subjected to a bending moment of 136 *in.kips*.

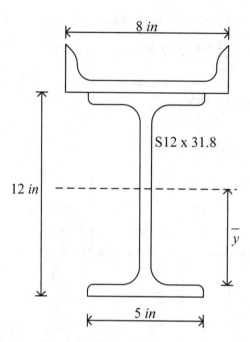

Required: Maximum bending stress and its location in the beam

Solution:

Step 1: Let channel section be 1 and the I-section be 2. The sectional properties of the rolled steel sections are taken from standard tables provided by the American Institute of Steel Construction (AISC).

Determine the centroid and the centroidal moment of inertia

$A_1 = 3.38 \ in^2$

$\overline{y_1} = 12 + 0.571 \ in$

$A_2 = 9.35 \ in^2$

$\overline{y_2} = 6 \ in$

$A\overline{y} = A_1\overline{y_1} + A_2\overline{y_2} = 3.38 \times 12.571 + 9.35 \times 6 = 98.59 \ in^3$

$\overline{y} = \dfrac{98.59 \ in^3}{(3.38 + 9.35) \ in^2} = 7.74 \ in$ from the bottom.

$I_{XX} = I_{NA} = \sum (\overline{I} + Ad^2) = (\overline{I_1} + A_1d_1^2) + (\overline{I_2} + A_2d_2^2)$

$\overline{I_1} = I_X$ (from tables) $= 218 \ in^4$

$\overline{I_2} = I_Y$ (from tables) $= 1.32 \ in^4$

$A_1d_1^2 = 9.35 \times (7.74 - 6)^2 = 28.4 \ in^4$

$A_2d_2^2 = 3.38 \times (7.74 - 12.57)^2 = 78.85 \ in^4$

$I_{NA} = 326.5 \ in^4$

Step 2: Determine the stress equation and find the bending (flexural) stresses at the top and bottom fibers

$$\sigma = -\frac{My}{I} = -\frac{(136,000 lb.in)(y)}{326.5 in^4} = -416.54(y) \, psi$$

$y_{top} = 12 + 2.26 = 14.26 \, in.; \quad \therefore \sigma_{top} = -416.54 \times 14.26 = -5840 \, psi \quad \text{(compression)}$

$y_{bottom} = -7.74 \, in.; \quad \therefore \sigma_{bottom} = -416.54 \times (-7.74) = 3224 \, psi \quad \text{(tension)}$

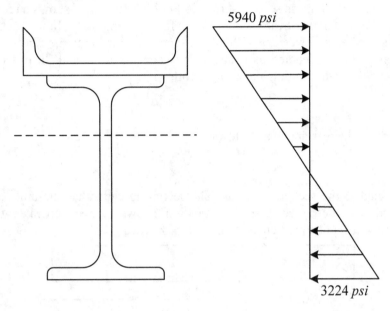

7.5   Design for bending

The theoretical description presented so far in this chapter pertains to the basic issues related to the calculation of flexural stresses. The computation of maximum flexural stress, whether in tension or compression, has also been described. This section now describes the usage of these concepts for designing a beam subjected to bending.

The primary concept in the design of a beam is to arrive at the cross section dimensions given the beam span and loading to which it is subjected to. This is achieved by determining the maximum bending stress in tension and compression and setting it equal to the allowable stress in bending.

$$\sigma_x = -\frac{My}{I_{NA}} \leq \sigma_{all.}$$

The following sections outline the steps involved in the design of a beam.

7.5.1   Allowable Stress and Section Modulus

The allowable stress in bending is denoted henceforth as $\sigma_{all.}$. For all isotropic materials, in the elastic range of behavior the allowable stress in bending is same in both compression and tension. In what is traditionally known as the *allowable stress design (ASD)* the allowable stress is determined by dividing the yield stress of the material σ_y by a factor of safety (*F.O.S*) and is given as follows

$$\sigma_{all.} = \frac{\sigma_y}{F.O.S}$$

However, in materials such as concrete, the allowable stresses in tension and compression are vastly different. For example, concrete is very weak in tension compared to compression. In this chapter the discussion is restricted to isotropic materials only.

The second concept in the design of the cross section of a beam is the concept of section modulus. Consider the beam cross section shown in Figure 7.10, which shows a rectangular and a T-shaped beam. The rectangular beam is considered first for simplicity. In the rectangular beam, the neutral axis is located at the center of the cross section and the extreme fibers in compression (top) and tension (bottom), denoted as y_t and y_b, respectively are equal. In order to define the section modulus consider the bending equation as follows

$$-\sigma_{all.} = -\frac{M_{max.} y_t}{I_{NA}}$$

The equation can now be rearranged as follows

$$\frac{M_{max.}}{\sigma_{all.}} = \frac{I_{NA}}{y_t} = S_t$$

where, S_t, is defined as the section modulus. The section modulus has the units of cube of the length. It should also be noted that the equation shown above separates the geometric characteristics and the applied moment and material properties.

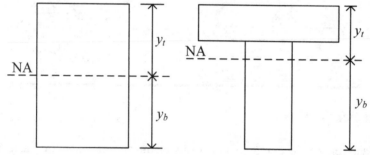

Figure 7.10: Cross section of a rectangular and a T-beam showing the location of the neutral axis

For a rectangular section, the section modulus is expressed as follows

$$S_t = \frac{I_{NA}}{y_t} = \frac{bh^3/12}{h/2} = \frac{bh^2}{6}$$

For a section that is not symmetric about the neutral axis, such as the T-shaped cross section shown in Figure 7.10, the section modulus for the top and the bottom fibers are different. In the design of a cross section, the determination of the cross section properties can not be done directly. A cross section size may be assumed and then the section modulus of the top and bottom fibers can be determined and compared with the allowable values.

Example 7-5: Design of beam sections for flexural stresses

Problem Statement: The beam 16 *ft.* long is loaded by concentrated loads as shown. If the allowable stress in bending is 24 *ksi*, design an appropriate rectangular cross section for the beam.

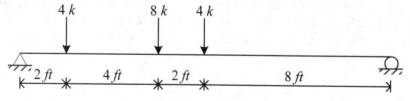

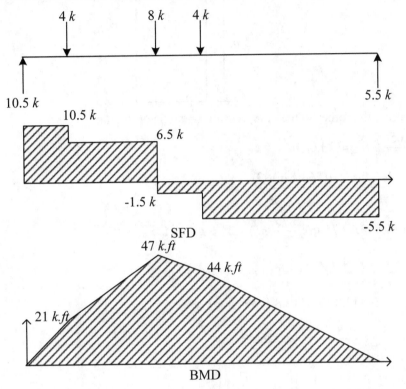

Required: Cross section dimensions for the rectangular beam

Solution:

Step 1: Determine the reactions and draw the shear force and bending moment diagrams

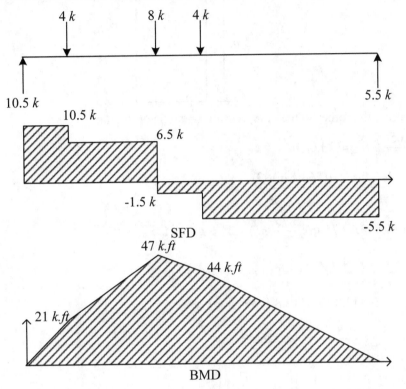

Step 2: From the bending moment diagram, determine the maximum bending moment and the required section properties

$$M_{max} = 47 \ k.ft = (47 \times 12) \ k.in = 564 \ k.in$$

$$S_{req} = \frac{M}{\sigma_{all}} = \frac{564 \ k.in}{24 \ ksi} = 23.5 \ in^3$$

In order to determine the size of the rectangular cross section, let us assume that $h=2b$, which is the depth of the beam, is twice the width (any other suitable assumption can be made here)

$$S = \frac{I}{c} = \frac{\frac{bh^3}{12}}{\frac{h}{2}} = \frac{bh^2}{6}$$

$$\therefore 23.5 = \frac{b \times (2b)^2}{6}$$

or $b = 3.24 \ in$

Design choice can be $3.5 \ in \times 7.5 \ in$.

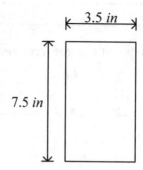

Step 3: Determine the forces in the compression and tension region

$$I_{NA} = \frac{bh^3}{12} = \frac{3.5 \times 7.5^3}{12} = 123.05 \ in^4$$

$$F = -\frac{MQ}{I_{NA}} = -\frac{M(A\bar{y})}{I_{NA}} = -\frac{(564 \ k.in)(Q)}{123.05 \ in^4}$$

$$Q_{bottom} = A\bar{y} = (3.5 \ in \times 3.75 \ in)(\frac{3.75}{2} \ in.) = 24.6 \ in^3$$

$$F_{bottom} = -\frac{(564 \ k.in.)(24.6 \ in^3)}{123.05 \ in^4} = -112.8 \ k. \ (compression)$$

$$F_{top} = -F_{bottom} = -(-112.8 \ k) = 112.8 \ k \ (tension)$$

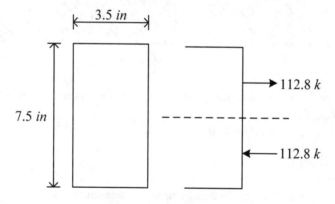

7.6 Beams made of two materials – Composite beams

An application of the principles of bending is now considered for beams whose cross section is made of two different types of materials. Consider a beam made of a wooden cross section. In order to strengthen the beam if two metal plates are attached at the top and bottom, it forms a composite beam. It will be seen later that the addition of a thin metallic plate which has a higher elastic modulus results in significant additional moment capacities. This section describes the principles involved in the computation of stresses, and consequently the maximum values, in both the materials. The theoretical foundation is laid out first, followed by a simpler approach to the solution of such problems.

Consider a composite beam cross section, as shown in Figure 7.11, which shows a central rectangular area made of a material with an elastic modulus E_A. It has a width of b and a depth of d. It is attached to two thin rectangular plates of thickness t at both the top and the bottom. It is to be noted that the two materials are combined with connectors along the span which keeps the unit acting as one piece. The two plates have an elastic modulus E_B, such that $E_B > E_A$. For simplicity, the width of both the materials is considered to be equal, although this is not a requirement and the approach illustrated below is valid even if the widths of the two materials are unequal, as shown in Figure 7.12. It is also to be noted that the approach is valid for non symmetric sections as well, for instance if there were a plate only at the top and none at the bottom.

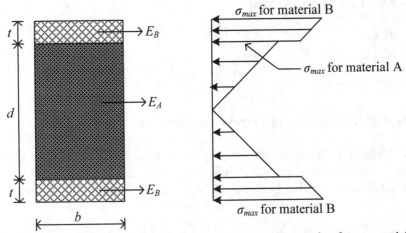

Figure 7.11: Composite Beam of symmetric cross section made of two materials

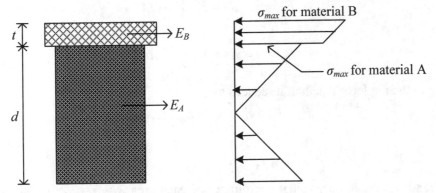

Figure 7.12: Composite Beam of unsymmetric cross section made of two materials

7.6.1 Principles of Composite Beams

There are two main principles on which the theory of composite materials is based on.

1. **Strain Compatibility:** Since the assumption that plane sections remain plane after bending is valid in this situation also, the first principle on which the theory is developed is that the strain distribution across the depth follows a linear distribution, with compression at the top and tension at bottom for a positive bending moment. The neutral axis lies at the location where the strain is zero. Since the materials are firmly connected to each other it can be assumed that the strain at the interface of the two materials is the same, *i.e.* there is no relative slip at the interface. This is shown in Figures 7.11 and 7.12 that at location where the strain ε_2 is the same in materials A and B. Mathematically this concept can be given as

$$\varepsilon_x = -\frac{y}{\rho}$$

Note: It is important to note that the location of neutral axis is *not necessarily* at the geometric centroid of the cross section. Its location will be determined later.

2. **Elastic Behavior:** As usual elastic behavior is assumed which implies that the stresses in the material are directly proportional to the strain in the material, *i.e.* $\sigma_A = E_A \varepsilon$ and $\sigma_B = E_B \varepsilon$. Hence, it can be seen that at the interface although the strains are the same due to strain compatibility, the stresses are not equal. This concept is illustrated in Figure 7.11 and 7.12. The stresses can now be expressed as

$$\sigma_A = E_A \varepsilon_x = -\frac{E_A y}{\rho}$$

$$\sigma_B = E_B \varepsilon_x = -\frac{E_B y}{\rho}$$

7.6.2 Location of Neutral Axis and Stress Computation

Neutral Axis: Following the assumptions of pure bending, it is taken that the cross section experiences only a bending moment and a shear force. As there is no axial force action $P=0$. Let the areas for the two materials be A_A and A_B. The net axial force due to internal stresses can be written as

$$Force_A + Force_B = F_A + F_B = 0$$

The forces in the two materials are now given as

$$F_A = \int_{A_A} \sigma_x dA = E_A \int_{A_A} \frac{-y}{\rho} dA$$

$$F_B = \int_{A_B} \sigma_x dA = E_B \int_{A_B} \frac{-y}{\rho} dA$$

Substituting in the net force equation it reduces to

$$F_A + F_B = E_A \int y dA + E_B \int y dA = 0$$

or

$$E_A \overline{y}_A A_A + E_B \overline{y}_B A_B = 0$$

where, $\overline{y}_A$ and $\overline{y}_B$ are the centroidal coordinates of each area *with respect to the neutral axis.* This concept is used in order to determine the neutral axis of the composite section.

Stress Computation: The stresses are now computed by the application of the second moment of area principle. Let M_A and M_B be the moments carried by the two components. They can now be expressed as follows

$$M_A = \int_{A_A} y \sigma_A dA = \frac{E_A}{\rho} \int y^2 dA = \frac{E_A}{\rho} I_A$$

$$M_B = \int_{A_B} y \sigma_B dA = \frac{E_B}{\rho} \int y^2 dA = \frac{E_B}{\rho} I_B$$

where, I_A and I_B are the moments of inertia of the two sections about the neutral axis. Since the total moment is the sum of the two component moments it can be written as

$$M = M_A + M_B = \frac{E_A}{\rho} I_A + \frac{E_B}{\rho} I_B$$

or

$$M = \frac{1}{\rho}\left(E_A I_A + E_B I_B\right)$$

or

$$\frac{1}{\rho} = \frac{M}{\left(E_A I_A + E_B I_B\right)}$$

The stresses can now be computed as

$$\sigma_A = -\frac{E_A y}{\rho} = -\frac{M E_A y}{\left(E_A I_A + E_B I_B\right)}$$

$$\sigma_B = -\frac{E_B y}{\rho} = -\frac{M E_B y}{\left(E_A I_A + E_B I_B\right)}$$

7.6.3   Alternative Method: Transformed Area Method

The applications of the equations, while theoretically elegant and consistent are not always the easiest way to solve a problem involving composite sections. An alternate method, involving transformed sections is illustrated in this section. In order to apply the bending stress equation directly, it must be ensured that the *entire section* be made of the *same material*. Although it was not evident it must be kept in mind that the determination of the moment of inertia of the cross sectional area assumes that the entire area is made of the same material. In the case of composite sections, however this condition cannot be satisfied. Hence, a transformed area method is adopted. The idea is to transform the area of one of the materials, here the one with the higher modulus, to an equivalent area with the elastic modulus of the other material.

The transformed area method uses two transforms. They are;
1. Geometric transformation, in which the width of one of the materials is transformed,
2. Stress transformation

Geometric Transform: This is the first step in the process in which the width (*never the thickness*) of one material, here the one with the higher elastic modulus, is transformed.
Principle: In the original section the stress distribution across the depth is not continuous. There is a jump at the interface of the two materials. However, the bending stress equation assumes a linear stress distribution. Also, the resultant of the axial forces due to bending stresses in the original and transformed areas must remain the same. Expressing this in an equation form, the width transformation equation can be derived as shown below.

$$F_{original} = F_{transformed}$$

$$\left(\int \sigma_x dA\right)_{original} = \left(\int \sigma_x dA\right)_{transformed}$$

$$\left(\int \frac{E_A y}{\rho} b_{or.} dy\right)_{original} = \left(\int \frac{E_B y}{\rho} b_{tr.} dy\right)_{transformed}$$

$$E_A b_{or.}\left(\int y dy\right) = E_B b_{tr.}\left(\int y dy\right)$$

$$E_A b_{or.} = E_B b_{tr.}$$

It can be noted that from a physical perspective, if we change the width of the material with a higher modulus to that of a lower elastic modulus, the width should increase.

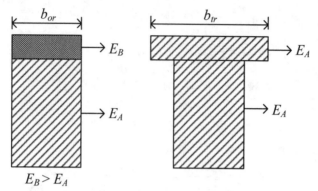

$$E_B > E_A$$

Figure 7.13: Principle to illustrate the width transform

Stress Transform: The stress transformation principle is based on the strain compatibility at the interface. This can be expressed in equation form as shown below.

$$\varepsilon_x = \frac{\sigma_A}{E_A} = \frac{\sigma_B}{E_B}$$

Steps involved in problem solution: The following steps are involved in the computation of stresses in a composite section subjected to a bending moment M.

Step 1: Transform the width of the material with a higher modulus using the geometric transform equation. It is easier to change the width of the material with a higher modulus. In this case the new width is equal to the original width multiplied by the ratio of the elastic modulus of the higher to the lower values.

Step 2: Since now the entire transformed section has the same elastic modulus, determine the centroid and the moment of inertia of the cross section.

Step 3: Using the bending stress equation determine the linear stress distribution equation across the depth.

Step 4: Using the stress transform equation transform the stresses in the transformed area part to the actual values. If the higher modulus material was transformed, it will result in an increase in stresses in this portion.

The above concepts are now illustrated using the example below.

Example 7-6: Analysis for beams made of two materials

Problem Statement: A beam cross section is made of a wooden core of size 150×250 *mm* and is attached to two aluminum plates of size 150×25 *mm* as shown, to form a composite beam section made of two materials. Given that the maximum allowable bending stresses in wood and aluminum is 45 *MPa* and 210 *MPa* respectively, determine the maximum moment capacity of the cross section. It is also given that the elastic modulus of wood and aluminum are 14 *GPa* and 70 *GPa* respectively.

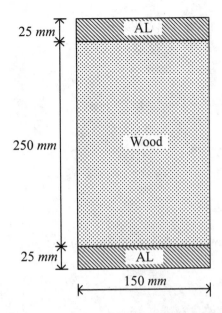

Required: Determine the moment capacity of the cross section made of two materials.

Solution:

Step 1: Transform the cross section such that it is made of the same material. In this problem the aluminum portion is transformed into an equivalent wood section. Remember that if you transform the width of a material with a higher modulus, its width will increase. Hence, the total composite section is made of an equivalent wooden cross section.

$$b_{new} = b_{old} \times \frac{E_{AL}}{E_{wood}} = 150 \ mm \times \frac{70 \ GPa}{14 \ GPa} = 750 \ mm$$

The depth of the transformed cross section does not change.

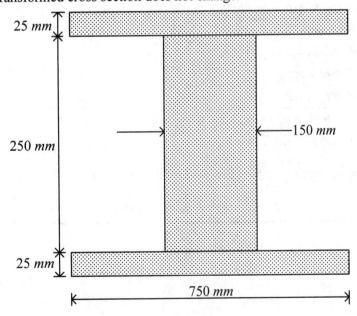

Step 2: Determine the composite section centroidal moment of inertia. In this problem since the symmetry is maintained in both axes, the centroid lies at the center of the I-section.

$$I_{composite} = \sum (\overline{I} + Ad^2) = 2(\overline{I_1} + A_1 d_1^2) + (\overline{I_2} + A_2 d_2^2)$$

$$\overline{I_1} = \frac{750 \times 25^3}{12} = 975,562.5 \ mm^4$$

$$A_1 = 750 \times 25 \ mm^2; d_1 = \left(\frac{250}{2} + \frac{25}{2}\right) mm = 137.5 \ mm$$

$$\overline{I_2} = \frac{150 \times 250^3}{12} = 195,312,500 \ mm^4$$

$$A_2 = 150 \times 250 \ mm^2; d_2 = 0$$

$$\overline{I}_{composite} = 9.0625 \times 10^8 \ mm^4$$

Step 3: Convert the actual allowable stress in aluminum into an equivalent wood allowable stress

$$\left(\frac{\sigma}{E}\right)_{wood} = \left(\frac{\sigma}{E}\right)_{Al.}$$

$$\sigma_{all, as.wood} = \left(\frac{\sigma}{E}\right)_{Al.} (E_{wood})$$

$$\sigma_{all, as.wood} = \left(\frac{210 \ MPa}{70 \ GPa}\right)_{Al.} (14 \ GPa) = 42 \ MPa$$

Step 4: Determine the moment capacity from the two allowable stress considerations

$$\sigma = -\frac{My}{I_{NA}} = \frac{-M(150 \ mm)}{9.0625 \times 10^8 \ mm^4}$$

At top fiber (Aluminum location)

$$M_{all} = \frac{(42 \ MPa)(9.0625 \times 10^8 \ mm^4)}{150 \ mm}$$

$$= 2.5375 \times 10^8 \ N.mm = 253.75 \ kN.m$$

At bottom fiber (Top of wood)

$$M_{all} = \frac{(45 \ MPa)(9.0625 \times 10^8)}{125 \ mm}$$

$$= 3.2625 \times 10^8 \ N.mm = 326.25 \ kN.m$$

Step 5: Maximum moment capacity is the lesser of the two values

$$M_{max} = 253.75 \ kN.m$$

7.7 Summary

In chapter 7 bending or flexural stresses in the beam were studied. The keywords introduced in this chapter are as follows.
1. **Longitudinal Axis:** It is the axis that runs along the length of the beam passing through the centroid of the cross section at the two ends.
2. **Transverse/Lateral Axes:** The axis that is perpendicular to the longitudinal axis is the transverse axis, also called lateral axis. The cross sections of the beam lie in this axis.
3. **Pure Bending:** Pure bending is said to occur when the bending moment at the two ends of the beam are equal in magnitude.
4. **Warping:** If plane sections do not remain plane after bending the sections is said to be warping.
5. **Radius of Curvature:** The radius of the neutral axis is called the *radius of curvature* (ρ) of the beam.
6. **Neutral Axis:** The axis about which the applied bending moment acts is called the neutral axis. The neutral axis of the cross section is also called *centroidal axis*.
7. **Flexural Stress:** A beam subjected to bending moment at the two ends experiences compression stresses at the top and tensile stresses at the bottom. These stresses are also termed as Flexural stresses.

$$\sigma_x = -\frac{My}{I_{NA}}$$

8. **Flexural Strain:** The strain caused in the beam subjected to bending moment is termed as Flexural strain.

$$\varepsilon_x = -\frac{y}{\rho} = -\frac{My}{EI_{NA}}$$

9. **Allowable Stress:** The allowable stress is determined by dividing the yield stress of the material (σ_y) by a factor of safety (F.O.S.) and is given by,

$$\sigma_{all.} = \frac{\sigma_y}{F.O.S}$$

10. **Section Modulus:** The section modulus is determined by dividing moment of inertia of the cross section about its centroidal axis by the distance between the neutral axis and the extreme fiber in tension or compression. For a section that is not symmetric about the neutral axis, such as the T-shaped cross section, the section modulus for the top and the bottom fibers are different.

$$S_t = \frac{I_{NA}}{y_t} \text{ and } S_b = \frac{I_{NA}}{y_b}$$

7.8 Problems

7.1 A cantilever beam is fixed at B is loaded as shown in the figure below. Its cross section is rectangular with a width of 150 *mm* and depth of 700 *mm*. Determine the magnitude and location of the maximum bending stress. Draw the bending stress distribution at the support and determine the forces in the cross section due to bending stresses.

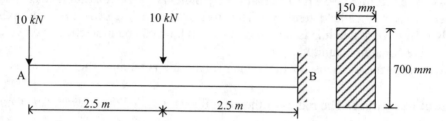

7.2 A cantilever beam, of length 5*m*, is fixed at end A and is loaded with an udl of 250 *kN/m* throughout its length. The cross section is shown in the figure below. Determine the magnitude and location of the maximum bending stress. Draw the bending stress distribution at the support and determine the forces in the cross section due to bending stresses.

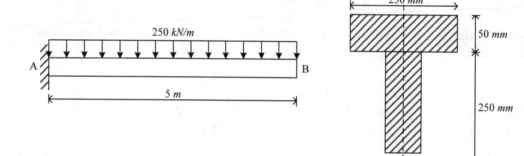

7.3 A simply supported beam of length 9 *ft* has a point load of 100 *lbs* at a distance of 4 *ft* from its right end. The beam has a rectangular cross section of width 6 *in* and depth of 18 *in*. Determine the magnitude and location of the maximum bending stress. Draw the bending stress distribution at the support and determine the forces in the cross section due to the bending stresses.

7.4 If the beam in the above problem has a cross section as shown in figure below, determine the magnitude and location of the maximum bending stress. Draw the bending stress distribution at the support and determine the forces in the cross section due to the bending stresses.

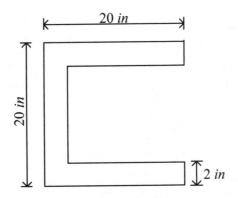

7.5   Determine the magnitude and location of the maximum bending stress in the beams with the loading and cross section as shown in figure below. Also draw the bending stress distribution at the support and determine the forces in the cross section due to the bending stresses.

a.

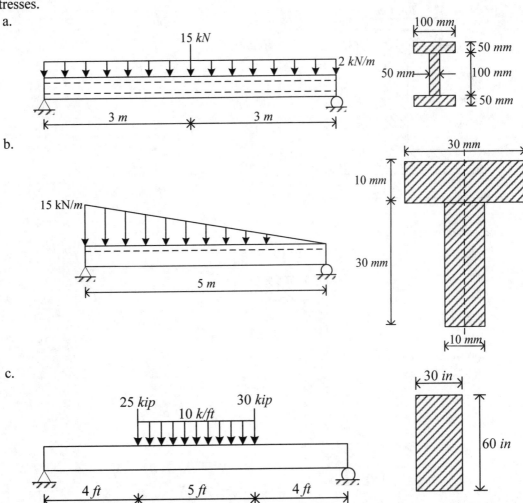

b.

c.

7.6 Determine the magnitude of the maximum bending stress in the cross sections given below. The moment to which the cross section is subjected to is also given below. Draw the bending stress distribution and determine the forces in the cross section due to bending stresses.

a.   Moment = 150 *k in*

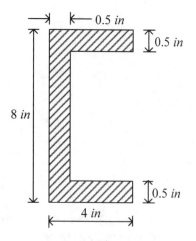

b. Moment = 50 $kN\,m$

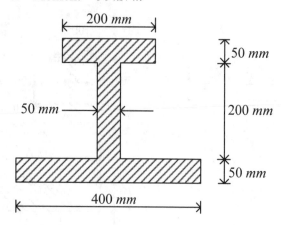

c. Moment = 36 $kN\,m$

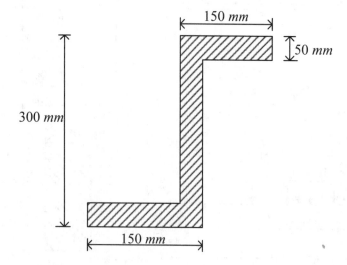

d. Moment = 100 $k\,in$

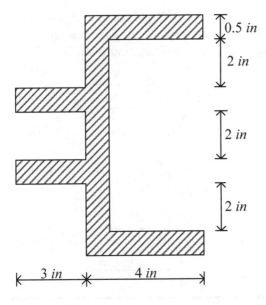

e. Moment = 40 $kN\,m$

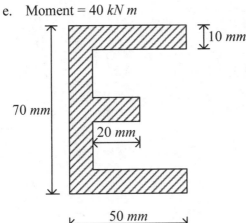

7.7 The cantilever beam 2.5 m. long is loaded uniformly with the load of 6 kN/m throughout the length of the cantilever. If the allowable stress in bending is 50 MPa, design an appropriate rectangular cross section for the beam.

7.8 A simply supported beam of length 10 ft is uniformly loaded with 20 lb/ft and carries a concentrated load of 60 lbs at a distance of 4 ft from right. If the allowable stress in bending is 30 ksi, design an appropriate rectangular cross section for the beam.

7.9 A simply supported beam of length 6 m is loaded as shown in figure below. If the allowable stress in bending is 45 MPa, design an appropriate rectangular cross section for the beam.

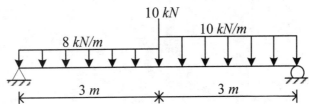

7.10 Given that the maximum allowable bending stresses in wood and aluminum is 45 *MPa* and 210 *MPa* respectively, determine the maximum moment capacity of the cross sections given below. It is also given that the elastic modulus of wood and aluminum are 14 *GPa* and 70 *GPa* respectively.

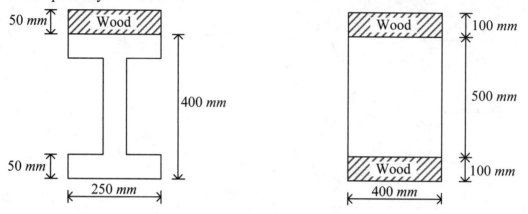

Chapter 8

Shear Stresses in Beams

Goal: The learning objectives of this chapter are as follows:

1. Introduce the concept of shear flow and shear stresses
2. Outline the concept of shear flow and discuss application examples in built up sections
3. Describe the concept of shear stresses in solid rectangular and I sections
4. Discuss the concept of shear center
5. Application of the concepts of shear to various problems

8 Shear Stresses in Beams

8.1 Introduction

In two dimensional problems of a beam bending under applied loads, it has been seen from the method of sections that there are three internal forces (axial force P, bending moment M and shear force V) that must be resisted by internal stresses in the beams. The stresses due to axial force are normal to the cross section and have been studied in detail in Chapter 3. The internal stresses due to the bending moment are also normal to the cross sectional area and have been studied in Chapter 7.

This chapter deals with the third internal force, namely the Shear Force V, the nature of stresses it causes on the cross section of a beam and the stress distribution across the cross section. The first concept covered is *shear flow*, which was introduced in the chapter on torsion, and some of its applications in practice. This is followed by the derivation of the formula used to determine shear stress in beams and the equations for maximum shear stresses in beams. Finally, this chapter concludes with a discussion of the concept of shear center in beams.

8.1.1 Concept of Shear Stresses in Perspective

Consider the beam, in two dimensions, loaded as shown in Figure 8.1. After the determination of reactions, the internal forces on a cross section are also shown. The axial force P, acting at the centroid of the cross section causes *uniform normal stress*, as shown in Figure 8.2. The bending moment M, acting about an axis coming out of the plane of the paper and with an origin at the centroid of the cross section, causes *non uniform normal stress*, as shown in Figure 8.2.

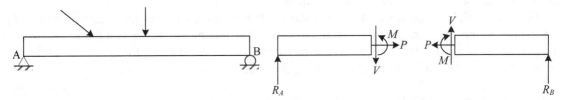

Figure 8.1: Beam loaded and the internal forces in the beam

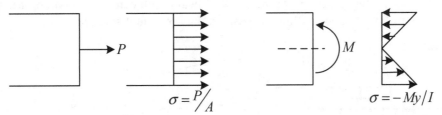

$$\sigma = P/A \qquad \sigma = -My/I$$

Figure 8.2: Internal stress distributions due to axial force and bending moment

The shear force V, on the cross section causes a stress that is parallel to the cross section and is in the direction of the of the shear force, as shown in Figure 8.3. The nature of the distribution across the cross section and the maximum values and their locations are now discussed in detail.

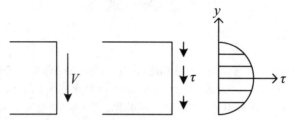

Figure 8.3: Internal stresses due to shear force

8.2 Shear Flow

The concept of shear stress is introduced by first discussing shear flow q. Consider a stack of beams, as shown in Figure 8.4, subjected to lateral loads which causes bending as shown. If the stack of beams is not rigidly connected to each other, by what are known as shear connectors, they will separate and slide relative to each other, as shown in Figure 8.4.

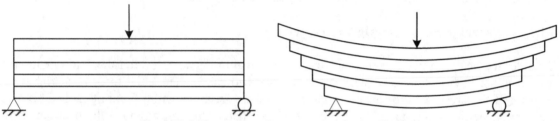

Figure 8.4: Separation of unconnected stack of beams

Q: Why do the beams slide relative to each other?
A: The beams slide in the horizontal direction relative to each other as they experience a shear force at the interfaces in the horizontal direction. The phenomenon in commonly known as *horizontal shear* and is caused by the variation of bending moment along the span. The horizontal shear force is explained through the concept of shear flow.

8.2.1 Horizontal Shear Flow and Horizontal Shear Force

Figure 8.5 shows an internal section of the stack of beams subjected to a bending moment and a shear force. The following steps outline the basis of the horizontal shear in beams.

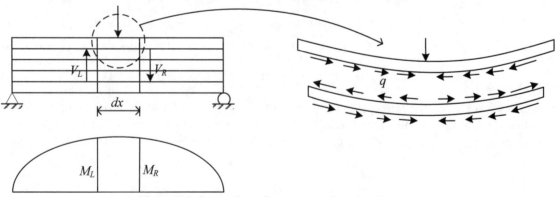

Figure 8.5: Separation of unconnected stack of beams

Consider a small segment of the beam dx. The shear force and bending moment on the left and right hand side is designated as V_L, M_L and V_R, M_R respectively.

Step a: Axial force due to bending: The bending moment M, causes a linear distribution of the internal normal stress. Since the magnitudes of the moment on the left and right hand sides are different the magnitudes of these stresses are different on the left and right hand sides. The magnitudes of the axial forces on the uppermost stack of wood, on the left F_L and right hand side F_R, can now be determined from the equation for axial forces due to bending that was derived in chapter 7. These horizontal forces are shown in Figure 8.6 and can be expressed as shown below

$$F_L = \frac{M_L Q}{I_{NA}} = \frac{M_L(A\bar{y})}{I_{NA}}$$

$$F_R = \frac{M_R Q}{I_{NA}} = \frac{M_L(A\bar{y})}{I_{NA}}$$

where, Q is the first moment of areas of the cross section $A\bar{y}$ representing the top most beam of the stack. The first moment of area is the product of the cross section area A and the distance of the centroid of the area from the neutral axis of the overall cross section $\bar{y}$, as shown in Figure 8.6.

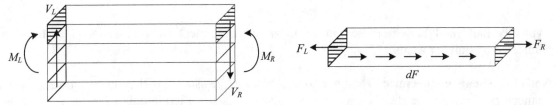

Figure 8.6: Axial force, horizontal shear and shear flow

Step b: Horizontal Shear: Since the bending moments on the two sides of the section are different the horizontal forces F_L and F_R are different. The difference in these two horizontal forces manifests itself as a shear at the interface between two pieces of the stack of wood. The horizontal force at the interface is called the *horizontal shear* caused by the change in bending moment across the span. The horizontal shear at the bottom face in the small segment is designated as dF, and is given as

$$dF = F_R - F_L = \frac{M_R Q}{I_{NA}} - \frac{M_L Q}{I_{NA}}$$

$$dF = \frac{(M_R - M_L)Q}{I_{NA}} = \frac{(dM)Q}{I_{NA}}$$

Step c: Shear Flow q: This horizontal shear force experienced by the bottom length of the beam dx, can be expressed as a shear flow by dividing the shear force by the length over which it acts as shown below. Using $V = \dfrac{dM}{dx}$, the equation for the horizontal shear flow in the beam can now be derived as follows.

$$q = \frac{dF}{dx} = \frac{1}{dx}\frac{(dM)Q}{I_{NA}} = \frac{dM}{dx}\frac{Q}{I_{NA}}$$

$$q = \frac{VQ}{I_{NA}}$$

Q: How to prevent the stack of beams from sliding relative to each other?

As all the interfaces of the beams experience a relative horizontal force between them which causes them to slide relative to each other, the beam can be connected by vertical bolts or shear connectors (Figure 8.7), in order to prevent the slide.

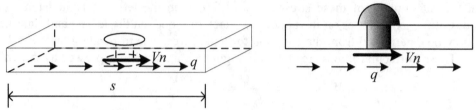

Figure 8.7: Shear connectors in beams; depiction of force per connector

8.2.2   Shear Connectors and Design of Connectors

From Figure 8.7 it can be seen that the shear connectors, placed at a spacing s, keeps the beams as an integral unit. Hence, the design of these connectors involves the strength of the connectors and the horizontal spacing at which they must be placed. These shear connectors experience a horizontal force (Figure 8.7)

$$V_n = q_n s \leq V_{sh\_cap}$$

Typically nails and bolts are used in wood as shear connectors, whereas steel sections are connected by bolts or welds.

Nails as shear connectors: This horizontal force is resisted by the nails acting as shear connectors. For nails the shear capacity of a nail V_{sh_cap} is specified in either *lbs.* or *Newtons* as a force value.

Welds as shear connectors: As it is expected that the student might have not had an introduction or an exposure to welding and the specification of the strength of a weld, the weld strength can often be specified by a shear flow form of expression q_{all} with the units of (*lb /in*). Hence, the determination of the shear flow at a certain level automatically specifies the strength of the weld that is required at that interface. The shear capacity of welds is specified as

$$q_{all} \geq q_n$$

Bolts as shear connectors: Common bolts, when used as shear connectors, resist the horizontal force in the form of shear stress in bolts (single or double shear). Hence, the design shear strength of the bolts V_{bolt} *must* be greater than or equal to the horizontal shear force experienced by them, as shown below

$$V_{sh\_cap} \geq V_n$$

$$V_{sh\_cap} = V_{bolt} = \left(\tau_{all.}\right) A_{bolt} = \left(\tau_{all.}\right) n \frac{\pi d^2}{4}$$

where, $\tau_{all.}$ is the allowable shear stress in the bolts, n is equal to one if the bolt experiences single shear and two if it experiences double shear and d is the diameter of the bolt. Hence, the spacing and diameter of the bolts can be related to the applied shear force V as follows

$$q_n = \frac{VQ}{I_{NA}}$$

$$V_n = q_n s$$

$$V_{bolt} \geq V_n$$

$$(\tau_{all.})n\frac{\pi d^2}{4} \geq \left(\frac{VQ}{I_{NA}}\right)s$$

Example 8.1: Shear capacity of a built up wooden section

Problem Statement: A wooden beam is made of five wooden pieces of dimension $0.5\ in \times 0.1\ in$ thick and stacked on top of each other as shown in the figure. The five pieces are connected by screws which are at $0.75\ in$ spacing in the longitudinal direction. The screws are $1/8\ in$ in diameter. If the allowable shear stress in the screws is $4000\ psi$, determine the maximum shear capacity of the section.

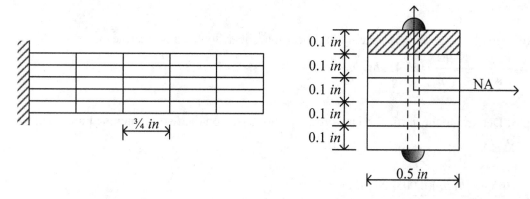

Required: Determine the shear capacity of the built up wooden section.

Solution:

Notes: The basic form of the shear flow equation from which the shear capacity, V, of the beam is determined is given as

$$q = \frac{VQ_{NA}}{I_{NA}} \text{ or } V = \frac{qI_{NA}}{Q_{NA}}$$

In this equation, for a given section, the quantities q and I_{NA} remain constant. Hence, the shear force V depends on the first moment of area Q_{NA}. There are three choices for the determination, as shown in the figure, for the determination of Q_{NA}.

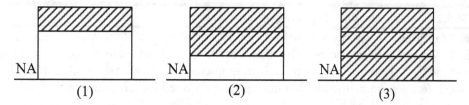

The longitudinal or horizontal shear flow can occur only between either the topmost and the second wooden piece or the second and third piece. The screw is provided in order to carry the shear flow as a horizontal shear force. The third choice shown in the figure above is not considered as there is no interface at the bottom of the section.

Step 1: Determine the moment of area for the two cases

$A_1 = 0.5 \times 0.1 = 0.05 \; in^2$

$\overline{y_1} = 0.05 + 0.1 + 0.05 = 0.2 \; in.$

$Q_{1NA} = A_1 \times \overline{y_1} = 0.05 \times 0.2 = 0.01 \; in^3$

$I_{NA} = \dfrac{1}{12}bd^3 = \dfrac{1}{12}0.5 \times 0.5^3 = 0.005208 \; in^4$

$A_2 = 0.5 \times 0.2 = 0.1 \; in^2$

$\overline{y_2} = 0.05 + 0.1 = 0.15 \; in.$

$Q_{2NA} = A_2 \times \overline{y_2} = 0.1 \times 0.15 = 0.015 \; in^3$

$I_{NA} = \dfrac{1}{12}bd^3 = \dfrac{1}{12}0.5 \times 0.5^3 = 0.005208 \; in^4$

Step 2: Determine the shear flow capacity of the section from the allowable shear stress in the screw.

a) Shear capacity of the bolt

$$V_{bolt} = \tau_{all.} \times A_{bolt} = 4000 \, psi \times \left(\frac{\pi \times (1/8)^2}{4} \, in^2 \right)$$

$$= 49 \; lbs.$$

b) Since the bolts are at ¾ in spacing the allowable shear flow at any interface is

$$q_{all.} = \frac{V_{bolt}}{s} = \frac{49 \; lbs.}{\frac{3}{4} \; in.} = 65.45 \; lbs/in.$$

Step 3: Determine the vertical shear force capacity based on the two moments of areas calculated

$$V_{all} = \frac{q_{all.}I_{NA}}{Q_{NA}}$$

$$V_{1all} = \frac{(65.45 \; lb/in.)(0.005208 \; in^4)}{(0.01 \; in^3)}$$

$$= 34.1 \; lbs.$$

$$V_{2all} = \frac{(65.45 \; lb/in.)(0.005208 \; in^4)}{(0.015 \; in^3)}$$

$$= 22.73 \; lbs.$$

Note: The maximum allowable value of shear force is the lower of the two values computed.
$V_{max} = 22.73 \; lbs$
It must be noted the moment of area with the two planks governed.

Example 8.2: Determination of spacing of lag screws

Problem Statement: A simply supported beam is loaded by a uniformly distributed load of 200 *lbs/ft.* as shown in the figure below. The cross section is made of many wooden pieces as shown. Given that the lag screws to be used are ½ *in* in diameter and the allowable shear force in each lag screw is 500 *lbs.*, determine the longitudinal spacing required for lag screws at A and B.

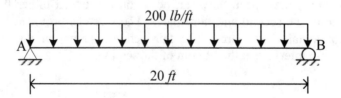

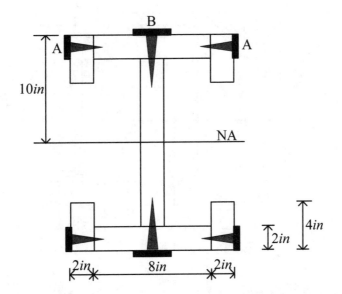

Required: To find the spacing for the lag screws at A and B of the cross section.

Solution:

Step 1: Determine the reactions, draw the shear force diagram and determine the maximum vertical shear force to be taken by the section

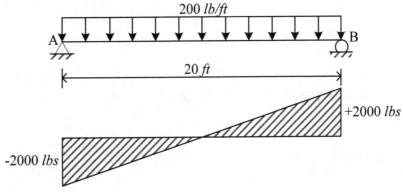

$$\sum F_x = 0: \ A_x = 0$$

$$\sum F_y = 0: \ A_y + B_y - (200 \ lb/ft.)(20 \ ft.) = 0$$

$$\sum M_A = 0: -(200 \ lb/ft.)(20 \ ft.)(10 \ ft.) + B_y(20 \ ft.) = 0$$

$$\therefore A_y = B_y = 2000 \ lbs \uparrow$$

$$V_{max} = 2000 \ lbs$$

Step 2: Determine the shear flow q_A and q_B of the section at lag screws A and B

a) Determine the area A and hence the moment of that area about the neutral axis Q_{NA}. The area to be identified can be thought of as the area of the cross section that would *fall off* if the screw were not present. Alternatively the area can be thought of as that part that is being connected to the main part, with the main part being defined as the one containing the neutral axis.

In both the cases the moment of inertia in all the calculations is the moment of inertia of the *entire* section about the neutral axis.

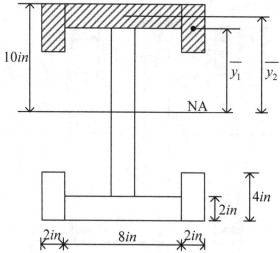

$$I_{NA} = \sum \overline{I} + Ad^2$$

$$= 4\left[\left(\frac{1}{12}2\times4^3\right)+(2\times4)\times8^2\right]+2\left[\left(\frac{1}{12}8\times2^3\right)+(2\times8)\times9^2\right]+\left[\left(\frac{1}{12}2\times16^3\right)\right]$$

$$= 6,060 \ in^4$$

$A_1 = 4\times2 = 8 \ in^2$

$\overline{y}_1 = 10-2 = 8 \ in.$

$Q_{A,NA} = A_1\times\overline{y}_1 = 8\times8 = 64 \ in^3$

$A_1 = 4\times2 = 8 \ in^2; \ \overline{y}_1 = 10-2 = 8 \ in.$

$A_2 = 8\times2 = 16 \ in^2; \ \overline{y}_2 = 10-1 = 9 \ in$

$Q_{B,NA} = 2\times A_1 \times \overline{y}_1 + A_2 \times \overline{y}_2 = 2\times8\times8+16\times9 = 272 \ in^3$

b) The vertical shear force in the cross section is the same, *i.e.* V_{max}= 2000 *lbs*. The shear flow in each of the two lag screw locations is determined as shown below

$$q_A = \frac{V_{max}Q_{A,NA}}{I_{NA}}$$

$$= \frac{(2000 \ lbs)(64 \ in^3)}{6,060 \ in^4} = 21.12 \ lbs/in.$$

$$q_B = \frac{V_{max}Q_{B,NA}}{I_{NA}}$$

$$= \frac{(2000 \ lbs)(272 \ in^3)}{6,060 \ in^4} = 90 \ lbs/in.$$

Step 3: Determine the spacing of each lag screw

$$s_A = \frac{V_{screw}}{q_A}$$

$$= \frac{(500 \ lbs)}{21.12 \ lbs/in.} = 23.67 \ in.$$

$$s_B = \frac{V_{screw}}{q_B}$$

$$= \frac{500 \ lbs}{90 \ lbs/in.} = 5.56 \ lbs/in.$$

Note: The spacing actually provided should be less than the above values and for practical reasons rounded off as shown.

$s_A = 23 \ in.$ center to center

$s_B = 5.5 \ in.$ center to center

8.3   Shear Stress in Beams

The concept of shear stress in beams follows directly from the idea of shear flow. It was seen in an earlier section, that shear flow is useful to determine the flow or force in the connectors. In the case where the entire beam is monolithic the transfer of this shear occurs in the form of a shear stress.

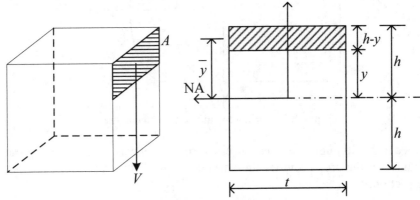

Figure 8.8: Solid section subjected to shear stress

8.3.1   Shear Stress Distribution Formula

Q: How to determine the shear stress at any point?
Consider a solid section, as shown in Figure 8.8, which shows a solid section subjected to a shear force V. The aim is to determine the shear stress τ at a distance y from the neutral axis. The following steps outline the concepts and procedures involved in the determination of the shear stress.

Step a: Determine the shear flow at a section at a distance y from the neutral axis. As shown in Figure 8.8, the area A above (away from the neutral axis) is considered and the horizontal shear flow is given by the equation

$$q = \frac{VQ}{I_{NA}} = \frac{V\left(A\overline{y}\right)}{I_{NA}}$$

where, Q is the first moment of the area about the neutral axis.

Step b: The horizontal shear stress is the shear flow divided by the width of the section, as shown in Figure 8.8

$$\tau = \frac{q}{t} = \frac{VQ}{I_{NA}t} = \frac{V\left(A\overline{y}\right)}{I_{NA}t}$$

Step c: Consider an incremental element, as shown in Figure 8.9, which shows the shear stress on the element at the section. Since shear stresses always exist in pairs, the horizontal shear stress causes an equal amount of vertical shear stress in the cross section, which is the required shear stress equation.

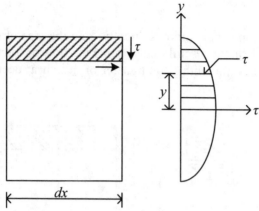

Figure 8.9: Horizontal and vertical shear stress

It is to be noted that although the shear stress formula appears to have a constant value, the centroidal distance of the area provides the variable. This is illustrated for two specific cases in the following section.

8.3.2   Rectangular Cross Sections

The shear stress magnitude, distribution and maximum value is now determined for a simple rectangular shape. Figure 8.8 shows a rectangular section with dimensions b and $2h$, whose neutral axis lies at the center of the depth. The shear stress at a distance y from the neutral axis is now determined.

a)   Determine the shear flow at a distance y from the neutral axis by considering the area above that point $A = b(h - y)$. Hence, the shear flow is given as

$$q = \frac{VQ}{I_{NA}}$$

$$I_{NA} = \frac{b(2h)^3}{12} = \frac{2bh^3}{3}$$

$$Q = A\bar{y}$$

$$A = b(h-y) \text{ and } \bar{y} = y + \frac{h-y}{2} = \frac{h+y}{2}$$

$$Q = b(h-y)\frac{h+y}{2} = \frac{b(h^2 - y^2)}{2}$$

$$q = V\frac{1}{2bh^3/3}\frac{b\left(h^2 - y^2\right)}{2} = \frac{3V\left(h^2 - y^2\right)}{4h^3}$$

b)   The shear stress is the shear flow divided by the width of the cross section b and is given as

$$\tau = \frac{q}{b} = \frac{VQ}{I_{NA}b}$$

$$\tau = \frac{3V\left(h^2 - y^2\right)}{4bh^3}$$

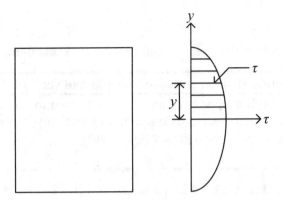

Figure 8.10: Shear stress distributions across a rectangular section

It can be seen from the shear stress distribution formula for rectangular sections that it is
a) parabolic in nature (function of the square of y)
b) zero at the extremes ($y=h$) and maximum at the neutral axis ($y=0$)
Figure 8.10 shows the typical distribution of the shear stress across the depth of a rectangular cross section.

8.3.3   I Shaped Sections

The shear stress distribution across the depth of an I-shaped section, which is a commonly used structural shape, is now described. It closely follows the rectangular shape distribution with one important variation, in that the width of the cross section changes. Since the width of the flange is very high the stress magnitude is very low. At the web portion where the width decreases sharply, the magnitude of the shear stress increases rapidly. Example 8.3 illustrates this concept and figure 8.11 shows the distribution.

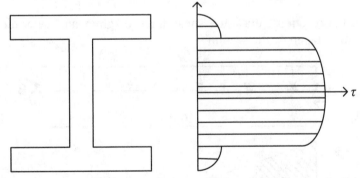

Figure 8.11: Distribution of shear stress across the depth of an I-section.

From the distribution of shear stress across the I-sections, some important observations which are of practical use in design considerations are as follows
a) The magnitude of the maximum shear stress in the flanges is almost negligible compared to the magnitude of the stress values in the web (both at the top and center of the web).
b) Due to (a) it can be practically taken that the web of an I-section carries all the shear force and the flanges do not contribute to taking the shear stress.
c) *Average Shear Stress:* Since the difference in the values of the shear stress at the top and the center of web is not significant, it can be reasonably assumed that the stress distribution across the web practically constant and is given by an average value of

$$\tau_{ave.} = \frac{V}{A_{web}} = \frac{V}{t_w h}$$

where h is the total depth of the I-section and t_w is the thickness of the web.

Example 8.3: Determination of shear stress (horizontal and vertical) in I beams

Problem Statement: A simply supported beam is loaded by a uniformly distributed load of 5 k/ft. as shown in the figure. The cross section is made of an I-section with the dimensions as shown. Draw the shear stress distribution across the cross section

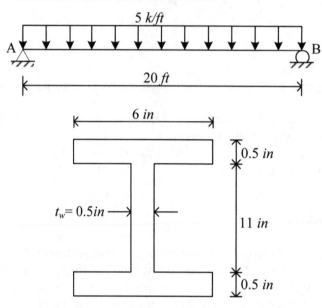

Required: To find the shear stress distribution across the cross section?

Solution:

Step 1: Determine the reactions, draw the shear force diagram and determine the maximum vertical shear force to be taken by the section

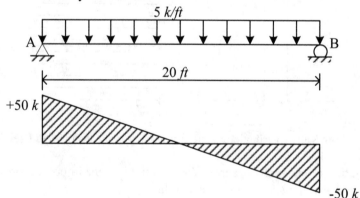

$$\sum F_x = 0 : A_x = 0$$

$$\sum F_y = 0 : A_y + B_y - (5 \, k / ft.)(20 \, ft.) = 0$$

$$\sum M_A = 0 : -(5 \, k / ft.)(20 \, ft.)(10 \, ft.) + B_y(20 \, ft.) = 0$$

$$\therefore A_y = B_y = 50 \, k \uparrow$$

$$V_{max} = 50 \, k$$

Step 2: Determine the moment of inertia in all the calculations is the moment of inertia of the *entire* section about the neutral axis.

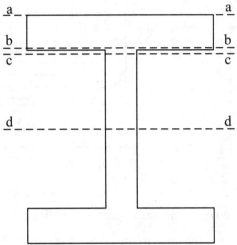

$$I_{NA} = \sum \overline{I} + Ad^2$$

$$= 2\left[\left(\frac{1}{12}6\times0.5^3\right)+(6\times0.5)\times5.5^2\right]+\left[\left(\frac{1}{12}0.5\times11^3\right)\right]$$

$$= 254 \ in^4$$

The vertical shear force in the cross section is the same, *i.e.* V_{max}= 50 *kips*. The shear stress across the depth of the section can be determined as shown below. The stress is determined at four sections (*a-a*, *b-b*, *c-c* and *d-d*) as shown below

$$\tau_{a-a} = \frac{V_{max}Q_{a-a,NA}}{I_{NA}b}$$

$$Q_{NA} = A\overline{y} = (0)(6 \ in) = 0$$

$$b = 6 \ in$$

$$\tau_{a-a} = \frac{(50 \ k)(0 \ in^3)}{(254 \ in^4)(6 \ in)} = 0 \ ksi$$

$$\tau_{b-b} = \frac{V_{max}Q_{b-b,NA}}{I_{NA}b}$$

$$Q_{NA} = A\overline{y} = (0.5\times6)(6-0.25) = 17.25 \ in^3$$

$$b = 6 \ in$$

$$\tau_{b-b} = \frac{(50 \ k)(17.25 \ in^3)}{(254 \ in^4)(6 \ in)} = 0.57 \ ksi$$

$$\tau_{c-c} = \frac{V_{max}Q_{c-c,NA}}{I_{NA}b}$$

$$Q_{NA} = A\overline{y} = (0.5\times6)(6-0.25) = 17.25 \ in^3$$

$$b = 0.5 \ in$$

$$\tau_{c-c} = \frac{(50 \ k)(17.25 \ in^3)}{(254 \ in^4)(0.5 \ in)} = 6.8 \ ksi$$

$$\tau_{d-d} = \frac{V_{max}Q_{d-d,NA}}{I_{NA}b}$$

$$Q_{NA} = A\overline{y} = (0.5\times6)(6-0.25)+(0.5\times5.5)\left(\frac{5.5}{2}\right)$$

$$= 24.81 \ in^3$$

$$b = 0.5 \ in$$

$$\tau_{d-d} = \frac{(50 \ k)(24.81 \ in^3)}{(254 \ in^4)(0.5 \ in)} = 9.78 \ ksi$$

Step 3: The distribution of the *vertical* shear stress is shown in the figure below

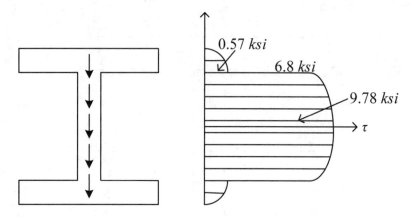

Step 4: The distribution of the *horizontal* shear stress in the flanges is calculated as shown below.

Consider the section at a distance x from the edge. The area to be used for the determination of the moment of area in the shear flow calculation is shown by the hatched area in the figure below.

$$\tau_{x-x} = \frac{V_{max}Q_{x-x,NA}}{I_{NA}b}$$

$$Q_{NA} = A\bar{y} = (0.5 \times x)(6-0.25) = 2.875x \ in^3$$

$$b = 0.5 \ in$$

$$\tau_{x-x} = \frac{(50 \ k)(2.875x \ in^3)}{(254 \ in^4)(0.5 \ in)} = 1.132x \ ksi$$

$$\tau_{x=0} = 0$$

$$\tau_{x=3} = 1.132 \times 3 = 3.4 \ ksi$$

The final shear stress distribution in the I-section is shown below.

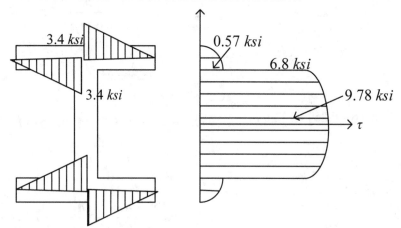

Notes:
1. The magnitude of the vertical shear stress in the web (6.8 *ksi*) is twice the horizontal shear stress value in the flanges (3.4 *ksi*).
2. The shear flow in the flanges from the two sides $q = \tau t$ add up to form the shear flow in the web, which results in twice the stress values in the web.

8.3.4 Maximum shear stress

From the shear stress distribution equation derived in the two previous sections for a rectangular and an I-section, another important expression that is used for design purposes is the maximum value of the shear stress.

Rectangular Section: For a rectangular section the maximum shear stress value occurs at the center of the cross section ($y=0$). The value can now be derived, knowing that the area of the cross section is $A=b(2h)$, as follows

$$\tau_{max.} = \frac{3V\left(h^2 - 0^2\right)}{4bh^3} = \frac{3Vh^2}{4bh^3} = \frac{3V}{4bh}$$

$$\tau_{max.} = \frac{3V}{2A} = \frac{3}{2}\tau_{avg.}$$

where, the average shear stress is defined as the shear force divided by the area of the cross section.

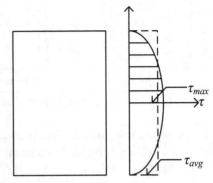

I-section: Since the flanges are assumed to carry no shear stress and all the shear is carried by the web and considering that the difference between the maximum and minimum values of the shear stress in the web is not significant, it can be taken as

$$\tau_{max.} = \tau_{avg.} = \frac{V}{ht_w}$$

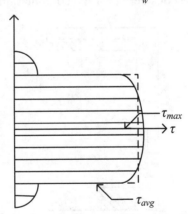

8.4 Shear in Thin Walled Cross-sections

There are many applications wherein thin walled closed cross sections, such a circular, rectangular and square tubes, are suitable and used in practice. In an earlier chapter on torsion shear stresses, in thin walled sections subjected to torsion, was considered. The behavior of such sections, when subjected to a predominant shear force is now discussed.

As in the chapter in torsion, shear in thin walled sections can be visualized as a *shear flow*. It can be thought of as a flow of water through the thin section. This visualization leads to two concepts namely,
a) Shear stress in the thin walls
b) Shear force in the thin walls

The following description gives the details of the nature and computation of shear forces in the thin walled cross section.

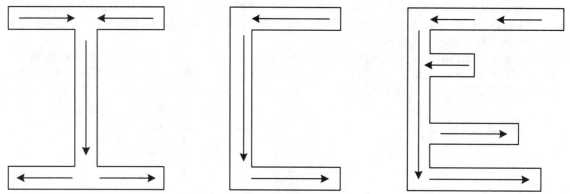

Figure 8.12: Shear stress direction in thin walled sections

Nature of shear stresses in a thin walled section: Figure 8.12 shows the 'flow' of shear stresses through a thin walled section subjected to a shear force. It can be visualized as being
a) Parallel to the direction of the wall
b) Equal in magnitude across the cross section thickness
The shear flow and shear stress equation used in the earlier sections are the same as described earlier. The main question now to be answered is, *what is the area to be considered for the determination of the moment of area Q?* This area can be visualized as 'all the area beyond the point under consideration' (it must be kept in mind that the reason all the area beyond is being considered is that the horizontal force due to bending is being caused by this area). Figure 8.13 shows the hatched area that is to be considered for the computation of the moment of area Q.

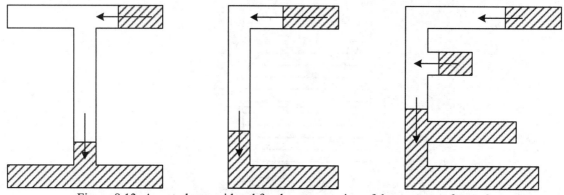

Figure 8.13: Area to be considered for the computation of the moment of area Q

Shear force in the thin walls: Any cross section experiencing a stress will have net resultant force acting on it. Since thin walls subjected to shear force experience a shear stress, the overall area will experience a shear force. Often this shear force is caused by a non uniform shear stress; hence integration techniques will have to be adopted. The general formula for the determination of this shear force can be given as

$$F = \int \tau dA = \int q ds$$

Hence, thin walled sections that are horizontal will experience horizontal shear stresses and horizontal shear force, although the externally applied shear force in only vertical in nature. Section 8.5 illustrates how a C-section subjected to shear force is subjected to shear stresses, horizontal and vertical shear force and the steps involved in their computation.

8.5   Shear Center for Singly Symmetric Cross Sections

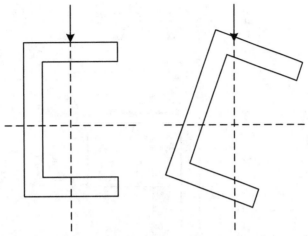

Figure 8.14: Experiment to illustrate the concept of shear center

Simple experiment: Perform a simple experiment as shown in Figure 8.14, which shows a pictorial representation of a plastic spoon, which has a C- shaped handle. Hold the spoon firmly keeping the handle horizontal and apply a vertical force with a finger at the end of the spoon, as shown. It can be seen that the cross section twists, although no external torsion is applied. Why is an apparent *internal torsion* caused due to a purely vertical external shear force? This question can be answered through the concept of *Shear Center*.

An alternate question to ask is: *Is there a point through which the force can be applied without causing a twist of the cross section?* The answer is yes and this point is called the *Shear Center* of the cross section. For a doubly symmetric section this point lies at the centroid of the cross section. However for singly symmetric cross section it lies on the axis of symmetry and the following concepts illustrates the ideas involved in its computation.

a)   Figure 8.15(a) shows a C-shaped section subjected to a vertical shear force

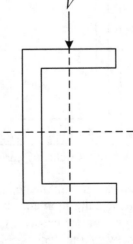

Figure 8.15(a): C-shaped section subjected to vertical force.

b) The shear flow causes internal shear stresses whose direction is shown in Figure 8.15(b). The magnitude of the shear flow at any point is given by the equation

$$q = \frac{VQ_{NA}}{I_{NA}} = \frac{V\left(A\bar{y}\right)}{I_{NA}}$$

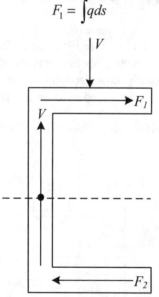

Figure 8.15(b): Shear flow in the section

c) The internal shear flow can be combined into resultant shear forces in each of the segments as shown in Figure 8.15(c). The shear force in each segment can be computed using the equation

$$F_1 = \int q\,ds$$

Figure 8.15(c): Resultant shear forces

d) It can now be clearly seen that there is a net imbalance in moments which results in a torque, as shown in Figure 8.15(d). By taking the moment about the mid point of the web of the shape it can be seen that the twisting moment caused by the shear flow forces in the flange is (h is the center to center distance between the flanges)

$$M = F \times h$$

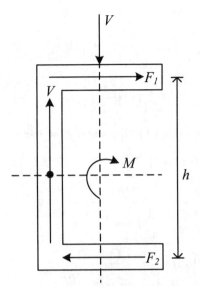

8.15(d): Moment caused in section

e) The internal moment can be balanced by moving the applied the force to the shear center, as shown in Figure 8.15(e). It can be now seen that the shear center for this case does not lie in the cross section area itself. Hence, the balancing moment is given as Ve, where e is the distance of the shear center from the center of the web. The shear center can now be determined from the acting and balancing moment as

$$Ve = F_1 h$$

$$e = \frac{F_1 h}{V}$$

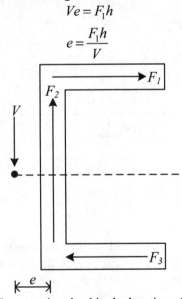

Figure 8.15(e): Concepts involved in the location of the shear center

Important: The derivation, shown below, using symbolic calculations shows that the *shear center depends purely on the geometry of the cross section*. It should also be noted that the following derivation and equations are valid only for the C section and should NOT be used for other types of cross sections.

The moment of inertia for the C shape can be shown to be

$$I_{NA} = \frac{1}{12}th^3 + 2\left[\frac{1}{12}bt^3 + (bt)\left(\frac{h}{2}\right)^2\right]$$

$$I_{NA} = \frac{1}{12}th^3 + 2\left[(bt)\left(\frac{h}{2}\right)^2\right] = \frac{1}{12}th^3 + \frac{(bt)h^2}{2}$$

The shear force in the entire flange F_1 due to the shear flow can be shown to be

$$Q_{NA} = A\overline{y} = (bt)\frac{h}{2}$$

$$q = \frac{VQ_{NA}}{I_{NA}} = \frac{V(bth/2)}{\dfrac{1}{12}th^3 + \dfrac{(bt)h^2}{2}}$$

$$F_1 = \int qds = \int \frac{V(bth/2)}{\dfrac{1}{12}th^3 + \dfrac{(bt)h^2}{2}}ds$$

$$F_1 = \frac{V(bth/2)}{\dfrac{1}{12}th^3 + \dfrac{(bt)h^2}{2}}\int_0^b ds$$

$$F_1 = \frac{V(bth/2)}{\dfrac{1}{12}th^3 + \dfrac{(bt)h^2}{2}} \times b = \frac{V(b^2th/2)}{\dfrac{1}{12}th^3 + \dfrac{(bt)h^2}{2}}$$

From the moment balance equation the shear center can now be derived as shown below

$$e = \frac{F_1 h}{V}$$

$$e = \frac{(b^2th^2/2)}{\dfrac{1}{12}th^3 + \dfrac{(bt)h^2}{2}} = \frac{(b^2h^2/2)}{\dfrac{h^3}{12} + \dfrac{bh^2}{2}}$$

$$\boxed{e = \frac{b^2/2}{h/12 + b/2}}$$

Example 8.5 illustrates the concepts involved in the computation of shear center. As an advanced example 8.5 shows the computation of shear center through the concepts of integration for a section that has the shape of an arc.

Example 8.5: Determination of shear center of the thin walled section shown below

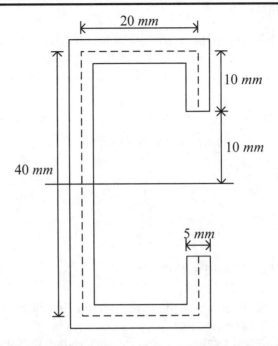

Required: Determine the shear center of the thin walled section shown in the figure

Solution:

Step 1: Draw the shear flow diagram (force diagram) and determine the shear center equation from the moment balance equation

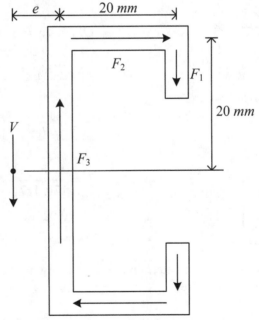

$F_1 = \int q_1 ds$ Force in the lip

$F_2 = \int q_2 ds$ Force in the flange

Determine the shear center from the moment equation. The origin for considering moments is taken to be the center of the main web.

By considering the web, the force in the web does not have to computed.

$$Ve = 2\left(F_1 \times 20 + F_2 \times 20\right)$$

$$e = \frac{40 \times \left(F_1 + F_2\right)}{V}$$

Step 2: Determine the moment of inertia of the cross section

$$I_{NA} = \frac{th^3}{12} + 2\left[\frac{th_1^3}{12} + \left(h_1 t\right)\left(\frac{h + h_1}{2}\right)^2\right]$$

$$I_{NA} = \frac{5 \times 40^3}{12} + 2\left[\frac{5 \times 10^3}{12} + \left(10 \times 5\right)\left(\frac{20 + 10}{2}\right)^2\right]$$

$$I_{NA} = 26,666.66 + 2\left[416.67 + 11,250\right] = 50,000 \ mm^4$$

Step 3: In order to determine the forces in the flange and the lips the moment of area calculations, to determine the shear flow, is the next step.

For determining the shear flow the entire area beyond that section must be considered as shown in the figure

$$A = yt = 5y$$

$$\bar{y} = 10 + \frac{y}{2}$$

$$Q_{NA} = A\bar{y} = 5y\left[10 + \frac{y}{2}\right]$$

$$q_1 = \frac{VQ_{NA}}{I_{NA}} = \frac{V}{130,417}\left[50y + \frac{5y^2}{2}\right]$$

$$F_1 = \int_0^{10} q_1 dy = \int_0^{10} \frac{V}{130,417}\left[50y + \frac{5y^2}{2}\right] dy$$

$$F_1 = \frac{V}{130,417}\left[25y^2 + \frac{5y^3}{6}\right]_0^{10} = \frac{3,333.33V}{130,417}$$

$$F_1 = 0.026V$$

Find the force in the flange. In order to determine the shear flow in the flange, the lip area which remains constant must also be considered.

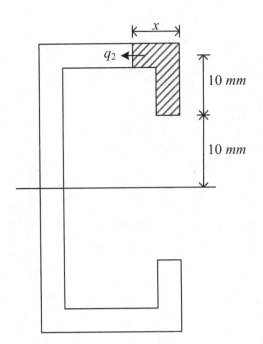

$$A_1 = 10 \times 5 = 50 mm^2$$

$$\bar{y}_1 = 15 mm$$

$$A_2 = 5x$$

$$\bar{y}_2 = 20 mm$$

$$Q_{NA} = A_1\bar{y}_1 + A_2\bar{y}_2 = 50 \times 15 + 100x$$

$$q_2 = \frac{VQ_{NA}}{I_{NA}} = \frac{V}{103,417}[750 + 100x]$$

$$F_2 = \int_0^{20} q_2 dx$$

$$F_2 = \int_0^{20} \frac{V}{103,417}[750 + 100x] dx$$

$$F_2 = \frac{V}{103,417}\left[750x + 50x^2\right]_0^{20} = \frac{35,000V}{103,417}$$

$$F_2 = 0.338V$$

Step 3: Determine the shear center from the balance of moment equation.

$$e = \frac{40 \times (F_1 + F_2)}{V} = \frac{40 \times (0.026V + 0.338V)}{V}$$

$e = 14.56\ mm$ to the LEFT of the web

Step 4: Determine the shear stress distribution in the thin walled section. The shear stress is the shear flow divided by the thickness of the cross section
Shear stress in the lips:

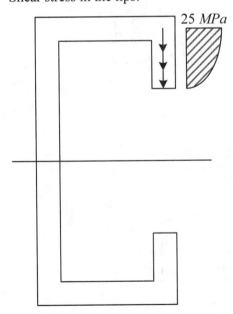

$$q_1 = \frac{VQ_{NA}}{I_{NA}} = \frac{V}{50,000}\left[150y - \frac{5y^2}{2}\right]$$

$$\tau = \frac{q}{t} = \frac{5,000N}{5 \times 50,000}\left[150y - \frac{5y^2}{2}\right]$$

$$\tau = 0.02\left[150y - \frac{5y^2}{2}\right]\frac{N}{mm^2}$$

$$\tau_{y=0} = 0$$

$$\tau_{y=10} = 25 MPa$$

Shear stress distribution in the flange:

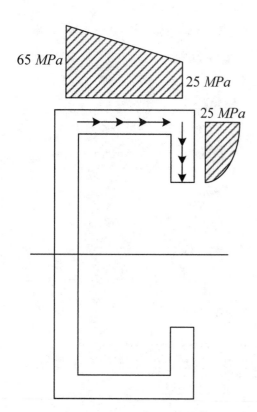

$$q_2 = \frac{VQ_{NA}}{I_{NA}} = \frac{5,000N}{50,000}\left[1250 + 100x\right]$$

$$\tau = \frac{q_2}{t} = \frac{5,000N}{5 \times 50,000}\left[1250 + 100x\right]$$

$$\tau = 0.02\left[1250 + 100x\right]\frac{N}{mm^2}$$

$$\tau_{x=0} = 25 MPa$$

$$\tau_{x=20} = 65 MPa$$

Shear stress distribution in the web:

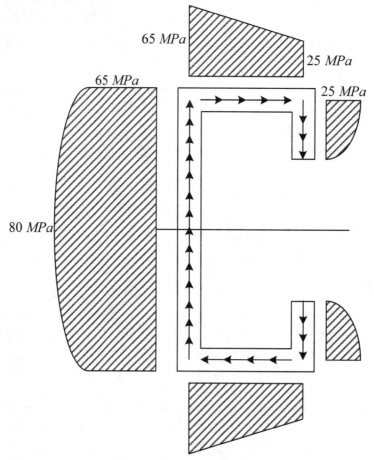

$$A_1 = 10 \times 5 = 50 \ mm^2; \ \overline{y}_1 = 25 \ mm$$

$$A_2 = 20 \times 5 = 100 \ mm^2; \ \overline{y}_2 = 20 \ mm$$

$$A_3 = 5 \times y = 5y; \ \overline{y}_3 = 20 - \frac{y}{2}$$

$$Q_{NA} = A_1 \overline{y}_1 + A_2 \overline{y}_2 + A_3 \overline{y}_3$$

$$Q_{NA} = 50 \times 25 + 100 \times 20 + 5y \left[20 - \frac{y}{2} \right]$$

$$q_3 = \frac{V Q_{NA}}{I_{NA}} = \frac{5,000 \ N}{50,000} \left[3250 + 100y - \frac{5y^2}{2} \right]$$

$$\tau = \frac{q}{t} = \frac{5,000 \ N}{5 \times 50,000} \left[3250 + 100y - \frac{5y^2}{2} \right]$$

$$\tau_{y=0} = 65 \ MPa$$

$$\tau_{y=10} = 80 \ MPa$$

Example 8.5: Determination of shear center of the thin walled section shaped as an arc

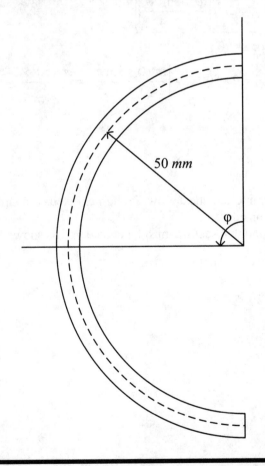

Data:

Radius	r=50 mm
Thickness	t=5 mm
Arc angle	φ=90 degrees

50 mm

φ

Required: Determine the shear center of the arc shape

Step 1: Determine the moment of inertia of the cross section

$$I_{NA} = \int y^2 \, dA$$

In order to determine the moment of inertia for a circular section the variables are changed to the radius r and θ as

$$y = r\sin(\theta) = 50\sin\theta$$

$$dA = t\,ds = t(r\,d\theta) = 250\,d\theta$$

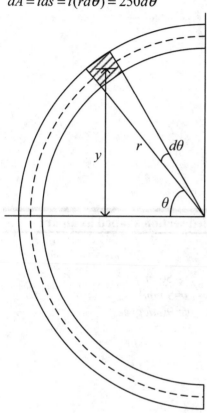

$$I_{NA} = \int \left(r\sin(\theta)\right)^2 tr\,d\theta = \int r^3 t \sin^2(\theta)\,d\theta$$

$$I_{NA} = 2\int_0^\phi r^3 \sin^2(\theta)\,td\theta = 2r^3 t \int_0^\phi \left(\frac{1-\cos(2\theta)}{2}\right)d\theta$$

$$I_{NA} = 2r^3 t\left[\int_0^\phi \frac{d\theta}{2} - \int_0^\phi \frac{\cos(2\theta)}{2}d\theta\right]$$

$$I_{NA} = 2r^3 t\left[\frac{\theta}{2}\Big|_0^\phi - \frac{\sin 2\theta}{4}\Big|_0^\phi\right]$$

$$\boxed{I_{NA} = 2r^3 t\left[\frac{\phi}{2} - \frac{\sin 2\phi}{4}\right]}$$

For $\phi = 90$

$$I_{NA} = 2\times 50^3 \times 5 \times \left[\frac{\pi/2}{2} - \frac{\sin\pi}{4}\right] = \frac{\pi \times 50^3 \times 5}{2}$$

$$I_{NA} = 99,472 \ mm^4$$

Step 2: The moment of area calculation, to determine the shear flow, is the next step. The area beyond the point (as shown in the figure must be considered).

For determining the shear flow the entire area beyond that section must be considered as shown in the figure

$$A = r\theta$$

$$\bar{y} = \frac{r\sin\phi + r\sin\theta}{2}$$

$$Q_{NA} = A\bar{y} = r^2\theta\left[\frac{\sin 90° + \sin\theta}{2}\right]$$

$$q = \frac{VQ_{NA}}{I_{NA}} = \frac{V(50^2)\theta}{99,472}\left[\frac{1+\sin\theta}{2}\right]$$

$$q = (0.02571)V\theta\left[\frac{1+\sin\theta}{2}\right]$$

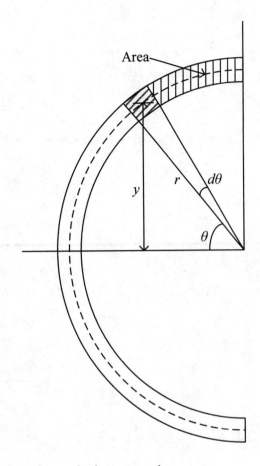

Find the force and the moment due to the incremental area

$$dF = qdA = qtds = qtrd\theta$$

$$dF = 50 \times 5 \times qd\theta = 250qd\theta$$

$$dF = 250 \times 0.02571V\theta\left[\frac{1+\sin\theta}{2}\right]d\theta$$

$$dF = 6.2.3V\theta\left[\frac{1+\sin\theta}{2}\right]d\theta$$

$$dM = r \times dF = 6.283V\left[\frac{\theta+\theta\sin\theta}{2}\right]d\theta$$

$$M = 2\int_{\pi/2}^{0} 6.283V\left[\frac{\theta+\theta\sin\theta}{2}\right]d\theta$$

$$M = 6.283V\left[\int_{\pi/2}^{0}\theta d\theta + \int_{\pi/2}^{0}\theta\sin\theta d\theta\right]$$

$$M = 6.283V\left[\theta\Big|_{\pi/2}^{0} + \theta\int\sin\theta d\theta - \int 1\int\sin\theta d\theta\right]$$

$$M = 6.283V\left[\theta\Big|_{\pi/2}^{0} - \theta\cos\theta\Big|_{\pi/2}^{0} + \int\cos\theta d\theta\right]$$

$$M = 6.283V\left[\theta\Big|_{\pi/2}^{0} - \theta\cos\theta\Big|_{\pi/2}^{0} + \sin\theta\Big|_{\pi/2}^{0}\right]$$

$$M = 62.83V\left[-\frac{\pi}{2} + \frac{\pi}{2}\cos\left(\frac{\pi}{2}\right) - \sin\left(\frac{\pi}{2}\right)\right]$$

$$M = 6.283V\left[-1.5707 + 0 - 1.0\right]$$

$$M = 16.15V$$

Step 3: Determine the shear center from the balance of moment equation. The origin is taken to be the center of the arc.

$$Ve = M$$

$$e = \frac{M}{V} = 16.15V/V = 16.15 \ mm$$

8.6   Summary

This chapter has addressed the concept of shear flow and shear stresses in beams caused by the bending moment and shear force acting along the beam's span. The keywords introduced in this chapter are as follows.

1. **Allowable stress:** The allowable stress is the lower of the yield stress f_y divided by a factor or safety. $f_{all} = \dfrac{f_y}{F.O.S}$

2. **Average/Maximum shear stress in an I section:** The average shear stress in an I shaped section is the shear force divided by the area of the web. $\tau_{max} \approx \tau_{ave.} = \dfrac{V}{A_{web}} = \dfrac{V}{t_w h}$

3. **Average/Maximum shear stress in a rectangular section:** The average shear stress in a rectangular section is the shear force divided by the area. The maximum shear force in a rectangular section is one and a half times the average shear stress.

$$\tau_{ave.} = \frac{V}{A_{web}} = \frac{V}{t_w h}$$

$$\tau_{max} = 1.5\tau_{ave.}$$

4. **Factor of safety:** The factor with which the shear yield stress is divided in arriving at the allowable stress in shear.

5. **Moment of area:** The moment of area of a cross section is the product of the area A and the distance of the centroid of the area to the neutral axis $\bar{y}$ and is given as $Q_{NA} = A\bar{y}$

6. **Shear center:** The shear center of a cross section is defined as the point through which the shear force must be applied for no shear induced torsion to occur in the cross section.

7. **Shear flow:** The beams slide in the horizontal direction relative to each other as they experience a shear force at the interfaces in the horizontal direction. The phenomenon in commonly known as *horizontal shear* and is caused by the variation of bending moment along the span.

$$q = \frac{VQ}{I_{NA}}$$

8. **Shear stress:** The shear stress is the stress parallel to the cross section caused by the shear force and is expressed as $\tau = \dfrac{q}{t} = \dfrac{VQ}{I_{NA}t} = \dfrac{V\left(A\bar{y}\right)}{I_{NA}t}$

9. **Shear yield stress:** The stress value, specific to a material, at which the material starts yielding and exhibits plastic behavior.

8.7   Problems:

8.1 Define *shear flow q*?

8.2 Determine the moment of area about the neutral axis Q_{NA} of the sections shown in the following diagram.

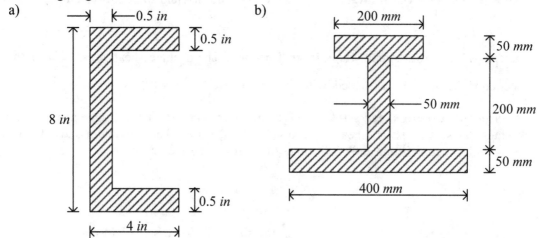

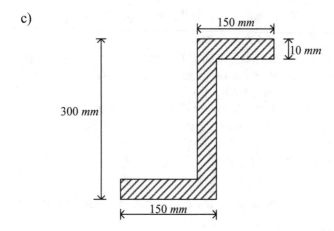

8.3 A beam is made of a T-section by nailing two wooden planks as shown in the figure below. If the shear force in the cross section is a) 2500 *lbs.* and b) 10 *kN* in the US and SI units version of the problem, determine the spacing required for the nails. Assume the nail has a shear force capacity of a) 200 *lbs.* and b) 800 *N* respectively.

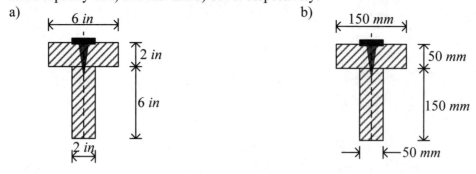

8.4 In problem 8.3, if the wooden planks are glued together, instead of being nailed, determine the required strength of the glue in each case. Express your answers in appropriate units in each case.

8.5 An I beam is made of three wooden planks and is subjected to the loading as shown in figure below. The flanges are nailed to the web with nails of strength of 300 *lbs*. Determine the spacing of the nails required at top and bottom.

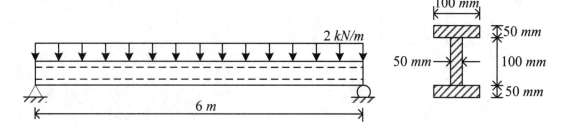

8.6 A simply supported beam of length 9 *ft* has a point load of 10 *kips* at a distance of 4 ft from its right end. The beam has a rectangular cross section of width 6 *in* and depth of 18 *in*.
   a) Determine the magnitude and location of the maximum shear stress.
   b) Draw the shear stress distribution across the depth at the point of maximum shear force.
   c) Compare the answer of the maximum shear stress with that calculated from the direct maximum shear stress equation for a rectangular equation

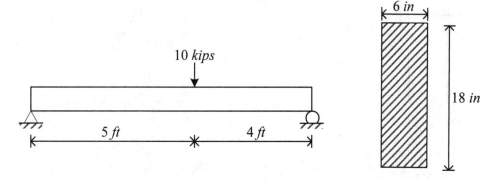

8.7 A beam is loaded as shown in the figure and has a shape as shown in the figure. Determine the maximum shear stress in the beam. Draw the shear stress distribution across the depth of the cross section.

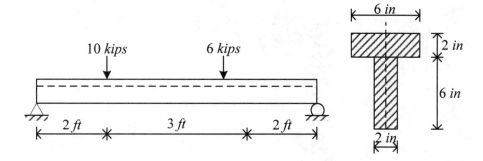

8.8 A beam is loaded as shown in the figure and has a shape as shown in the figure. Determine the maximum shear stress in the beam. Draw the shear stress distribution across the depth of the cross section.

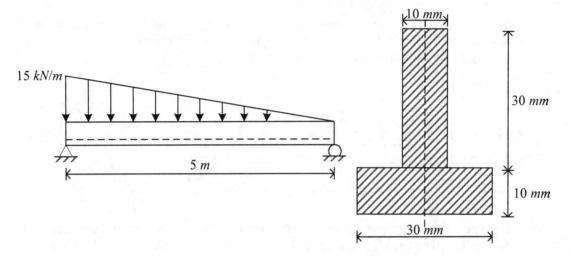

8.9 In the following problems, the cross section is subjected to a shear force of 5 *kips* (for US units problems) and 20 *kN* (for SI units problems). In each case, determine the
   a) Maximum shear stress in the cross section
   b) Draw the shear stress distribution across the cross section

a)   b)

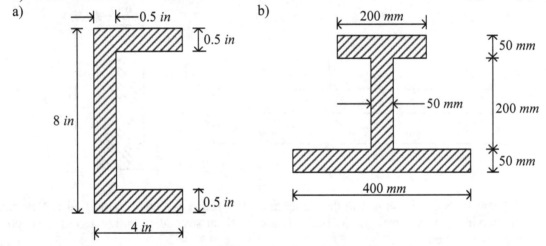

c)

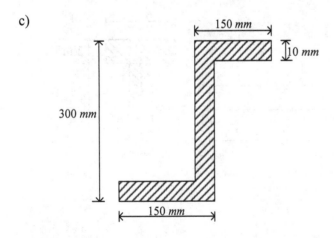

8.10 Define *shear center* in your own words. Under what conditions of the cross section does the shear center of a cross section not coincide with the center of gravity?

8.11 Determine the shear center of the following cross sections.

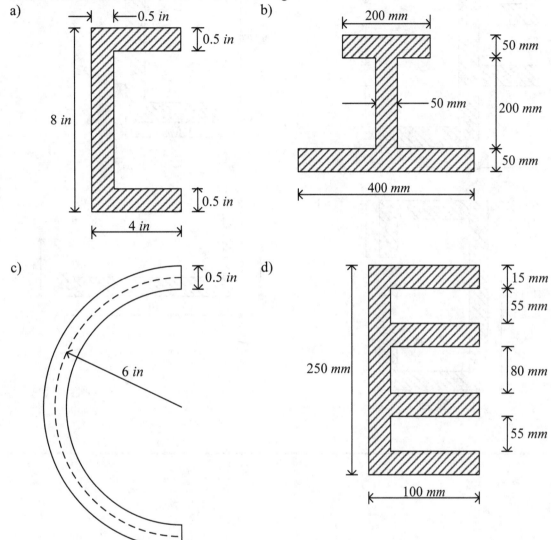

a)

0.5 in

0.5 in

8 in

0.5 in

4 in

b)

200 mm

50 mm

50 mm

200 mm

50 mm

400 mm

c)

0.5 in

6 in

d)

15 mm

55 mm

250 mm

80 mm

55 mm

100 mm

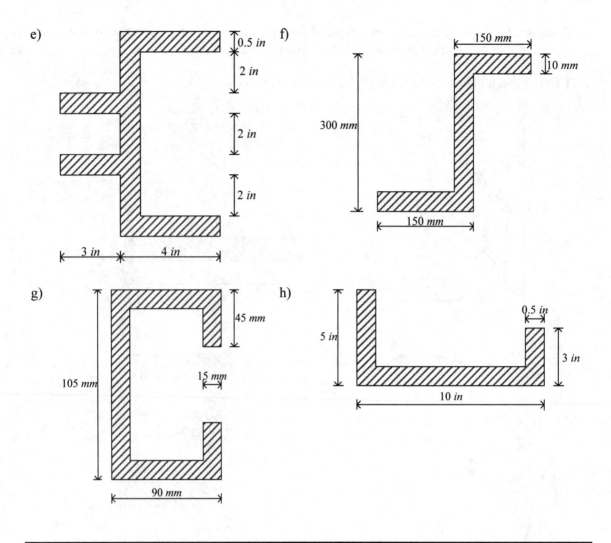

e)

0.5 in

2 in

2 in

2 in

3 in

4 in

f)

150 mm

10 mm

300 mm

150 mm

g)

45 mm

15 mm

105 mm

90 mm

h)

0.5 in

5 in

3 in

10 in

Chapter 9

Transformation of Stresses

Goal: The learning objectives to this chapter are as follows:

1. Demonstrate the concept and the physical need to do stress transformations
2. Derive the equations related to stress transformations
3. Illustrate the methodology to find principal stresses and maximum shear stress
4. Demonstrate the relationship between brittle and ductile failure of materials and to the principal stresses and maximum shear stresses determined
5. Demonstrate the application issues using some common practical problems

9 Transformation of Stresses

9.1 Introduction and Purpose of this Chapter

It was seen in Chapter 4 that a body subjected to a set of forces is subjected to internal stresses and in general there are six independent stresses that must be determined in order to completely characterize the state of stress at any point. They are $\sigma_x, \sigma_y, \sigma_z, \tau_{xy}, \tau_{xz}, \tau_{yz}$. The definitions of these stresses have been given in Chapter 4. Consider an object as shown in Figure 9.1 subjected to a set of forces. The stresses, at any point, are defined on a small cubical element A and they are shown in Figure 9.1(a). At the same point consider another cubical element B of the same size, but oriented at a different angle. It can be seen that although the point is the same, the stresses on element B are different from that on element A. The stresses on the element at B are shown in Figure 9.1(b).

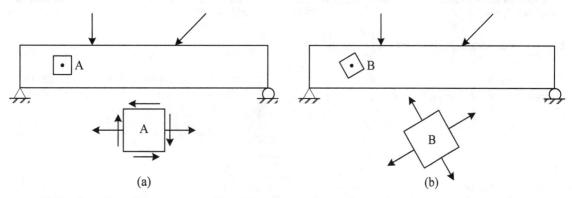

Figure 9.1: Change in stresses acting on an element due to change in orientation of the element.

9.1.1 Purpose of this Chapter

The purpose of this chapter is to examine the relationship between the stresses in the elements A and B, as shown in Figure 9.1. Both the elements are located at the same point and it is assumed that the geometric relationship between the orientations of the two elements is known. It will be shown here the relationship can be established by a mathematical principle called the *stress transformation*. However, some examples of stresses in cubic elements are shown first, in order to get a physical idea of how these arise due to forces applied to a structure. Two different methods are addressed in this chapter, namely
1. Using equations of transformations of stresses
2. A geometric method called the Mohr's circle method.

9.1.2 Maximum Normal and Shear Stresses

As seen in Figure 9.1, two, in fact infinite, different states of stress exist at the same point in a body. As the element, on which these stresses are determined, is rotated the values of the shear and normal stresses changes. It will be seen that one of these rotated elements will have a maximum value of normal stress and another orientation will correspond to a maximum value of the shear stress. The determination of *maximum normal stresses* and *maximum shear stresses* is important in characterization of failure of brittle and ductile materials. Figure 9.2 shows a cylindrical object made of a brittle (cast iron) and a ductile (aluminum) material subjected to a uniform torque. It can be seen that the failure modes are clearly different. The determination of the maximum normal and shear stresses, as outlined in this chapter, is important in the determination of the manner of failure of these materials.

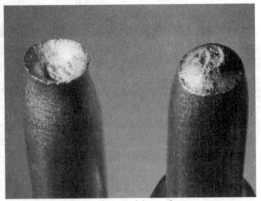

Figure 9.2: Failure of brittle (cast iron) and ductile (aluminum) material, when subjected to a torque

9.1.3   Mathematical Representation of Stress

The mathematical representation of a the six stresses at any point in a three dimensional structure is shown in matrix form as follows

$$\begin{pmatrix} \sigma_{xx} & \tau_{xy} & \tau_{xz} \\ \tau_{yx} & \sigma_{yy} & \tau_{yz} \\ \tau_{zx} & \tau_{zy} & \sigma_{zz} \end{pmatrix}$$

It can be seen that the form is symmetric about the diagonal as $\tau_{xy} = \tau_{yx} ; \tau_{xz} = \tau_{zx} ; \tau_{yz} = \tau_{zy}$. In case the body is subjected to stresses in only one plane, a two dimensional state of stress exists and the matrix form of stress can be written as follows

$$\begin{pmatrix} \sigma_{xx} & \tau_{xy} \\ \tau_{yx} & \sigma_{yy} \end{pmatrix}$$

9.1.4   Common Examples of Stresses in Cubic Elements

A few examples are shown here, in order to help the student visualize the concept of stress in cubic elements, to show how a body is subjected to stresses internally, when subjected to external forces and moments. Some of these examples have been done before, but are repeated for emphasis.

a) **Rod subjected to axial force:** Consider a rod subjected to an axial force as shown. Two sections, one perpendicular (element A) and one inclined to the axial direction (element B), is considered. The stresses in these two elements are shown in Figure 9.3. This example has been considered in earlier chapters. The matrix form of representation of this stress state is

For element A: $\begin{pmatrix} \sigma & 0 \\ 0 & 0 \end{pmatrix}$ and for element B: $\begin{pmatrix} \sigma_{xx} & \tau_{xy} \\ \tau_{yx} & \sigma_{yy} \end{pmatrix}$

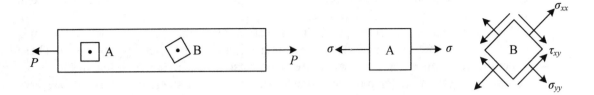

Figure 9.3: Rod subjected to axial load and stresses in elements A and B

b) **Rod subjected to a pure torsion:** Consider a circular rod subjected to a pure torsional moment as shown in Figure 9.4. It has been seen in an earlier chapter that a section taken perpendicular to the longitudinal axis experiences a pure shear stress condition. By considering a cubic element on this section, as shown in Figure 9.4, it can be seen that the element is in pure shear. The matrix representation of this state of stress is

$$\begin{pmatrix} 0 & \tau \\ \tau & 0 \end{pmatrix}$$

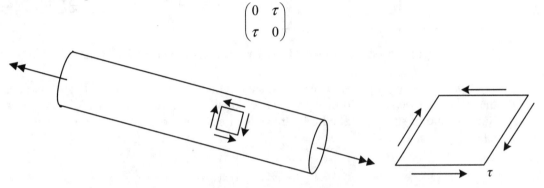

Figure 9.4: Rod subjected to pure torsion and stresses on element A

c) **Closed ended thin cylinder subjected to internal pressure:** Consider a thin cylinder which is closed at the ends by plates, as shown in Figure 9.5. If this cylinder is filled with any liquid the walls of the cylindrical shell are subjected to two kinds of stress, namely an axial pull due to the fluid trying to push the end plates away and the cylindrical wall restraining them, and the fluid pressure on the cylinder walls causing a hoop tension in the walls. The schematic and the stresses on an element of the cylinder are shown in Figure 9.5. It can be clearly seen that although this is a three dimensional problem, the state of stress in the cylindrical wall is purely a state of *plane stress*. It might be surprising to the student to realize that although there is an internal pressure against the wall, there is no stress in the thickness direction in the element. The no stress condition occurs only when the walls of the cylinder are very thin.

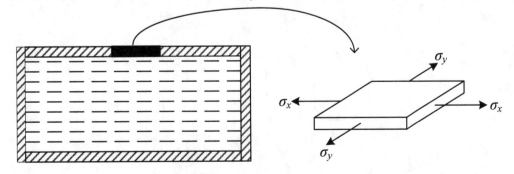

Figure 9.5: Closed ended cylinder subjected to internal pressure

d) **Beam subjected to external forces and moments:** Examples of this kind have been seen extensively in this book. Consider a simply supported beam, as shown in Figure 9.6, subjected to a set of forces and moments. A section perpendicular to the longitudinal axis is subjected to internal forces (shear and axial) and moment (bending moment). These internal forces cause axial and shear stresses. Consider three elements, one at the top or bottom of the section (element A), one at the neutral axis (element B) and one at a location in between the two (element C). The stresses in the elements A, B and C are shown in Figure 9.6. The calculation of the magnitude of these stresses has been discussed in earlier chapters.

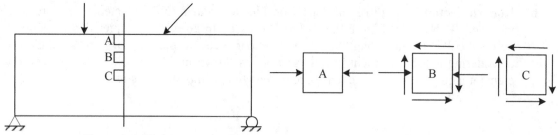

Figure 9.6: Simply supported beam and stresses in elements A, B and C.

e) **Hydrostatic state of stress:** Consider a small cube immersed in a fluid. The six faces of the cube experience uniform compressive stress, a pressure $-p$ and no shear stresses. Such a state of stress is called a hydrostatic stress. The mathematical form of this stress can be written as

$$\begin{pmatrix} -p & 0 & 0 \\ 0 & -p & 0 \\ 0 & 0 & -p \end{pmatrix}$$

9.2 Stress Transformation for Plane Stress

The principle of stress transformation is described in this section for a two dimensional plane stress case. Figure 9.7 shows a body subjected to a set of arbitrary forces. Consider a point A within the body where it is desired to determine the stresses. The state of stress on element A, in Figure 9.7, is a state of plane stress and can be represented in matrix form as follows

$$\begin{pmatrix} \sigma_{xx} & \tau_{xy} \\ \tau_{yx} & \sigma_{yy} \end{pmatrix}$$

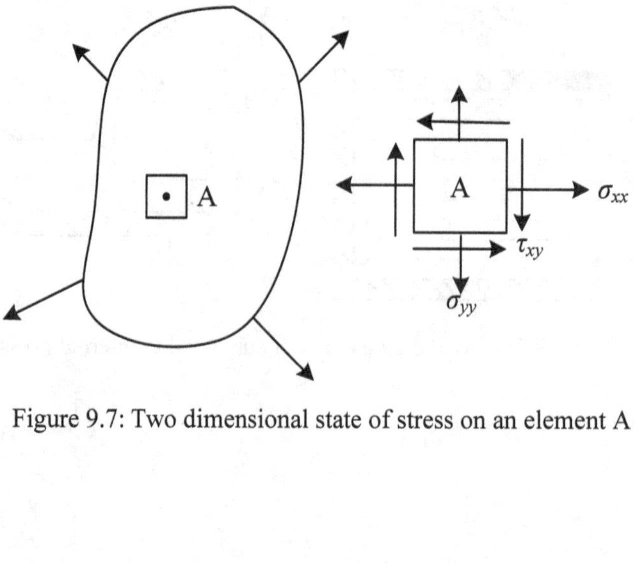

Figure 9.7: Two dimensional state of stress on an element A

There are a number of questions that are of importance in practical cases, which will be addressed in this section. Some of these questions are
a) What is the state of stress at A but on an inclined element?
b) What is the maximum normal stress experienced at point A?
c) What is the maximum shear stress experienced at point A?

9.2.1   Stress on an arbitrary plane

Consider a plane adjacent to the inclined section b-b in Figure 9.8. The axis perpendicular to this plane is designated x' and the axis system as x'-y'. The axis system corresponding to the element adjacent to plane a-a, is x-y. Let θ be the angle between x and x'. Let the state of stress corresponding to the plane x'-y' is designated as shown below and in Figure 9.8.

$$\begin{pmatrix} \sigma_{x'x'} & \tau_{x'y'} \\ \tau_{y'x'} & \sigma_{y'y'} \end{pmatrix}$$

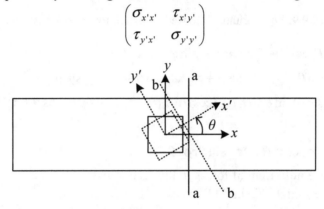

Figure 9.8: Schematic of an inclined element with axes x' and y'

The relationship between the two stress states is derived as shown below. The concept used is that forces in each of the two systems can be expressed in terms of each other. Consider the element to have a small area Δt in the y-z plane.

Step 1: Determine the forces on element in two systems.
The axial and shear forces can be written as follows

$$F_x = \sigma_x \Delta A_x \quad F_{x'} = \sigma_{x'} \Delta A$$
$$T_x = \tau_{xy} \Delta A_x \quad T_{x'} = \tau_{x'y'} \Delta A$$
$$F_y = \sigma_y \Delta A_y$$
$$T_y = \tau_{xy} \Delta A_y$$

where, $\Delta A_x = \Delta A \sin \theta$ and $\Delta A_x = \Delta A \cos \theta$

Step 2: Force Equilibrium.
Consider the equilibrium of the section as shown in Figure 9.9, in the x' direction

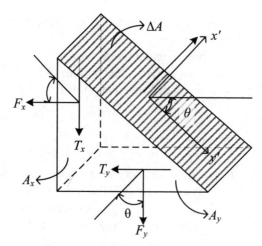

Figure 9.9: Equilibrium of the wedge section for stress transformation

$$F_{x'} = F_x \sin\theta + F_y \cos\theta + T_x \cos\theta + T_y \sin\theta$$

$$\sigma_{x'}\Delta A = \sigma_x \Delta A_x \sin\theta + \sigma_y \Delta A_y \cos\theta + \tau_{xy}\Delta A_x \cos\theta + \tau_{yx}\Delta A_y \sin\theta$$

$$\sigma_{x'}\Delta A = \sigma_x(\Delta A \sin\theta)\sin\theta + \sigma_y(\Delta A \cos\theta)\cos\theta + \tau_{xy}(\Delta A \sin\theta)\cos\theta + \tau_{yx}(\Delta A \cos\theta)\sin\theta$$

or

$$\sigma_{x'} = \sigma_x \sin^2\theta + \sigma_y \cos^2\theta + 2\tau_{xy}\sin\theta\cos\theta$$

Similarly consider the equilibrium of forces in the section in the y' direction

$$T_{x'} = -F_x \cos\theta + F_y \sin\theta - T_x \sin\theta + T_y \cos\theta$$

$$\sigma_{x'}\Delta A = -\sigma_x \Delta A_x \cos\theta + \sigma_y \Delta A_y \sin\theta - \tau_{xy}\Delta A_x \sin\theta + \tau_{yx}\Delta A_y \cos\theta$$

$$\sigma_{x'}\Delta A = -\sigma_x(\Delta A \sin\theta)\cos\theta + \sigma_y(\Delta A \cos\theta)\sin\theta - \tau_{xy}(\Delta A \sin\theta)\sin\theta + \tau_{yx}(\Delta A \cos\theta)\cos\theta$$

or

$$\tau_{x'y'} = -\sigma_x \sin\theta\cos\theta + \sigma_y \sin\theta\cos\theta + \tau_{xy}\cos^2\theta - \tau_{xy}\sin^2\theta$$

Step 3: Apply trigonometric transformations

$$\sigma_{x'} = \sigma_x \sin^2\theta + \sigma_y \cos^2\theta + 2\tau_{xy}\sin\theta\cos\theta$$

$$\sigma_{x'} = \sigma_x \frac{1-\cos 2\theta}{2} + \sigma_y \frac{1+\cos 2\theta}{2} + \tau_{xy}\sin 2\theta$$

or

$$\sigma_{x'} = \frac{\sigma_x + \sigma_y}{2} + \frac{\sigma_x - \sigma_y}{2}\cos 2\theta + \tau_{xy}\sin 2\theta$$

$$\tau_{x'y'} = -\sigma_x \sin\theta\cos\theta + \sigma_y \sin\theta\cos\theta + \tau_{xy}(\cos^2\theta - \sin^2\theta)$$

or

$$\tau_{x'y'} = -\frac{\sigma_x - \sigma_y}{2}\sin 2\theta + \tau_{xy}\cos 2\theta$$

Step 4: Summary.

Thus given the stresses in one plane the stresses in any other plane can be determined and summarized as follows.

$$\boxed{\begin{aligned} \sigma_{x'} &= \frac{\sigma_x + \sigma_y}{2} + \frac{\sigma_x - \sigma_y}{2}\cos 2\theta + \tau_{xy}\sin 2\theta \\ \tau_{x'y'} &= -\frac{\sigma_x - \sigma_y}{2}\sin 2\theta + \tau_{xy}\cos 2\theta \end{aligned}}$$

Eqn (9.1)

The stresses on any other plane can be determined by finding the angle θ between the x axis and the axis perpendicular to the required plane and substituting it in the above equations.

Sum of normal stresses always remains a constant: Another important point is now derived. Consider the stresses on a plane perpendicular to the x' plane, called the y' plane. The expression for this plane is derived as shown below

$$\sigma_{y'} = \frac{\sigma_x + \sigma_y}{2} + \frac{\sigma_x - \sigma_y}{2}\cos 2(\theta + \frac{\pi}{2}) + \tau_{xy}\sin 2(\theta + \frac{\pi}{2})$$

$$\sigma_{y'} = \frac{\sigma_x + \sigma_y}{2} - \frac{\sigma_x - \sigma_y}{2}\sin 2\theta + \tau_{xy}\cos 2\theta$$

The addition of the stresses on the x' and the y' plane results in the cancellation of the sine and cosine terms and results in

$$\sigma_{x'} + \sigma_{y'} = \sigma_x + \sigma_y$$

Eqn (9.2)

In other words, the *sum of the normal stresses on any set of perpendicular planes always remains a constant*. This useful equation can be used to determine one of the normal stress values, instead of going through the lengthy computations.

For example consider a plane stress example $\left(\sigma_x = 12ksi, \sigma_y = 4ksi, \tau_{xy} = -5ksi\right)$ as shown below.

The transformed stress values $\left(\sigma_{x'}, \sigma_{y'}\right)$ are plotted in Figure 9.10

$$\sigma_{x'} = \frac{\sigma_x + \sigma_y}{2} + \frac{\sigma_x - \sigma_y}{2}\cos 2\theta + \tau_{xy}\sin 2\theta$$

$$\sigma_{x'} + \sigma_{y'} = \sigma_x + \sigma_y$$

$$\boxed{\begin{aligned} \sigma_{x'} &= \frac{12+4}{2} + \frac{12-4}{2}\cos 2\theta - 5\sin 2\theta = 8 + 4\cos 2\theta - 5\sin 2\theta \\ \sigma_{y'} &= 12 + 4 - \sigma_{x'} = 16 - \sigma_{x'} \end{aligned}}$$

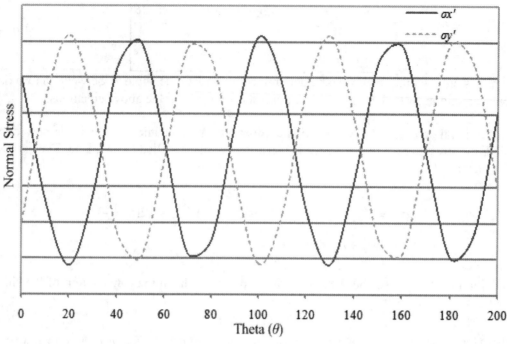

Figure 9.10: Normal stresses $\left(\sigma_{x'}, \sigma_{y'}\right)$ on two perpendicular planes.

9.2.2 Maximum Normal Stress and Maximum Shear Stress

It was seen in the previous section that the stresses, both normal and shear, change with the orientation of the plane containing the element, as a sinusoidal function. Two issues were apparent in the section and the example presented. They are

a) The maximum normal stress occurs on a section at a certain orientation with respect to the original x axis. The maximum normal stresses are also called the *Principal Stresses* and the angle corresponding to the orientation of the element for this case is called the *Principal Angle.*

b) The maximum shear stress occurs at an orientation different from that of the principal stresses. There is no specific name for the angle corresponding to the plane on which maximum shear stresses occurs.

9.2.2.1 Principal Stress and Principal Angle

From the example it can be seen that the variation of the normal stress with the angle of the element follows a sinusoidal pattern. Consequently, within one wave length the value has a maximum and a minimum value which are called *Principal Stresses* and the angle corresponding to those values are called the *Principal Angles.* The values of these quantities are determined using the principle of derivatives. The principal angle can be determined by taking the first derivative to the normal stress with respect to the angle and setting it equal to zero, as shown below,

$$\frac{d\sigma_{x'}}{d\theta} = \frac{\sigma_x - \sigma_y}{2}(-2\sin 2\theta) + \tau_{xy} 2\cos 2\theta = 0$$

to get the following expression for the principal angles.

$$\tan 2\theta_p = \frac{2\tau_{xy}}{\sigma_x - \sigma_y} \qquad \text{Eqn (9.3)}$$

Visualization of the Principal angle: The principal angle equation derived above can be set up geometrically as shown in Figure 9.11, in order to determine the magnitude of the principal stresses.

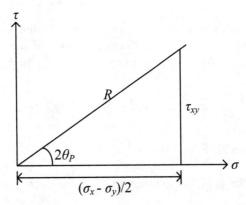

Figure 9.11: Geometric representation of the principal angle equation

From Figure 9.10 it can be clearly seen that the base can be represented as $\dfrac{\sigma_x - \sigma_y}{2}$ and the side can be represented as τ_{xy}. Consequently, the hypotenuse is

$$R = \sqrt{\left[\frac{\sigma_x - \sigma_y}{2}\right]^2 + \tau_{xy}^2} \qquad \text{Eqn (9.4)}$$

Hence, the following expressions can be written

$$\cos 2\theta_p = \frac{\sigma_x - \sigma_y}{2R}$$

$$\sin 2\theta_p = \frac{\tau_{xy}}{R} \qquad \text{Eqn (9.5)}$$

Substituting these values in equation 9.1 for the normal stress the equations representing the principal stresses can be written as follows

$$\sigma_{x'} = \frac{\sigma_x + \sigma_y}{2} + \frac{\sigma_x - \sigma_y}{2}\cos 2\theta_p + \tau_{xy}\sin 2\theta_p$$

$$\sigma_{x'} = \frac{\sigma_x + \sigma_y}{2} + \frac{\sigma_x - \sigma_y}{2}\frac{\sigma_x - \sigma_y}{2R} + \tau_{xy}\frac{\tau_{xy}}{R}$$

$$\sigma_{x'} = \frac{\sigma_x + \sigma_y}{2} + \frac{[\sigma_x - \sigma_y]^2}{4R} + \frac{\tau_{xy}^2}{R}$$

The equation for the principal stresses can now rewritten as after substituting for R as follows

$$\sigma_{1,2} = \frac{\sigma_x + \sigma_y}{2} \pm \sqrt{\left[\frac{\sigma_x - \sigma_y}{2}\right]^2 + \tau_{xy}^2} \qquad \text{Eqn (9.6)}$$

Shear Stress on Principal Planes: An interesting phenomenon that is observed is now derived. The shear stresses on the principal stresses are zero as shown below

$$\tau_{x'y'} = -\frac{\sigma_x - \sigma_y}{2}\sin 2\theta_p + \tau_{xy}\cos 2\theta_p$$

$$\tau_{x'y'} = -\frac{\sigma_x - \sigma_y}{2}\frac{\tau_{xy}}{R} + \tau_{xy}\frac{\sigma_x - \sigma_y}{2R} = 0$$

Eqn (9.7)

9.2.3 Maximum Shear Stress and Associated Plane

The maximum shear stress that any point experiences can also be found in a manner similar to that of the principal stresses. By taking the first derivative of the shear stress transformation equation with respect to the axis of orientation, the angle at which the maximum shear stress occurs is found as follows.

$$\frac{d\tau_{x'y'}}{d\theta} = -\frac{\sigma_x - \sigma_y}{2}2\cos 2\theta - \tau_{xy}2\sin 2\theta = 0$$

$$\tan 2\theta_s = -\frac{\sigma_x - \sigma_y}{2\tau_{xy}}$$

The cosine and the sine of the angle of the maximum shear stress can now be written as shown below

$$\cos 2\theta_s = \frac{\tau_{xy}}{R}$$

$$\sin 2\theta_s = \frac{\sigma_x - \sigma_y}{2R}$$

Eqn (9.8)

Substituting this in the expression for the shear and normal stress transformation equation it can shown that

$$\sigma_{x'} = \frac{\sigma_x + \sigma_y}{2} + \frac{\sigma_x - \sigma_y}{2}\frac{\tau_{xy}}{R} + \tau_{xy}\left(-\frac{\sigma_x - \sigma_y}{2}\right)$$

$$\sigma_{x'} = \frac{\sigma_x + \sigma_y}{2}$$

$$\tau_{x'y'} = -\frac{\sigma_x - \sigma_y}{2}\left(-\frac{\sigma_x - \sigma_y}{2R}\right) + \tau_{xy}\frac{\tau_{xy}}{R}$$

Eqn (9.9)

$$\tau_{x'y'} = \tau_{max} = \sqrt{\left(\frac{\sigma_x - \sigma_y}{2}\right)^2 + \left(\tau_{xy}\right)^2}$$

From the derivations it can be seen that the maximum shear stress is equal to R and the normal stress on the maximum shear stress planes is equal to the average value of the normal stresses.

9.2.4 Relation between the orientations of principal stress and maximum shear stress

From the expressions for the angle of orientation of the planes that represent the principal stress and the maximum shear stress, it can be shown that

$$\tan 2\theta_p = -\frac{1}{\tan 2\theta_s}$$

Eqn (9.10)

Geometrically this is possible only if $2\theta_s = 2\theta_p + \dfrac{\pi}{2}$ or if $\theta_s = \theta_p + \pi/4$. In other words the two sets of planes are oriented at 45 degrees to each other. This concept is represented in Figure 9.12 serves as a good starting point

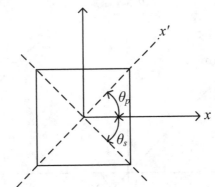

Figure 9.12: Orientation of principal and maximum shear planes

9.3   Mohr's Circle Method

In the early days when calculators were not in existence, the stress transformations were done graphically using a method devised by a German engineer Otto Mohr (1835-1918). Hence, the method is called the Mohr's circle. Although, it is easier to do the transformation equations now with calculators, the Mohr's circle method helps to visualize the process. Secondly, there are numerous failure theories of materials, such as those for soils that are based on the Mohr's circle method. Hence, it is still useful to learn this technique.

9.3.1   Drawing a Mohr's circle

The circle shown in Figure 9.14 serves as a good starting point for the introduction to this method. The x – axis of the Mohr's circle method represents the normal stress σ and the y – axis represents the shear stress τ. Consider the state of plane stress, as shown in Figure 9.13, which has the full complement of stresses in two dimensions, namely σ_x, σ_y and τ_{xy}.

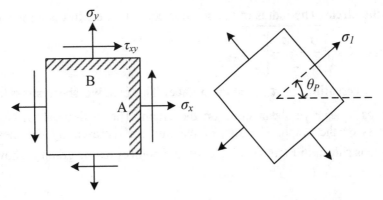

Figure 9.13: State of plane stress and principal stress planes

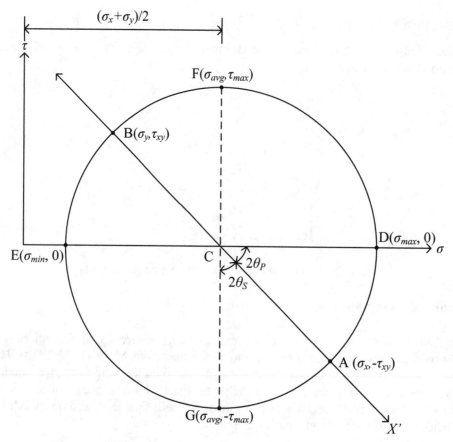

Figure 9.14: Mohr's circle representation of the plane stress and principal stress

The following salient points outline the steps required to draw of the Mohr's circle and the plane stress state representation on it.

1) **Center of the circle:** The center of the circle lies on the normal stress axis or the x-axis. The center is located at a distance of $C = \left(\dfrac{\sigma_x + \sigma_y}{2} \right)$ from the origin.

2) **Radius of the circle:** The radius of the circle is equal to the expression for R derived earlier and is given as $R = \sqrt{\left[\dfrac{\sigma_x - \sigma_y}{2} \right]^2 + \tau_{xy}^2}$

3) **Point 'A' representing** $\left(\sigma_x, \tau_{xy} \right)$ **on the x-face:** The positive shear stress on the x-face is represented as a negative shear stress on the graph. The positive shear on the y-face is a positive stress on the graph. The sign convention for representing the shear stress on the Mohr's circle is shown in Figure 9.15. Hence, the point A on the graph is shown as $\left(\sigma_x, -\tau_{xy} \right)$, as shown in Figure 9.14.

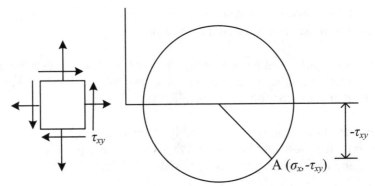

Figure 9.15: Representation of shear stress on Mohr's circle

4) **Point 'B' representing** $\left(\sigma_y, \tau_{xy}\right)$ **on the y-face:** The y-face stress is represented by point B as shown in Figure 9.14. It can be seen that the y-face stress is diagonally opposite to the x-face stress. Hence, in a Mohr's circle the stress states that are 180 degrees apart represent stress states on faces that are 90 degrees apart in reality.

Other points to note:

1) Figure 9.13 shows the physical representation of the of the plane stress state along with the corresponding principal stress planes and their orientation. The corresponding representation on the Mohr's circle is shown in Figure 9.14, in which it can be seen that the points of intersection of the circle with the x-axis represent the principal stress states. Point E represents the minimum principal stress $(\sigma_{min}, 0)$ and point D represents the maximum principal stress $(\sigma_{max}, 0)$. It can be seen from Figure 9.14 that at points D and E the shear stress is zero, which was derived earlier through mathematical expressions. It can also be seen graphically the principal stress values can be written as follows

$$\sigma_{max} = C + R$$
$$\sigma_{min} = C - R$$

Eqn (9.11)

which is the expression for the principal stress values derived earlier mathematically.

2) The angle between the diameter representing the plane stress state and the horizontal diameter is equal to twice the principal angle $2\theta_p$.

3) The maximum shear stress in Figure 9.14 is represented by the topmost and bottom most points (F $[\sigma_{ave}, \tau_{max}]$ and G$[\sigma_{ave}, -\tau_{max}]$) on the circle. On the y-axis the value can be seen to be equal to the radius R or $\tau_{max} = R$ while the x-axis value is the center C of the circle.

4) The angle between the planes representing the principal stresses (diameter DE) and the maximum shear stress (diameter FG) on the Mohr's circle is equal to 90 degrees. This implies the physical angle between the two planes is 45 degrees, another observation derived earlier mathematically.

9.3.2 Solution using Mohr's Circle Method

The three problems in this topic are now setup using the Mohr's circle method. The three basic problems described in this chapter are

a) Given the state of plane stress, what are the stresses on any arbitrary plane oriented at an angle θ to the original orientation

b) Given the state of plane stress, determine the values of the principal stresses and their orientations

c) Given the state of plane stress, determine the maximum shear stress values, the associated normal stresses and the orientation of the corresponding planes.

The earlier section (9.3.1) outlines the step involved in finding the principal stresses and maximum shear stress and their orientation given a state of plane stress. The steps involved in finding the stress at any arbitrary plane are as follows:

In this problem the state of stress is completely defined on a given plane, represented by its normal – the x axis. It is now required to find the stresses on a plane normal to the x' axis. The angle between x' and the x axis is given as θ, as shown in Figure 9.16.

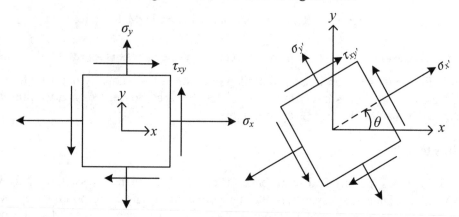

Figure 9.16: Problem definition for a general state of stress

Step 1: Draw the Mohr's Circle.

Step 2: Draw the point A representing the state of stress on the given plane, represented by the x-axis. Join the center C and the point A which is radius CA.

Step 3: Draw another radius at an angle 2θ to CA. The angle drawn is clockwise or counterclockwise and depends on the angle between the actual x and x' axis. The angle on the Mohr's circle is clockwise if the actual angle between the plane stress and the arbitrary plane is anticlockwise and vice a versa.

Step 4: Determine graphically the state of stress at the new point, which represents the stress on the plane corresponding to the x' axis.

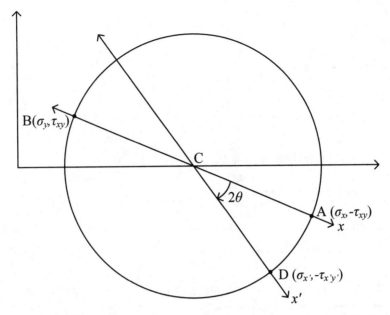

Figure 9.17: Determination of stress on a general plane using Mohr's circle

Example 9.1: Normal and Shear Stress in a Beam

Problem Statement: Determine the Shear and Normal stresses in the beam shown in figure.

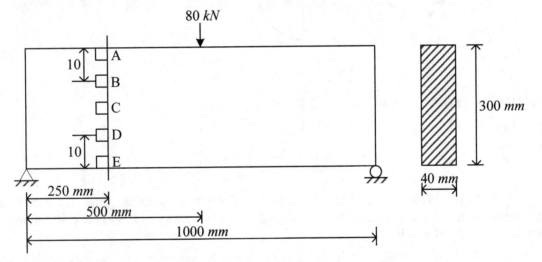

Required: The shear stress and normal stress at the section

Solution:

Step 1: Find Reaction at the supports

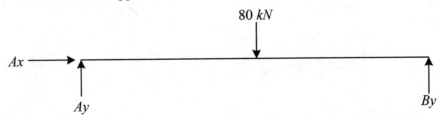

$$\sum F_x = 0; A_x = 0$$

$$\sum F_y = 0; A_y + B_y = 0$$

$$\sum M_A = 0; (80 \times 500) - B_y(1000) = 0$$

$$\therefore B_y = 40 \, kN$$

$$\therefore A_y = 40 \, kN$$

Step 2: Determine the shear and moment at the section

$M = 10 \, kN.m$

$V = 40 \, kN \downarrow$

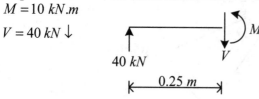

40 kN   V

M

0.25 m

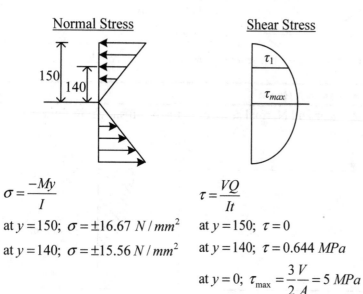

Normal Stress   Shear Stress

150   140

τ_1

τ_{max}

$\sigma = \dfrac{-My}{I}$ $\tau = \dfrac{VQ}{It}$

at $y = 150$; $\sigma = \pm 16.67 \, N/mm^2$ at $y = 150$; $\tau = 0$

at $y = 140$; $\sigma = \pm 15.56 \, N/mm^2$ at $y = 140$; $\tau = 0.644 \, MPa$

at $y = 0$; $\tau_{max} = \dfrac{3}{2}\dfrac{V}{A} = 5 \, MPa$

Step 3: From the bending and shear stress values at the two locations, draw the elemental representation of the stress values. The transformed principal stress values and the orientation are shown to the right of the element.

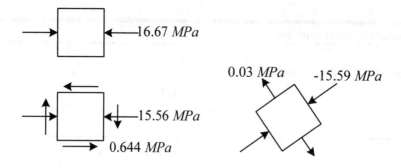

16.67 MPa

0.03 MPa   -15.59 MPa

15.56 MPa

0.644 MPa

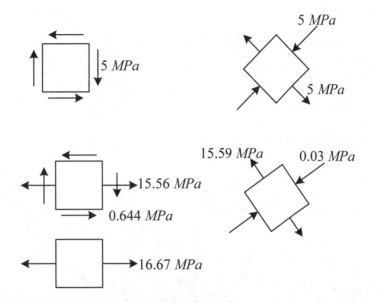

Example 9.2: Component of stress at a given angle

Problem Statement: The state of stress for an element is as shown in figure.

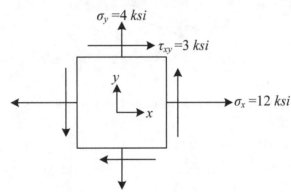

Required: a) Components of the stress associated with an element at $\theta = 15°$ CCW and show them on a properly oriented element.

b) Principal Normal Stress and show them on a properly oriented element.

c) Principal Shearing Stress and show them on a properly oriented element.

Solution:

Step 1: $\theta = 15°$ CCW ($\theta = +15°$)

$$\sigma_{x'} = (\frac{\sigma_x + \sigma_y}{2}) + (\frac{\sigma_x - \sigma_y}{2})\cos 2\theta + \tau_{xy}\sin 2\theta$$

$$= \frac{12+4}{2} + (\frac{12-4}{2})\cos 30° + 3\sin 30°$$

$$= 12.96 \; ksi$$

For y' axis ($\theta = 90+15=105°$)

$$\sigma_{y'} = \frac{12+4}{2} + (\frac{12-4}{2})\cos(2\times105°) + 3\sin(2\times105°)$$

$$= 3.036 \; ksi$$

$$\tau_{x'y'} = -\frac{(\sigma_x - \sigma_y)}{2}\sin 2\theta + \tau_{xy}\cos 2\theta$$

$$= -\frac{(12-4)}{2}\sin 30° + 3\cos 30°$$

$$= 0.6 \; ksi$$

Representation on properly orientation element

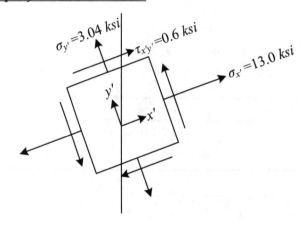

Step 2: Magnitudes of Principal Normal Stresses and their orientation

$$\tan 2\theta_p = \frac{2\tau_{xy}}{(\sigma_x - \sigma_y)} = \frac{2(3)}{(12-4)}$$

$$\therefore \theta_p = 18.43°$$

$\theta = 18.43°$ CCW ($\theta = +18.43°$)

$$\sigma_{x'} = (\frac{\sigma_x + \sigma_y}{2}) + (\frac{\sigma_x - \sigma_y}{2})\cos 2\theta + \tau_{xy}\sin 2\theta$$

$$= \frac{12+4}{2} + (\frac{12-4}{2})\cos(2\times18.43)° + 3\sin(2\times18.43)°$$

$$= 13 \; ksi$$

$$\sigma_x + \sigma_y = \sigma_{x'} + \sigma_{y'}$$

$$12 + 4 = 13 + \sigma_{y'}$$

$$\therefore \sigma_{y'} = 3 \; ksi$$

Representation on properly orientation element

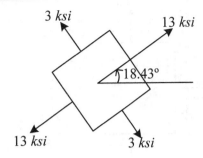

Step 2: Magnitudes of maximum shear stresses and their orientation

$$\tan 2\theta_s = -\frac{(\sigma_x - \sigma_y)}{2\tau_{xy}} = -\frac{(12-4)}{2(3)}$$

$$\therefore \theta_s = -26.66°$$

$\underline{\theta = 26.57° \text{ CW } (\theta = -26.57°)}$

$$\tau_{xy} = \sqrt{\left(\frac{\sigma_x - \sigma_y}{2}\right)^2 + \left(\tau_{xy}\right)^2} = \sqrt{\left(\frac{12-4}{2}\right)^2 + \left(3\right)^2}$$

$$\therefore \tau_{xy} = 5 \, ksi$$

$$\sigma_{x'} = \sigma_{y'} = \frac{\sigma_x + \sigma_y}{2} = \frac{12+4}{2}$$

$$\therefore \sigma_{x'} = \sigma_{y'} = 8 \, ksi$$

Representation on properly orientation element

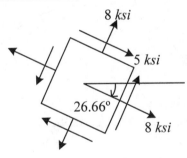

Example 9.3: Mohr's Circle

Problem Statement: The stresses acting on the body is shown in fugure.

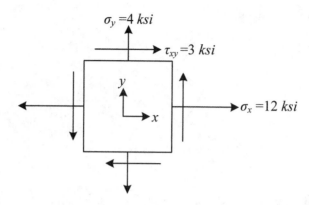

Required: Find the principal stress and plane of principal stress using Mohr's circle.

Solution:

Step 1: Draw Mohr's circle.

$\sigma_x = 12\ ksi$

$\sigma_y = 4\ ksi$

$\tau_{xy} = 3\ ksi$

$$C = \frac{\sigma_x + \sigma_y}{2} = \frac{12 + 4}{2} = 8\ ksi$$

$$R = \sqrt{\left(\frac{\sigma_x - \sigma_y}{2}\right)^2 + \tau_{xy}^2} = \sqrt{\left(\frac{12 - 4}{2}\right)^2 + 3^2} = 5\ ksi$$

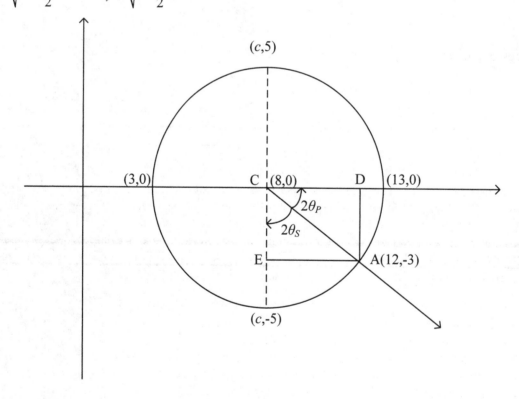

Step 2: Magnitude of Principal Stresses and their orientation

$$\sigma_1 = C + R = 13 \; ksi$$

$$\sigma_2 = 3 \; ksi$$

$$\tan 2\theta_p = \frac{AD}{CD} = \frac{3}{7} = 0.75$$

$$2\theta_p = 36.87°$$

$$\therefore \theta_p = 18.43°$$

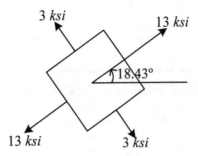

Step 3: Magnitude of maximum shear stresses and their orientation

$$2\theta_s = 90 - 2\theta_p = 53.13°$$

$$\therefore \theta_s = 26.66°$$

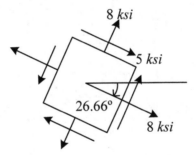

9.4 Design Issues and Failure of Ductile and Brittle Materials

The application of the principles of stress transformation methods is illustrated here in this section, for the determination of principal stresses and maximum shear stresses. The failure of many common brittle and ductile materials follows a typical pattern. Most materials have two separate and often independent allowable failure stress values in tension/compression σ_{all} and in shear τ_{all}. Brittle materials, such as glass, concrete etc., typically fail in tension when then condition $\sigma \le \sigma_{all}$ is violated, whereas ductile materials such as aluminum, steel, etc., fail in shear first when the condition $\tau \le \tau_{all}$ is violated. From the principles learned in this chapter it can be seen that the maximum stresses in a material can be found by determining the principal stresses and the maximum shear stresses. This section illustrates the application of principles learnt earlier in the determination of bending and shear stresses in combination with the transformation of stress principles, in order to determine the failure of structures. Two examples, one in beam bending and the other in combined torsion and bending is considered here to illustrate this point.

Example 9.4: Beam Bending Problem

Problem Statement: Consider a simply supported beam 10 *ft.* long and subjected to a central point load of 200 *kips*, as shown in Figure below. The beam has a rectangular cross section of 6 *in.* x 12 *in.* The type of material is not considered at this point. Determine the maximum normal stresses and the maximum shear stresses that the beam is subjected to.

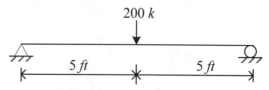

Required: Maximum normal and maximum shear stress

Solution:

Step 1: Determine the reactions, draw the shear force and bending moment diagrams in order to determine the maximum values. Since this is a simple example with a central load, it can be seen that the reactions are 100 *kips* at each end. The shear force and bending moment diagrams are shown below.

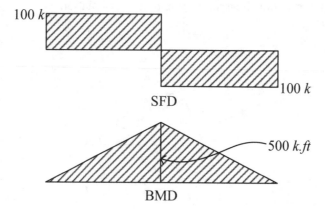

From the SFD and BMD the maximum values are $V_{max} = 100\ k$ occurring throughout the beam length, while the maximum moment value is $M_{max} = 500\ k.ft.$ occurring at the center of the beam.

Step 2: Consider a section at the center of the beam, where the maximum values of shear force and bending moment are simultaneously occurring. In this cross section, the values of shear stress and normal stresses due to bending are determined at various depths.

At any point in the cross section the normal stress and the shear stresses are determined by the equations

$$\sigma = -\frac{M_{max}.y}{I_{NA}}$$

$$\tau = \frac{VQ_{NA}}{I_{NA}b}$$

In the problem, the centroid and hence the neutral axis lies at the center of the rectangular section and hence the moment of inertia about the neutral axis is given as

$$I_{NA} = \frac{bh^3}{12} = \frac{6 \times 12^3}{12} = 864\ in^4$$

The value of *b*=6 *in.*, the width of the beam. Hence, the above equations reduce to a form as shown below

$$\sigma = -\frac{(500 \times 12 \ in.k)y}{864 \ in^4} = 6.94y \ ksi$$

$$\tau = \frac{VQ_{NA}}{I_{NA}b} = \frac{(100 \ k)Q_{NA}}{(864 \ in^4)(6 \ in.)} = 0.02Q_{NA} \ ksi$$

Step 3: Determine the stress values at various points on the depth, as indicated in Figure 9.13 and draw the stresses in incremental elements at the respective location.

At A ($y = 3 \ in.$)

$\sigma = -(6.94 \times 3) = -20.82 \ ksi$

$Q_{NA} = 0; \tau = 0$

At B ($y = 1.5 \ in.$)

$\sigma = -(6.94 \times 1.5) = -10.41 \ ksi$

$Q_{NA} = A\overline{y} = (1.5 \times 6)(3 + 3/2) = 40.5 \ in^3$

$\tau = 0.02 \times 40.5 = 0.81 \ ksi$

At C ($y = 0 \ in.$) (at the neutral axis)

$\sigma = -(6.94 \times 0) = 0 \ ksi$

$Q_{NA} = (3 \times 6)(3) = 54 \ in^3$

$\tau = 0.02 \times 54 = 1.08 \ ksi$

Step 4: Determine the maximum shear stress and the principal stresses at each point. The equation method is used in order to determine this, as shown below.

$$\tan 2\theta_p = \frac{2\tau_{xy}}{\sigma_x - \sigma_y}$$

At A: $\tan 2\theta_p = \dfrac{2(0)}{-20.84 - 0} = 0$ or $\theta_p = 0$

At B: $\tan 2\theta_p = \dfrac{2(0.81)}{-10.41 - 0} = 0$ or $\theta_p = -4.43°$

At C: $\tan 2\theta_p = \dfrac{2(1.08)}{0 - 0} = \infty$ or $\theta_p = 45°$

$$\sigma_{1,2} = \frac{\sigma_x + \sigma_y}{2} \pm \sqrt{\left[\frac{\sigma_x - \sigma_y}{2}\right]^2 + \tau_{xy}^2}$$

At A: $\sigma_{1,2} = \dfrac{-20.84 + 0}{2} \pm \sqrt{\dfrac{[-20.84 - 0]^2}{4} + 0}$

$\sigma_1 = -20.84 \ ksi \quad \sigma_2 = 0$

At B: $\sigma_{1,2} = \dfrac{-10.41 + 0}{2} \pm \sqrt{\dfrac{[-10.41 - 0]^2}{4} + 0.81^2}$

$\sigma_1 = 0.06 \ ksi \quad \sigma_2 = -10.47 \ ksi$

At C: $\sigma_{1,2} = \dfrac{0 + 0}{2} \pm \sqrt{\dfrac{[0 - 0]^2}{4} + 1.08^2}$

$\sigma_1 = -1.08 \ ksi \quad \sigma_2 = 1.08 \ ksi$

The orientation and the elements showing these values are shown in figure below

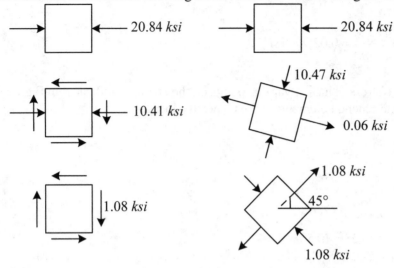

Step 5: Determine the maximum shear stresses and their orientation.

$$\tan 2\theta_s = -\frac{\sigma_x - \sigma_y}{2\tau_{xy}}$$

At A : $\tan 2\theta_s = -\dfrac{-20.84 - 0}{2(0)} = \infty; \ \theta_s = 45°$

At B : $\tan 2\theta_s = -\dfrac{-10.82 - 0}{2(0.81)} = 9.2; \ \theta_s = 41.9°$

At C : $\tan 2\theta_s = -\dfrac{0}{2(1.08)} = 0; \ \theta_s = 0°$

The orientation of the maximum shear stress directions is indicative of the plane in which a ductile material may fail.

$$\sigma_{x'} = \frac{\sigma_x + \sigma_y}{2}$$

$$\tau_{max} = \sqrt{\left(\frac{\sigma_x - \sigma_y}{2}\right)^2 + \left(\tau_{xy}\right)^2}$$

At A : $\sigma_{x'} = \sigma_{y'} = \dfrac{-20.84}{2} = -10.41; \tau_{max} = \sqrt{\left(\dfrac{-20.84 - 0}{2}\right)^2 + 0^2} = -10.41 \ ksi$

At B : $\sigma_{x'} = \sigma_{y'} = \dfrac{-10.42}{2} = -5.21; \ \tau_{max} = \sqrt{\left(\dfrac{-10.42 - 0}{2}\right)^2 + 0.81^2} = -5.47 \ ksi$

At C : $\sigma_{x'} = \sigma_{y'} = \dfrac{0}{2} = 0; \ \tau_{max} = \sqrt{\left(\dfrac{0 - 0}{2}\right)^2 + 1.08^2} = -1.08 \ ksi$

Combined Stresses

The determination and computation of the state of stress in a body, which is subjected to a combination of forces and moments in different directions, is often a very difficult process. Advanced techniques, such as the finite element method, is often used for the determination of stress in complex shaped bodies subjected to a complex state of forces.

In order to understand some of the fundamental principles involved in the determination of a combined state of three dimensional stress a few problems are illustrated below.

a. A circular shaft combined to a torsion, vertical shear force and bending moment
b. A hollow rectangular shaft subjected to a three dimensional state of stress, which causes biaxial bending, torsion, two shears and an axial force in the cross section. This example is a good example to understand the action of all force and moment components on a cross section.
c. Combined state of torsion and bending involved in the design of transmission shafts.

Example 9.5: Maximum Shear Stress in a shaft

Problem Statement: A shaft is subjected to
  a) Twist at 200 *lb-in*
  b) 60 *lb* vertical force as shown in the figure.

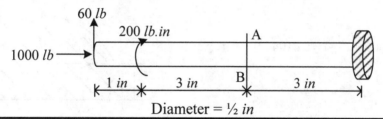

Diameter = ½ *in*

Required: Maximum shear stress at 4 *in* (section AB) from the free edge

Solution:

Step 1: Draw FBD of the Section

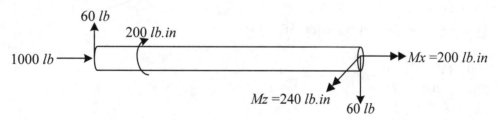

Internal forces at section AB

$V = 60 \ lbs \downarrow$

$T = 200 \ lb.in. \ (\text{CCW})$

Step 2: Determine the shear stresses due to vertical shear and torsion in order to determine the combined effect

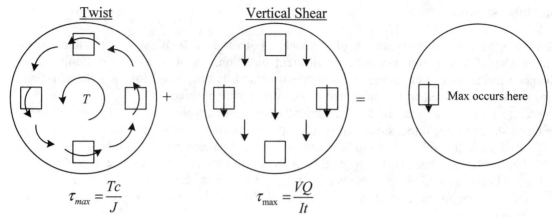

$$\tau_{max} = \frac{Tc}{J} \qquad\qquad \tau_{max} = \frac{VQ}{It}$$

<u>Twist:</u>

$$\tau_{max} = \frac{Tc}{J} = \frac{(200\ lb.in)(0.25\ in)}{(\pi \times \frac{0.5^4}{32})}$$

$$= 8150\ psi$$

<u>Direct:</u>

$$Q_{NA} = A\bar{y}$$

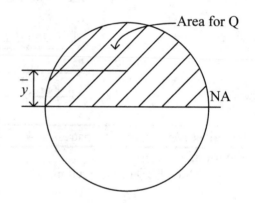

Area for Q

NA

$$= (\frac{\pi \times 0.25^2}{2})(\frac{4 \times 0.25}{3 \times \pi}) = 0.0104\ in^3$$

$$I_{NA} = \frac{\pi d^4}{4} = \frac{\pi \times 0.25^4}{4} = 0.00306\ in^4$$

$$t = \text{dia} = 0.5\ in$$

$$\therefore \tau_{bend} = \frac{60 \times 0.0104}{0.00307 \times 0.5} = 408\ psi$$

$$\tau_{total} = 408 + 8150$$

$$= 8560\ psi \text{ at the element at section AB}$$

<u>Normal Stress:</u>

$$\sigma = \frac{-1000}{0.196} - \frac{(60 \times 5\ in.lb)}{0.00306} \times 0.25$$

$$= 5102 - (98,039) \times 0.25$$

$$= -29,612\ psi$$

Example 9.6: Determination of stresses in a three dimensional problem

Problem Statement: The beam shown in figure is acting upon the force as shown in figure. Determine the state of stress at point A and B.

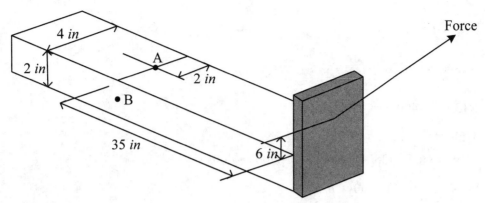

Details of the force:

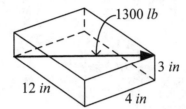

Section at A

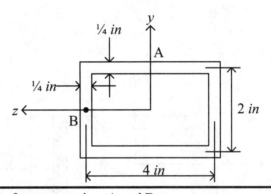

Required: Find: (a) State of stress at points A and B
(b) Draw the state of stress on the elements.

Solution:

Step 1: Determine the force-couple (internal) resultant at section

<u>Concept from Statics:</u> Find the force-couple at centroid of cross section –due to applied force.

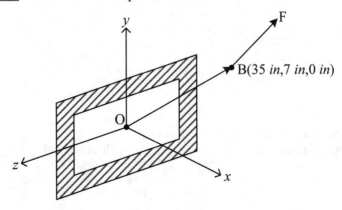

$$F_x = \frac{+12}{13} \times 1300 = 1200 \ lbs$$

$$F_y = \frac{+3}{13} \times 1300 = 300 \ lbs$$

$$F_z = \frac{-4}{13} \times 1300 = -400 \ lbs$$

Force-Couple at 0"

$$\vec{M}_o = \vec{r} \times \vec{F} = \vec{OB} \times \vec{F} = (35\underline{i} + 7\underline{j}) \times (1200\underline{i} + 300\underline{j} - 400\underline{k})$$

$$\vec{M}_o = -2800\underline{i} + 14000\underline{j} + 2100\underline{k} \quad lb.in$$

$$\vec{F}_o = 1200\underline{i} + 300\underline{j} - 400\underline{k} \quad lbs$$

Axial Force: $F_x = P = 1200 \ lbs$

Shear Forces: $V_y = 300 \ lbs$

$$V_z = -400 \ lbs$$

Torque: $M_x = -2800 \ lb.in$

Bending Moments: $M_y = 14000 \ lb.in$

$$M_z = 2100 \ lb.in$$

Step 2:

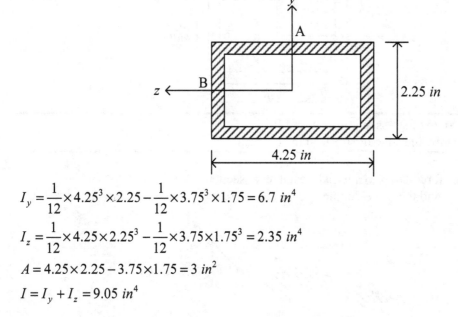

$$I_y = \frac{1}{12} \times 4.25^3 \times 2.25 - \frac{1}{12} \times 3.75^3 \times 1.75 = 6.7 \ in^4$$

$$I_z = \frac{1}{12} \times 4.25 \times 2.25^3 - \frac{1}{12} \times 3.75 \times 1.75^3 = 2.35 \ in^4$$

$$A = 4.25 \times 2.25 - 3.75 \times 1.75 = 3 \ in^2$$

$$I = I_y + I_z = 9.05 \ in^4$$

Step 3: Find the stresses at different points on section.

a)   Axial Stress: This is a situation with biaxial bending with axial load.

$$\sigma_x = \frac{P}{A} - \frac{M_z}{I_z}y + \frac{M_y}{I_y}z$$

$$= \frac{+2100 \ lbs}{3 \ in^2} - \frac{(2100 \ lb.in)}{2.35 \ in^2}y + \frac{(14000 \ lb.in)}{6.7 \ in^2}z$$

$$= 400 - 893.62y + 2089.6z$$

At A($y = 1.125, z = 0$)

  B($y = 0, z = 2.125$)

$\sigma_A = -605.3 \ psi$

$\sigma_B = 4840 \ psi$

b) Shear stress

Due to Torsion ($M_x = T = -2800 \ lb.in$)

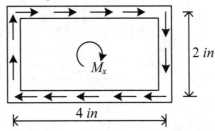

$$\tau = \frac{T}{2\boxed{A_m}t} = \frac{2800}{2(4 \times 2)(1/4)} = 700 \ psi \ \text{(clockwise direction because } M_x \text{ is negative)}$$

Shear stress due to shear force

i) Due to V_y (V along y direction, $\therefore$ NA is z-axis, Use I_z)

At A: $Q = 0$

$\qquad \therefore (\tau_{xy})_A = \tau_y = 0$

At B: $Q = A\overline{y} = (A_1\overline{y_1})_{outer} - (A_2\overline{y_2})_{inner}$ (point of interest is Neutral Axis)

$$= (1.125 \times 4.25)(\frac{1.125}{2}) - (0.875 \times 3.75)(\frac{0.875}{2})$$

$$= 1.254 \ in^3$$

$$(\tau_{xy})_B = \tau_B = \frac{V_y Q}{I_z t} = \frac{(300)(1.254)}{(2.35)(1/2)} = 320 \ psi$$

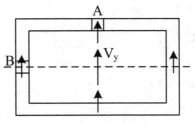

ii) Due to V_z (V_z along z direction, $\therefore$N.A. is y-axis, Use I_y)

At B: $A = 0 \therefore Q = 0$

$\therefore (\tau_{xz})_B = 0$

At A: $Q = A_1 \overline{y_1} - A_2 \overline{y_2}$

$$= (2.25 \times 2.125)(\frac{2.125}{2}) - (1.75 \times 1.875)(\frac{1.875}{2})$$

$$= 2.00 \ in^3$$

$$(\tau_{xz})_A = \tau_A = \frac{(400)(2.00)}{(6.7)(1/2)} = 239 \ psi$$

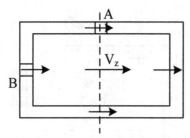

Step 4: Draw the state of stress.
Stress state at A:

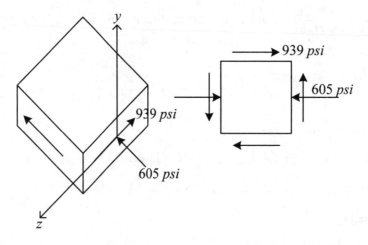

Stress state at B:

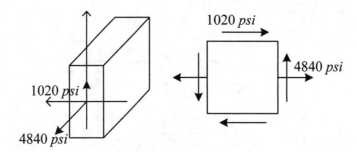

Example 9.7: Combined torsion and bending (Design of transmission shafts)

Problem Statement: In the chapter on torsion the design of circular shafts subjected to pure torsion was addressed. However, in many cases the design of shafts often involves both torsion and bending. Figure below shows a picture of a typical transmission shaft connected with gears. The forces are applied to the gears eccentric to the center of the shaft as shown.

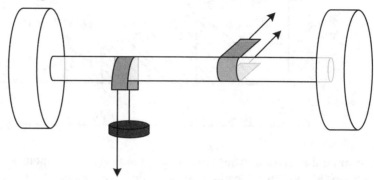

The eccentric connection results in the shaft being subjected to forces, possibly in multiple directions, and a moment couple at the center of the shaft. Consider the shaft shown in figure above subjected to the two forces acting on the gears as shown. Figure below shows the resulting action of these forces on the transmission shaft. The couple moments due to the forces are the torsion acting on the shaft, while the forces themselves result in bending moments in the member.

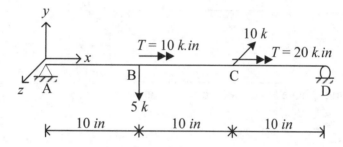

Action on the shaft: The following steps outline the action on the shaft and the manner in which the equations for the design are developed. It is to be expected that the ideal cross section in all this application is a circular or a hollow circular shaft.

Required: To design the circular shaft subjected to torsion and bending moment

Solution:

Step 1: Draw the bending moment diagram due to the forces acting. In general, since the forces acting can either be in the y or the z directions, two separate bending moment diagrams are drawn. The forces in the y direction cause a moment about the z-axis (M_z) while the forces in the z direction cause a moment about the y axis (M_y).

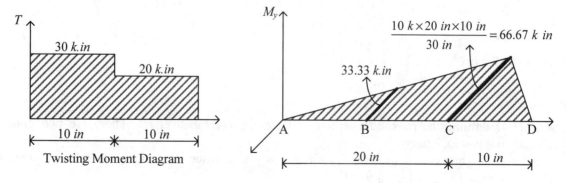

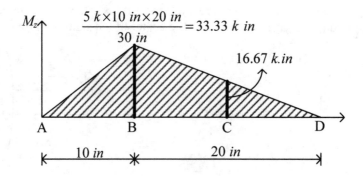

Step 2: Determine the location where the critical combination of moment and torsion can occur. For any problem, all possible locations have to be investigated. Figure below shows the cross section at B subjected to the combination of M_y, M_z and T. Since the cross section is circular, the two bending moments can be vectorially combined, since the moments of inertias associated with each of the moments are the moments of inertia about the diameter of the shaft and the location where the maximum stress is found is at the outer edge.

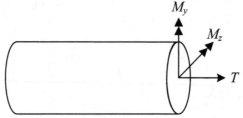

Cross section at B and C have to be checked for design.

$$\sigma_x = \pm\left(\frac{Mc}{I_{dia}}\right) \text{ and } \tau = \frac{Tc}{J}$$

$$M = \sqrt{M_y^2 + M_z^2}$$

At B:

$T_B = 30 \ k.in$

$M_y = 33.33 \ k.in$

$M_z = 33.33 \ k.in$

$\therefore M = \sqrt{33.33^2 + 33.33^2} = 47.14 \ k.in$

At C:

$T_C = 30 \ k.in$

$M_y = 66.66 \ k.in$

$M_z = 16.67 \ k.in$

$\therefore M = \sqrt{66.66^2 + 16.67^2} = 68.17 \ k.in$

Step 3: Determine the maximum stresses due to the combined effect. There are two points relevant to this step, namely

a) The polar moment of inertia of a circular shaft is twice its bending moment of inertia
$J = \pi c^4 / 2; \ I_{dia.} = \pi c^4 / 4 \text{ or } J = 2I_{dia.}$

b) At the outer edges where the bending and shear stresses due to torsion are a maximum, the shear stress due to the shear force is zero. Hence, the shear force diagram has not been drawn or used.

In this shaft, the outer element is subjected to both bending and normal stresses. This is an element subjected to plane state of stress as studied in this chapter. Hence, the following principles are used in order to determine the maximum design stress.

a) Since transmission shafts are made of ductile materials it can be expected that they will fail in shear.

b) The maximum shear stress in the shaft can be determined by using the principles of Mohr's circle outlined in this chapter, in which the equation of the radius represents the maximum shear stress, as follows

$$\tau_{max.} = \sqrt{\left(\frac{\sigma_x - \sigma_y}{2}\right)^2 + \tau^2} = \sqrt{\left(\frac{Mc}{2I_{dia.}}\right)^2 + \left(\frac{Tc}{J}\right)^2}$$

$$= \sqrt{\left(\frac{Mc}{J}\right)^2 + \left(\frac{Tc}{J}\right)^2}$$

Step 4: Determine the diameter of the shaft required by setting the maximum shear stress to its allowable value as follows.

$$\tau_{max} = \sqrt{\left(\frac{Mc}{J}\right)^2 + \left(\frac{Tc}{J}\right)^2} \leq \tau_{all.}$$

or

$$\frac{J}{c} = \frac{\pi c^4}{2c} = \frac{\pi c^3}{2} = \frac{\sqrt{M^2 + T^2}}{\tau_{all.}}$$

Assuming that the allowable shear stress is 24 ksi.

$$\frac{\pi c^3}{2} = \frac{\sqrt{68.71^2 + 30^2}}{24} = \frac{74.97}{24} = 3.12 \ in^3$$

$$\therefore c = 1.26 \ in$$

Adopt a shaft diameter of 1.3 *in*

9.5   Summary

This chapter has discussed the relationship between stresses on different sets of planes at the same point. The concept of stress transformation is used to relate the stresses on different planes. Two different stress transformation methods are addressed in this chapter, namely
a) Using equations of transformations of stresses
b) A geometric method called the Mohr's circle method.

1.   Given the stresses in one plane the stresses in any other plane can be determined using the following equations

$$\sigma_{x'} = \frac{\sigma_x + \sigma_y}{2} + \frac{\sigma_x - \sigma_y}{2}\cos 2\theta + \tau_{xy}\sin 2\theta$$

$$\tau_{x'y'} = -\frac{\sigma_x - \sigma_y}{2}\sin 2\theta + \tau_{xy}\cos 2\theta$$

where, θ is the angle between the x axis and the axis perpendicular to the required plane.

2.   The maximum and minimum normal stresses or the *principal stresses and the principal planes* are determined using the following equations. The shear stresses on principal planes are zero.

Equation for the principal planes $\left(\theta_p, \theta_p + \dfrac{\pi}{2}\right)$: $\tan 2\theta_p = \dfrac{2\tau_{xy}}{\sigma_x - \sigma_y}$

Equation for stresses on principal planes: $\sigma_{x'} = \dfrac{\sigma_x + \sigma_y}{2} + \dfrac{\sigma_x - \sigma_y}{2}\cos 2\theta_p + \tau_{xy}\sin 2\theta_p$

Minimum and maximum principal stresses $\sigma_{1,2} = \dfrac{\sigma_x + \sigma_y}{2} \pm \sqrt{\left[\dfrac{\sigma_x - \sigma_y}{2}\right]^2 + \tau_{xy}^2}$

3.   The maximum shear stress that any point experiences can also be found in a manner similar to that of the principal stresses. The angle at which the maximum shear stress occurs is

$$\tan 2\theta_s = -\frac{\sigma_x - \sigma_y}{2\tau_{xy}}$$

4.   The expression for the shear and normal stress transformation equation are

$$\sigma_{x'} = \sigma_{y'} = \frac{\sigma_x + \sigma_y}{2}$$

$$\tau_{max} = \sqrt{\left(\frac{\sigma_x - \sigma_y}{2}\right)^2 + \left(\tau_{xy}\right)^2}$$

5.   There are a number of examples for the determination of stresses due to the combined action of forces and moments. One of the common ones is the determination of the diameter of a transmission shaft subjected to combined action of bending and torsion and is given as follows

$$\frac{J}{c} = \frac{\pi c^4}{2c} = \frac{\pi c^3}{2} = \frac{\sqrt{M^2 + T^2}}{\tau_{all.}}$$

9.6 Problems:

9.1 The state of stress for an element is as shown in figure. Using the equation method, find $\sigma_{x'}$, $\sigma_{y'}$ and $\tau_{x'y'}$ at the angle shown in figure.

a.

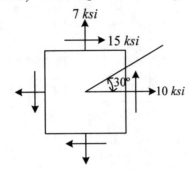

b.

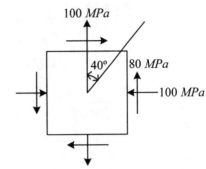

c.

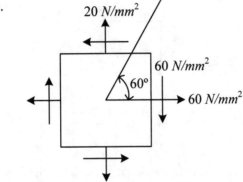

9.2 The state of stress for an element is as shown in figure. Using Mohr's circle method, find $\sigma_{x'}$, $\sigma_{y'}$ and $\tau_{x'y'}$ at the angle shown in figure.

a.

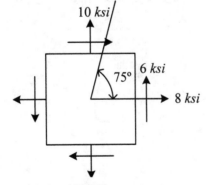

b.

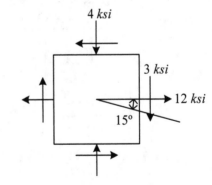

c.

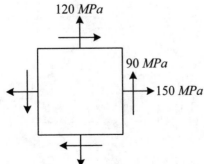

9.3 The state of stress for an element is as shown in figure. Using equation method find:

1. Principal Normal stress and show them on properly oriented element.
2. Principal Shearing stress and show them on a properly oriented element.

a.

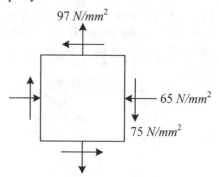

120 MPa

100 MPa

12°

90 MPa

b.

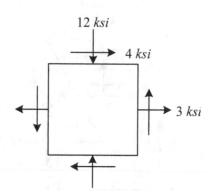

97 N/mm²

65 N/mm²

75 N/mm²

c.

14 ksi

8 ksi

16 ksi

d.

12 ksi

4 ksi

3 ksi

9.4 The state of stress for an element is as shown in figure. Using Mohr's circle method find:
1. Principal Normal stress and show them on properly oriented element.
2. Principal Shearing stress and show them on a properly oriented element.

a.

80 N/mm²

65 N/mm²

40 N/mm²

b.

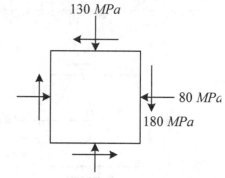

130 MPa

80 MPa

180 MPa

c.

15 ksi

6 ksi

9 ksi

d.

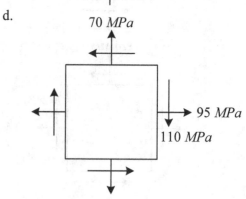

70 MPa

95 MPa

110 MPa

Chapter 10

Deflection in Beams

Goal: The learning objectives of this chapter are as follows:

1. Discuss the theory of deflection of beams in bending
2. Derive the differential equations for computing deflections
3. Derive the second order and fourth order differential equations for deflection
4. Discuss physical boundary conditions and their mathematical forms
5. Solve deflection problems using both second and fourth order equation forms
6. Discuss specific applications of the deflection equations

10 Deflection in Beams

10.1 Introduction

The design of beams and other members, as outlined in an earlier chapter, should satisfy the *three S* criteria; namely *Strength, Stiffness* and *Stability*. Most of the material leading up to this chapter dealt with the *design for strength*, wherein the size of the members is determined based on the maximum stresses not exceeding the allowable stress values. The second aspect of the design of members is now described, that is *design for stiffness*.

Stiffness Criterion: The main criterion involved in the design for stiffness in a beam is that the maximum deflection should be less than some specified value. Often the specified value is a subjective choice, although there are some prescribed values in some building codes and other engineering specifications.

This chapter describes the methodology involved in the determination of the deflection and slope of beams subjected to concentrated and distributed loads and moments, in statically determinate beams. It will be seen that this method lends itself very well for the determination of reaction forces and moments of statically indeterminate beams as well.

Definitions of Deflection and Slope (Sign Conventions): Consider a beam of length *L*, as shown in Figure 10.1. The positive direction for lateral loads and deflection is in the positive *y*-direction. The displaced position of the beam can be expressed by an equation *y(x)*, where *y* is defined as the deflection of the beam. This equation is also called the *elastic curve* of the beam. *Elastic curve* is a curve formed by the central axis of the deflected beam under loading. The *slope* of the beam is the tangent drawn to the elastic curve, as shown in Figure 10.1. A *positive slope* is considered a counterclockwise rotation of the slope, which is the angle that the tangent makes with respect to the positive *x*-axis. A *positive distributed load w(x)* is considered acting in the positive y-axis direction (upward).

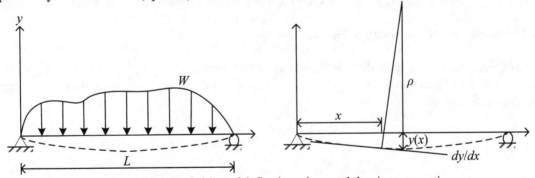

Figure 10.1: Definition of deflection, slope and the sign convention

The radius of curvature ρ of the neutral axis, as seen in Figure 10.1, is related to the bending moment *M*, the elastic modulus *E* and the moment of inertia about the neutral axis I_{NA} by the expression derived in chapter 7, as shown below

$$\frac{1}{\rho} = \frac{M}{EI_{NA}}$$

Eqn (10.1)

In general, the radius of curvature is related to the equation of a curve *y(x)* by the following expression

$$\frac{1}{\rho} = \frac{d^2y/dx^2}{\left[1+\left(\dfrac{dy}{dx}\right)^2\right]^{3/2}}$$

Eqn (10.2)

For small deflections, the slope of the curve dy/dx can be approximated as zero, as the curve is practically a straight line. Consequently, the expression of the radius of curvature reduces to the following simpler form

$$\frac{1}{\rho} = \frac{d^2y}{dx^2}$$

Eqn (10.3)

10.2 Differential Equations of Deflection

The expressions relating the equation of deflection/elastic curve to the bending moment, shear force and the distributed load equations are in the form of differential equations, as shown below.

10.2.1 Second Order Differential Equation

Using equation 10.1 and 10.3, the expression to find the deflection y can be related to the bending moment in the beam, in the form of *Second Order Differential Equation* as follows

$$\frac{1}{\rho} = \frac{d^2y}{dx^2} = \frac{M}{EI_{NA}}$$

or

$$M = EI_{NA}\frac{d^2y}{dx^2}$$

Eqn (10.4)

The term EI_{NA} is called the *flexural rigidity*. If the beam is made of the same cross section throughout the span and all deflections are considered when the beam is still within its elastic behavior range, then the flexural rigidity can be considered as a constant.

10.2.2 Fourth Order Differential Equation

It was seen in an earlier chapter that the derivative of the bending moment is the shear force in the beam. Hence the expression for shear force, in terms of the deflection equation of the beam can be expressed as follows

$$V = \frac{dM}{dx} = EI_{NA}\frac{d^3y}{dx^3}$$

or

$$\frac{d^3y}{dx^3} = \frac{V}{EI_{NA}}$$

Eqn (10.5)

which, is the third order differential equation. Similarly the derivative of the shear force is the magnitude of the distributed load $w(x)$. Hence, the fourth order differential equation expression, relating the deflection of the beam to the magnitude of the distributed load can be written as follows

$$w(x) = \frac{dV}{dx} = EI_{NA}\frac{d^4 y}{dx^4}$$

or   Eqn (10.6)

$$\frac{d^4 y}{dx^4} = \frac{w(x)}{EI_{NA}}$$

10.3 Solution of Differential Equations

Since the flexural rigidity is considered a constant, the solution to the second and fourth order differential equations can be derived by a direct integration process as shown below

10.3.1 Second Order Differential Equation

The second integral of *second order differential equation* gives the relation between the deflection of the beam and moment. Hence, the deflection equation can be derived from *second order differential equation* as follows

$$EI_{NA}\frac{d^2 y}{dx^2} = M(x)$$

$$EI_{NA}\frac{dy}{dx} = \int M(x)dx + A \qquad\qquad \text{Eqn (10.7)}$$

$$EI_{NA}y(x) = \iint M(x)dxdx + Ax + B$$

In order to solve this equation the expression for the bending moment $M(x)$ is needed, and is often found from the method of sections. The two constants of integration A and B are found by applying the boundary conditions.

Boundary Condition: Since the integrated values $EI_{NA}\frac{dy}{dx}$ and $EI_{NA}y(x)$ represent the *slope* and *deflection* respectively, the boundary condition to be sought for the solution must also correspond to the slope and deflections at the boundaries of the beams.

10.3.2 Fourth Order Differential Equation:

The fourth integral of *fourth order differential equation* gives the relation between the deflection of the beam and distributed load. Hence, the deflection equation can be derived from *fourth order differential equation* as follows

$$EI_{NA}\frac{d^4 y}{dx^4} = w(x)$$

$$EI_{NA}\frac{d^3 y}{dx^3} = \int w(x)dx + C_1$$

$$EI_{NA}\frac{d^2 y}{dx^2} = \iint w(x)dx + C_1 x + C_2$$

$$EI_{NA}\frac{dy}{dx} = \iiint w(x)dx + C_1\frac{x^2}{2} + C_2 x + C_3$$

$$EI_{NA}y = \iiiint w(x)dx + C_1\frac{x^3}{6} + C_2\frac{x^2}{2} + C_3 x + C_4$$

Boundary Conditions: The solution to the fourth order differential equation by the integration process involves four constants, which are determined by using appropriate boundary conditions. It can be seen that the constants represent the conditions of the Shear C_1, Moment C_2, Slope C_3 and the deflection C_4 at the initial point at $x = 0$.

10.4 Boundary Conditions and Application of Boundary Conditions

It has been seen that the determination of the constants involves the boundary conditions. The term *Boundary Conditions,* by definition imply two things
1. **Boundary:** One must look at the boundaries of the problem; this is typically at the ends or any intermediate support points
2. **Condition:** The term *condition* refers to a observable (typically a zero or known magnitude) value of the following quantities
    i. Deflection (y)
    ii. Slope (y')
    iii. Moment $\left(EIy'' \right)$
    iv. Shear $\left(ELy''' \right)$

The value of the boundary condition must be determined by a quick visual observation. This is often an easy determination with practice for a student new to this concept. Figure 10.2 shows some typical boundaries and the associated boundary conditions. Their associated values are also outlined below.

Application: The application of boundary conditions involves
1. The determination of the type of boundary and identifying its properties
2. The identification of the location of the boundary on the axis. This is done by finding the value of x at that boundary.

The following cases illustrate the nature of the boundaries and the manner in which they are applied to a particular problem.

Case A: At Outer Pin or Roller

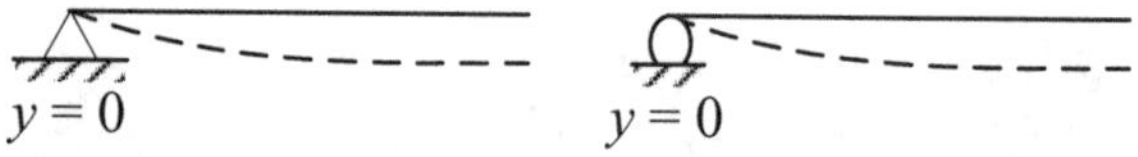

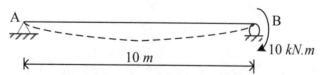
$$y = 0 \qquad\qquad y = 0$$

Figure 10.2(a): Boundary condition a pin and roller support.

At an outer pin or roller support, it can be seen that both the deflection and the moment value is zero. Hence, the boundary conditions for this case are
$$y = 0$$
$$M = EIy'' = 0$$

Special case:

A _ _ _ _ _ _ _ _ _ _ _ _ _ _ _ _ _ B

$10\ kN.m$

$10\ m$

Figure 10.2(b): A beam with pin and roller support with external moment

The figure shows a simply supported beam (pin at one end and a roller at the other end), with a concentrated moment at end B. This external moment modifies the boundary condition as follows

$$y_A = y(x = 0) = 0$$
$$y_B = y(x = 10) = 0$$
$$M_A = EIy''_B(x = 0) = 0 \ kN.m$$
$$M_B = EIy''_B(x = 10) = -10 \ kN.m$$

Case B: At Free End

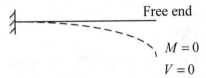

Figure 10.2(c): Boundary condition for free end

At the free end, where it is free to deflect as well as rotate, the only zero values are that of the moment or shear

$$M = EIy'' = 0$$
$$V = EIy''' = 0$$

However, if there is a concentrated value of shear or moment at the free end, as shown in the figure, they take on those values, accounting carefully for the sign.

Figure 10.2(d): A cantilever with external shear and moment at the free end

The boundary conditions for such a case are as follows,

$$M = EIy'' = -10 \ ft.k$$
$$V = EIy''' = +5 \ ft.k$$

Case C: At Fixed End

Figure 10.2(e): Boundary condition for a fixed end

At the fixed end both the deflection and the rotation are prevented. This is the reason why the fixed end reaction has both a force and a moment reaction. Hence, the moment and shear at the fixed end cannot be zero valued. Hence, the boundary conditions for this case are,

$$\text{Deflection} = EIy = 0$$
$$\text{Slope} = EIy' = 0$$

Application: The application of boundary conditions to a cantilever beam (fixed at one end and free end at the other) is illustrated below.

Figure 10.2(f): Cantilever beam with external shear and moment at the free end.

$y_A = y(x=0) = 0$

$y'_A = y(x=0) = 0$

$M_B = EIy''_B(x=10) = 0 \ kN.m$

$V_B = EIy'''_B(x=10) = 10 \ kN$

$y_A = y(x=0) = 0$

$y'_A = y(x=0) = 0$

$M_B = EIy''_B(x=10) = -10 \ kN.m$

$V_B = EIy'''_B(x=10) = 0 \ kN$

Note: It must be noted that for a distributed load, the shear and moment at the free end is still zero, as no concentrated load exists at that point.

Case D: At an Internal Pin support

At an internal support, typically resting either on a pin or a roller, there are two types of conditions. In such problems the deflection curve for each span is determined separately.

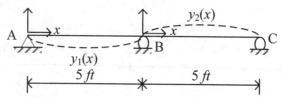

Figure 10.2(g): Deflection curve of a beam with internal support

As shown in the figure, the deflection curve in span AB is given by the equation $y_1(x)$ and that for span BC is given by equation $y_2(x)$. The x-axis is moved such that for span AB, $x=0$ at A and $x=5ft$ at B and for span BC, $x=0$ at B and $x=5ft$ at C. At the internal support the following conditions occur

1. Deflection is zero
2. The slope of the deflected shape of AB and BC are equal
3. The moment values from spans AB and BC are the same (equal in magnitude and opposite in nature/direction)

These physical boundary conditions can be represented by the following numerical boundary condition values

$$y_{1,B} = y(x=10) = 0$$

$$y_{2,B} = y(x=0) = 0$$

$$\text{Slope}_B = y'_{1,B}(x=10) = y'_{2,B}(x=0)$$

$$M_B = EIy''_{1,B}(x=10) = EIy''_{2,B}(x=0)$$

10.5 Solution Approaches of Second Order versus Solution Approaches of Fourth Order Differential Equation

Any problem can be solved using either second, third or fourth order differential equation approach. The two most commonly used ones are the second order and the fourth order approaches. Both these methods have their advantages and disadvantages which are described below along with the methodology to solve problems using the two approaches.

Second Order Approach: The starting point of the second order approach is the equation

$$EI_{NA}\frac{d^2y}{dx^2} = M(x)$$

The steps to get the solution are as follows:

Step 1: Determine the equation of $M(x)$ is determined from the method of sections learnt earlier

Step 2: Integrate the equation twice to get two constants

Step 3: Apply two boundary conditions, related only to displacement or slope, to determine the two constants of integration

Fourth Order Approach: The starting point of the second order approach is the equation

$$EI_{NA}\frac{d^4y}{dx^4} = w(x)$$

The steps to get the solution are as follows:

Step 1: Determine the equation of $w(x)$, which is the equation representing the distributed load. If no distributed load exists, the value of $w(x)$ is zero.

Step 2: Integrate the equation four times to get four constants

Step 3: Determine and apply four boundary conditions, related to displacement, slope, moment and shear, in order to determine the four constants of integration. It is often expeditious to apply any known zero valued boundary conditions, especially at $x = 0$, in order to simplify the mathematical solution process.

The advantages and disadvantages of the two approaches are illustrated using the simply supported beam problem shown in Figure 10.3. The beam is subjected to a uniformly distributed load of w kN/m acting downwards.

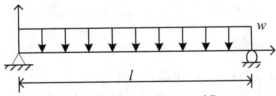

Figure 10.3: Simply Supported Beam

Second Order Approach
Step 1: Determine the reactions and the equation of the bending moment.
The reactions are $wl/2$ acting upwards as shown. From the method of sections and using the section diagram shown the moment equation is determined as follows

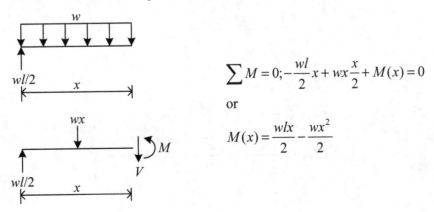

$$\sum M = 0; -\frac{wl}{2}x + wx\frac{x}{2} + M(x) = 0$$

or

$$M(x) = \frac{wlx}{2} - \frac{wx^2}{2}$$

Step 2: Set up the second order differential equation and integrate twice

$$EI_{NA}\frac{d^2y}{dx^2} = \frac{wlx}{2} - \frac{wx^2}{2}$$

$$EI_{NA}\frac{dy}{dx} = \frac{wlx^2}{4} - \frac{wx^3}{6} + C_1$$

$$EI_{NA}y(x) = \frac{wlx^3}{12} - \frac{wx^4}{24} + C_1x + C_2$$

Step 3: Determine and apply boundary conditions.
Since this is a simply supported beam the conditions applicable here are
a) deflection at A($x = 0$) = 0 and
b) deflection at B($x = l$) = 0.
Both these conditions are applicable only to the deflection equation derived in the previous step.

$$y_A = y(x = 0) = 0$$

$$EI_{NA}y(0) = \frac{wl(0)^3}{12} - \frac{w(0)^4}{24} + C_1(0) + C_2 = 0 \Rightarrow C_2 = 0$$

$$y_B = y(x = l) = 0$$

$$EI_{NA}y(l) = \frac{wl(l)^3}{12} - \frac{wl^4}{24} + C_1l = 0 \Rightarrow C_1 = -\frac{wl^3}{24}$$

The deflection equation can now be written as

$$EI_{NA}y(x) = \frac{wlx^3}{12} - \frac{wx^4}{24} - \frac{wl^3}{24}x$$

$$y(x) = \frac{w}{24EI_{NA}}(-x^4 - l^3x + 2lx^3)$$

Fourth Order Approach
Step 1: Determine the equation for the distributed load.
Since this is a uniformly distributed load acting downwards this equation is

$$w(x) = -w$$

Step 2: Integrate this equation four times and set up the constants of integration.

$$EI_{NA}\frac{d^4y}{dx^4} = -w$$

$$EI_{NA}\frac{d^3y}{dx^3} = -wx + C_1$$

$$EI_{NA}\frac{d^2y}{dx^2} = -\frac{wx^2}{2} + C_1x + C_2$$

$$EI_{NA}\frac{dy}{dx} = -\frac{wx^3}{6} + C_1\frac{x^2}{2} + C_2x + C_3$$

$$EI_{NA}y = -\frac{wx^4}{24} + C_1\frac{x^3}{6} + C_2\frac{x^2}{2} + C_3x + C_4$$

Step 3: Determine and apply the boundary conditions.

Since this is a simply supported beam, the deflection and moment values are zero at the two ends, as shown in an earlier section. Hence, the boundary conditions are

$$y_A = y(x = 0) = 0$$
$$y_B = y(x = l) = 0$$
$$M_A = EIy''_A(x = 0) = 0$$
$$M_B = EIy''_B(x = l) = 0$$

$y_A=0$ $y_B=0$

$x=0$ $x=L$

Apply these boundary conditions to the equations above to find the integral constants.

$$y(x = 0) = 0$$

$$EI_{NA}y = -\frac{w(0)^4}{24} + C_1\frac{(0)^3}{6} + C_2\frac{(0)^2}{2} + C_3(0) + C_4 = 0 \Rightarrow C_4 = 0$$

$$EIy''_A(x = 0) = 0$$

$$EI_{NA}\frac{d^2y}{dx^2} = -\frac{w(0)^2}{2} + C_1(0) + C_2 = 0 \Rightarrow C_2 = 0$$

$$EIy''_A(x = l) = 0$$

$$EI_{NA}\frac{d^2y}{dx^2} = -\frac{wl^2}{2} + C_1l = 0 \Rightarrow C_1 = \frac{wl}{2}$$

$$y(x = l) = 0$$

$$EI_{NA}y = -\frac{wl^4}{24} + \frac{wl}{2}\frac{l^3}{6} + C_3l = 0 \Rightarrow C_3 = -\frac{wl^4}{24}$$

The deflection equation now reduces to

$$EI_{NA}y(x) = \frac{wlx^3}{12} - \frac{wx^4}{24} - \frac{wl^3}{24}x$$

$$y(x) = \frac{w}{24EI_{NA}}(-x^4 - l^3x + 2lx^3)$$

which, is identical to the one derived from the second order method. Hence, it can be seen that although the fourth order solution starts from a simpler load function it has more boundary conditions that need to be considered in order to determine the constants.

Maximum value of deflection: The maximum value of deflection occurs at points, within a span, where the slope is zero. In the above example, the slope is zero valued at the center of the beam $(x = l/2)$. Setting this the maximum deflection for a simply supported beam subjected to a uniformly distributed load is given as

$$y\left(x = \frac{1}{2}\right) = \frac{w}{24EI_{NA}}\left[-\left(\frac{l}{2}\right)^4 - \left(\frac{l}{2}\right)l^3 + 2l\left(\frac{l}{2}\right)^3\right] = -\frac{5wl^4}{384EI_{NA}} \qquad \text{Eqn (10.8)}$$

Example 10.1: Deflection and slope at the free end of a cantilever

Problem Statement: The cantilever beam has the cross sectional properties as shown in the figure. The length of the beam is L and it is subjected to external force P at the free end.

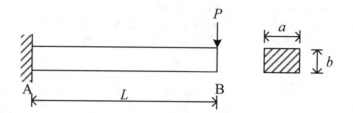

Required: To find deflection and slope at the free end of the cantilever using 2nd order method.

Solution:

Step 1: Find reactions using the force and moment equilibrium equations.

$$\sum F_y = 0 : R_A = P$$

$$\sum M_A = 0 : M_A - P \times L = 0$$

$$M_A = PL$$

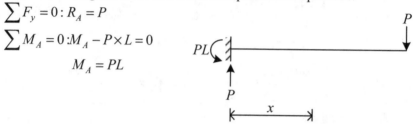

Draw a free body diagram and find moment equation using the method of sections

$$\sum M_x = 0 : PL + M(x) - Px = 0$$

$$\therefore M(x) = Px - PL$$

Step 2: Setup 2nd order equation and integrate.

$$EIy'' = M(x) = Px - PL$$

Slope: $EIy' = \dfrac{Px^2}{2} - PLx + c_1$ Eqn.(I)

Deflection: $EIy = \dfrac{Px^3}{6} - \dfrac{PLx^2}{2} + c_1 x + c_2$ Eqn.(II)

Step 3: Apply boundary conditions and solve for c_1 and c_2.

Fixed end

Boundary conditions: Slope = 0 at $x = 0$

                     Deflection = 0 at $x = 0$

Substituting the slope boundary condition in Eqn (I).

At $x = 0$, Slope $= 0$

$$\therefore EIy' = \dfrac{P \times 0^2}{2} - PL \times 0 + c_1 = 0$$

$$\therefore c_1 = 0$$

Substituting the deflection boundary condition in Eqn (II).

At $x = 0$, Deflection $= 0$

$$\therefore EIy = \frac{P \times 0^3}{6} - \frac{PL \times 0^2}{2} + c_1 \times 0 + c_2 = 0$$

$$\therefore c_2 = 0$$

Now the slope and deflection equation are:

$$y = \frac{P}{EI}\left(\frac{x^3}{6} - \frac{Lx^2}{2}\right)$$

$$y' = \frac{P}{EI}\left(\frac{x^2}{2} - Lx\right)$$

Step 4: Find the slope and deflection at the free end.

$$y_B(x = L) = \frac{P}{EI}\left(\frac{L^3}{6} - \frac{L^3}{2}\right) = -\frac{PL^3}{3EI}$$

$$y'_B(x = L) = \frac{P}{EI}\left(\frac{L^2}{2} - L^2\right) = -\frac{PL^2}{2EI}$$

Negative sign implies that the beam is deflecting in downward direction and undergoing a clockwise rotation.

Step 5: Find moment of inertia.

For a rectangular cross section the moment of inertia about the neutral axis is

$$I = I_{NA} = \frac{ab^3}{12}$$

The slope and deflection at the free end in terms of moment of inertia are

$$\text{Deflection} = -\frac{12PL^3}{3Eab^3} = -\frac{4PL^3}{Eab^3}$$

$$\text{Slope} = -\frac{12PL^2}{2Eab^3} = -\frac{6PL^2}{Eab^3}$$

Example 10.2: Maximum deflection problem

Problem Statement: A beam is subjected to triangular loading as shown in figure.

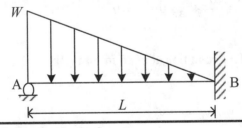

Required: Find maximum deflection in the beam.

Solution:

Note: Since reactions cannot be computed, 4th order method is suggested.

Step 1: Find the load function. As the load is acting downwards the load function will have a negative sign.

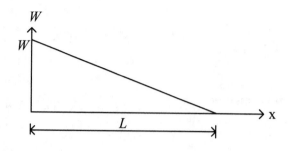

$$W(x) = -\frac{Wx}{L}$$

Step 2: Setup 4th order equation and integrate.

$$EIy'''' = -\frac{Wx}{L}$$

$$EIy''' = V = -\frac{Wx^2}{2L} + c_1 \qquad \text{Eqn.(I)}$$

$$EIy'' = M = -\frac{Wx^3}{6L} + c_1 x + c_2 \qquad \text{Eqn.(II)}$$

$$\text{Slope: } EIy' = -\frac{Wx^4}{24L} + \frac{c_1 x^2}{2} + c_2 x + c_3 \qquad \text{Eqn.(III)}$$

$$\text{Deflection: } EIy = -\frac{Wx^5}{120L} + \frac{c_1 x^3}{6} + \frac{c_2 x^2}{2} + c_3 x + c_4 \qquad \text{Eqn.(IV)}$$

Step 3: Identify boundary conditions and solve for c_1, c_2, c_3 and c_4. For simplicity set $x=0$ at B and $x=L$ at A.

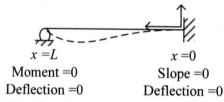

$$x = L \qquad\qquad\qquad x = 0$$
Moment = 0 Slope = 0
Deflection = 0 Deflection = 0

Substituting the deflection boundary condition at $x = 0$ in Eqn (IV).
At $x = 0$, Deflection $= 0$

$$\therefore EIy = -\frac{W \times 0^5}{120L} + \frac{c_1 \times 0^3}{6} + \frac{c_2 \times 0^2}{2} + c_3 \times 0 + c_4 = 0$$

$$\therefore c_4 = 0$$

Substituting the slope boundary condition at $x = 0$ in Eqn (III).
At $x = 0$, Slope $= 0$

$$\therefore ELy' = -\frac{W \times 0^4}{24L} + \frac{c_1 \times 0^3}{2} + c_2 \times 0 + c_3 = 0$$

$$\therefore c_3 = 0$$

Substituting the deflection boundary condition at $x = L$ in Eqn (IV).

At $x = L$, Deflection = 0

$$\therefore EIy = -\frac{WL^5}{120L} + \frac{c_1 L^3}{6} + \frac{c_2 L^2}{2} = 0$$

$$\therefore 0 = -\frac{WL^4}{120} + \frac{c_1 L^3}{6} + \frac{c_2 L^2}{2}$$

Dividing the equation by L^2

$$\therefore 0 = -\frac{WL^2}{120} + \frac{c_1 L}{6} + \frac{c_2}{2}$$

$$\therefore \frac{c_1 L}{6} + \frac{c_2}{2} = \frac{WL^2}{120} \qquad \text{Eqn (i)}$$

Substituting the moment boundary condition at $x = L$ in Eqn (II).

At $x = L$, Moment=0

$$\therefore EIy'' = -\frac{WL^3}{6L} + c_1 L + c_2 = 0$$

$$\therefore c_1 L + c_2 = \frac{WL^3}{6L} \qquad \text{Eqn (ii)}$$

Solving Eqn (i) and Eqn (ii) simultaneously, we get

$$c_1 = \frac{9WL}{40}$$

and

$$c_2 = -\frac{7WL^2}{120}$$

Step 4: Find reactions.

Substituting the value of c_1 and c_2 in the shear and moment equations we have

$$V = -\frac{Wx^2}{2L} + \frac{9WL}{40}$$

$$M = -\frac{Wx^3}{6L} + \frac{9WL}{40}x - \frac{7WL^2}{120}$$

By substituting $x=L$ we can find the reaction at A and by substituting $x=0$ we can get the reaction and moment at B.

$$V_A = -\frac{WL^2}{2L} + \frac{9WL}{40} = -\frac{WL}{2} + \frac{9WL}{40}$$

$$\therefore V_A = -\frac{11WL}{40}$$

$$V_B = -\frac{W \times 0^2}{2L} + \frac{9WL}{40}$$

$$\therefore V_B = \frac{9WL}{40}$$

$$M_B = -\frac{W \times 0^3}{6L} + \frac{9WL}{40} \times 0 - \frac{7WL^2}{120}$$

$$\therefore M_B = -\frac{7WL^2}{120}$$

Example 10.3: Maximum slope and deflection by 2nd order method.

Problem Statement: A $10ft$ long simply supported beam is subjected to a uniformly distributed load as shown in figure.

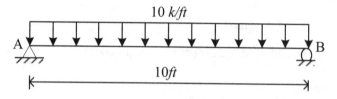

Required: Find maximum slope and deflection in the beam by 2nd order method.

Solution:

Step 1: Find reactions and moment function.

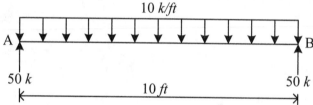

Drawing a free body diagram to find moment equation of the beam

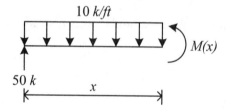

$$M(x) + \frac{10x^2}{2} - 50x = 0$$

$$\therefore M(x) = 50x - \frac{10x^2}{2}$$

$$\therefore M(x) = 50x - 5x^2$$

Step 2: Setup 2nd order equation and integrate.

$$EIy'' = M = 50x - 5x^2$$

Slope: $EIy' = \dfrac{50x^2}{2} - \dfrac{5x^3}{3} + c_1 = 25x^2 - \dfrac{5x^3}{3} + c_1$ Eqn(I)

Deflection: $EIy = \dfrac{25x^3}{3} - \dfrac{5x^4}{12} + c_1 x + c_2$ Eqn(II)

Step 3: Apply boundary conditions and solve for c_1 and c_2.

A _____ B

$x=0$ $x=10$

Moment $=0$ Moment $=0$

Deflection $=0$ Deflection $=0$

Substituting the deflection boundary condition at $x=0$ and $x=10$

At $x = 0$, Deflection$=0$

$$\therefore EIy = \frac{25 \times 0^3}{3} - \frac{5 \times 0^4}{12} + c_1 \times 0 + c_2 = 0$$

$$\therefore c_2 = 0$$

At $x = 10$, Deflection$=0$

$$\therefore EIy = \frac{25 \times 10^3}{3} - \frac{5 \times 10^4}{12} + c_1 \times 10 = 0$$

$$\therefore c_1 = -416.67$$

Step 4: Find maximum slope and deflection.

Slope in the beam is zero where the deflection is of maximum value. In this beam the slope is maximum at $x=0$ and $x=10$.

$$\text{Slope}_A = EIy'(x = 0) = 25 \times 0 - \frac{5 \times 0}{3} - 416.67$$

$$\therefore \text{Slope}_A = -\frac{416.67}{EI}$$

$$\text{Slope}_B = EIy'(x = 10) = 25 \times 10 - \frac{5 \times 10}{3} - 416.67$$

$$\therefore \text{Slope}_B = \frac{416.67}{EI}$$

The negative sign suggest that the slope is in clockwise direction whereas the positive sign suggest counter clock wise direction.

A   B

$416.67/EI$ $416.67/EI$

Maximum deflection in the beam occurs where the slope of the beam is zero. In this case the slope of the beam is zero at the center of the beam. Hence we can find maximum deflection by substituting $x=5$ in the deflection equation.

$$\therefore \text{Max. Deflection} = EIy(x = 5) = \frac{25 \times 5^3}{3} - \frac{5 \times 5^4}{12} + (-416.67) \times 5$$

$$\therefore \text{Max. Deflection} = -\frac{1302.1}{EI}$$

Problems with multiple regions: Solution to deflection problems can often involve integrating over multiple regions due to changes in either boundary conditions or loadings. In such problems the following basic steps are required when using the second order methods.

1. Determine the reactions
2. Determine the moment equations over each region using the method of sections
3. Integrate the second order equation over each region. The deflection equation and the constants of integration are designated separately for each region
4. Setup and apply two types of conditions, namely *boundary* and *continuity* conditions.
5. Solve for the constants of integration and determine the deflection equation for each region

---

Example 10.4: Deflection equations for multiple region problems

Problem Statement: A simply supported beam as shown in the figure is a steel wide flanged beam W8 x 12, $I_x = 75.3$ in^4. The beam has a length of 10 *ft* and is subjected to a load of P at a distance of 4 *ft* from A.

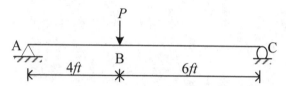

Required: To find deflection and slope equations using the 2nd order method.

Solution: In such a problem it is necessary to set up two different second order differential equations since the moment equations in regions AB and BC will be different. Consequently, the following two conditions are defined for the problem.

a) Region AB has origin at A and has the limits $0 < x < 4$ *ft* and region BC has the origin at B and has the limits of $0 < x < 6$ *ft*.

b) The deflection is represented by two different equations $y_1(x)$ in region AB and $y_2(x)$ in region BC

Step 1: Find reactions using the force and moment equilibrium equations.

$$\sum F_y = 0 : A_y + C_y - P = 0$$

$$\sum M_A = 0 : C_y(10\,ft) - P \times (4\,ft) = 0$$

$$C_y = 0.4P \uparrow$$

$$\therefore A_y = 0.6P \uparrow$$

0.6P   0.4P

Step 2: Draw a free body diagram and find moment equation using the method of sections

$M_1(x)$

0.6P

x

$$\sum M_x = 0 : -0.6Px + M_1(x) = 0$$

$$\therefore M_1(x) = 0.6Px \qquad 0 < x < 48 \ in$$

P

$M_2(x)$

0.6P   4ft x

$$\sum M_x = 0 : -0.6P(48 + x) + Px + M_2(x) = 0$$

$$\therefore M_2(x) = 28.8P - 0.4Px \qquad 0 < x < 72 \ in$$

It is advantageous to move the origin in the second region BC as it will ease the mathematical application of the boundary conditions, as seen in step 4.

Step 3: Setup 2nd order equations for each region and integrate.
Region AB $\quad 0 < x < 48in$

$EIy_1'' = M_1(x) = 0.6Px$

Slope: $EIy_1' = 0.3Px^2 + c_1$ $\qquad$ Eqn.(I)

Deflection: $EIy_1 = 0.1Px^3 + c_1x + c_2$ Eqn.(II)

Region BC $\quad 0 < x < 72in$

$EIy_2'' = M_2(x) = 28.8P - 0.4Px$

Slope: $EIy_2' = 28.8Px - 0.2Px^2 + c_3$ $\qquad$ Eqn.(III)

Deflection: $EIy_2 = 14.4Px^2 - \dfrac{0.2Px^3}{3} + c_3x + c_4$ Eqn.(IV)

Step 4: Identify and apply boundary conditions and solve for c_1, c_2, c_3, and c_4. Four boundary conditions are needed.

a) For span AB: $y_A = y_1(x = 0) = 0$
b) For span BC: $y_C = y_2(x = 72) = 0$
c) At point C: $y_B = y_1(x = 48) = y_2(x = 0)$
$\qquad\qquad\qquad y'_B = y'_1(x = 48) = y'_2(x = 0)$

Apply the boundary conditions.

a) Substituting the region AB deflection boundary condition in Eqn.(I).

$$\therefore EIy_1(x = 0) = \frac{0.6P \times 0^3}{6} + c_1 \times 0 + c_2 = 0$$

$$\therefore c_2 = 0$$

b) Substituting the region BC deflection boundary condition in Eqn (IV).

$$EIy_2(x = 72) = 14.4P \times 72^2 - \frac{0.2P \times 72^3}{3} + c_3 \times 72 + c_4 = 0$$

$$0 = 74649.6P - 24883.2P + 72c_3 + c_4$$

$$\therefore 0 = 49766.4P + 72c_3 + c_4 \dots\dots\dots(1)$$

c) Now the two continuity conditions can be written as

$$y_B = y_1(x = 48) = y_2(x = 0)$$

$$0.1P48^3 + c_1 48 + \cancel{c_2} = 14.4P \times 0^2 - \frac{0.2P \times 0^3}{3} + c_3 \times 0 + c_4$$

$$11059.2P + 48c_1 = c_4 \dots\dots\dots(2)$$

$$y'_B = y'_1(x = 48) = y'_2(x = 0)$$

$$0.3P \times 48^2 + c_1 = 28.8P \times 0 - 0.2P \times 0^2 + c_3$$

$$c_1 = -691.2P + c_3 \dots\dots\dots(3)$$

Solve equations (1), (2) and (3) algebraically to get the constants as follows

$$c_1 = -403.2P \; k$$

$$c_2 = 0$$

$$c_3 = -288P \; k$$

$$c_4 = -20,736 \; k.in^3$$

Step 5: Write the final expression for the slope and deflection of the beam

Region AB $0 < x < 48$ *in*

$$y_1' = \frac{1}{EI}\left(0.3Px^2 - 403.2P\right)$$

$$y_1 = \frac{1}{EI}\left(0.1Px^3 - 403.2Px\right)$$

Region BC $0 < x < 72$ *in*

$$y_2' = \frac{1}{EI}\left(28.8Px - 0.2Px^2\right)$$

$$y_2 = \frac{1}{EI}\left(14.4Px^2 - \frac{0.2Px^3}{3} - 288Px - 20,736P\right)$$

Step 5: The deflection at B ($x=48$ *in*) in terms of moment of inertia and the elastic modulus are

$$y_B = \frac{1}{EI}\left(0.1P\times 48^3 - 403.2P\times 48\right) = -\frac{8,294.4P}{EI} \ in$$

Example 10.5: Deflection equations for multiple region problems

Problem Statement: A two span overhanging beam carrying a load of 10 k is shown in the figure. Determine the maximum deflection in the span and at the free end. Assume that the beam is made of a steel wide flange section W8 x 31, with a moment of inertia of 110 in^4.

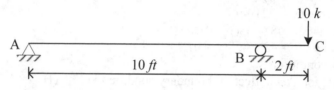

Required: To find the maximum deflection within the span region and at the free end.

Solution: In such a problem it is necessary to set up two different second order differential equations since the moment equations in regions AB and BC will be different. Consequently, the following two conditions are defined for the problem.

a)   Region AB has origin at A and has the limits $0<x<10$ *ft* and region BC has the origin at B and has the limits of $0<x<2$ *ft*.

b)   The deflection is represented by two different equations $y_1(x)$ in region AB and $y_2(x)$ in region BC

Step 1: Find reactions using the force and moment equilibrium equations.

$$\sum F_y = 0: A_y + B_y - 10\ k = 0$$

$$\sum M_A = 0:\ B_y(10\,ft) - 10\times(12\,ft) = 0$$

$$B_y = 12\ k \uparrow$$

$$\therefore A_y = 2\ k \downarrow$$

Step 2: Draw a free body diagram and find moment equation using the method of sections

$$\sum M_x = 0: 2x + M_1(x) = 0$$

$$\therefore M_1(x) = -2x \qquad 0 < x < 120\ in$$

$$\sum M_x = 0:$$

$$2(120 + x) - 12x + M_2(x) = 0$$

$$\therefore M_2(x) = -240 + 10x \qquad 0 < x < 24\ in$$

Step 3: Setup 2nd order equations for each region and integrate.

Region AB $0 < x < 120 in$

$EIy_1'' = M_1(x) = -2x$

Slope: $EIy_1' = -x^2 + c_1$ Eqn.(I)

Deflection: $EIy_1 = -\dfrac{x^3}{3} + c_1 x + c_2$ Eqn.(II)

Region BC $0 < x < 24 in$

$EIy_2'' = M_2(x) = 10x - 240$

Slope: $EIy_2' = 5x^2 - 240x + c_3$ Eqn.(III)

Deflection: $EIy_2 = \dfrac{5x^3}{3} - 120x^2 + c_3 x + c_4$ Eqn.(IV)

Step 4: Identify and apply boundary conditions and solve for c_1, c_2, c_3 and c_4. Four boundary conditions are needed.

a)   For span AB: $y_A = y_1(x = 0) = 0$
b)   For span BC: $y_B = y_1(x = 120) = 0$
c)   For span BC: $y_B = y_2(x = 0)$
d)   Continuity condition: $y'_B = y'_1(x = 120) = y'_2(x = 0)$

Apply the boundary conditions.

a) Substituting the region AB deflection boundary condition in Eqn.(I).

$\therefore EIy_1(x = 0) = -\dfrac{0^3}{3} + c_1 \times 0 + c_2 = 0$

$\therefore c_2 = 0 ....(1)$

b) Substituting the region AB deflection boundary condition in Eqn.(I).

$y_B = y_1(x = 120) = 0$

$-\dfrac{120^3}{3} + c_1 \times 120 + \cancel{c_2} = 0$

$\therefore c_1 = 4800 ....(2)$

c) Substituting the region BC deflection boundary condition in Eqn (IV).

$EIy_2(x = 0) = \dfrac{5 \times 0^3}{3} - 120 \times 0^2 + c_3 \times 0 + c_4 = 0$

$\therefore c_4 = 0 ....(3)$

d) Now the two continuity conditions can be written as

$y'_B = y'_1(x = 48) = y'_2(x = 0)$

$-120^2 + c_1 = 5 \times 0 - 240 \times 0 + c_3$

$\therefore c_3 = -9600 ....(4)$

Step 5: Find the slope and deflection equation.

Region AB $\left(0 < x < 120 \ in\right)$: $\ y_1 = \dfrac{1}{EI}\left(-\dfrac{x^3}{3} + 4800x\right)$

Region BC $\left(0 < x < 24 \ in\right)$: $\ y_2 = \dfrac{1}{EI}\left(\dfrac{5x^3}{3} - 120x^2 - 9600x\right)$

Step 6: Find some important slope and deflection values

$$EI = (29,000 \ ksi) \times (110 \ in^4) = 3,190,000 \ k.in^2$$

a) Deflection at C: $y_2 (x = 24 \ in)$

$$y_C = \frac{1}{EI} \left(\frac{5 \times 24^3}{3} - 120 \times 24^2 - 9600 \times 24 \right) = -\frac{276,480}{3,190,000} = -0.0866 \ in. = 0.866 \ in. \downarrow$$

b) Slope at A: $y_1' (x = 0 \ in)$

$$y_A' = \frac{1}{EI} \left(-0^2 + 4800 \right) = -\frac{4,800}{3,190,000} = -0.0015 \ rads$$

c) Slope at B: $y_1' (x = 120 \ in)$

$$y_B' = \frac{1}{EI} \left(-(120)^2 + 4800 \right) = -\frac{9,600}{3,190,000} = -0.003 \ rads$$

d) Maximum deflection:

  i) Find where the slope = 0

$$EIy_1' = \frac{1}{EI} \left(-x^2 + 4800 \right) = 0 \Rightarrow x = 69.28 \ in$$

  ii) Find the deflection at $x = 69.28 \ in.$

$$y_{max} = \frac{1}{EI} \left(-\frac{69.28^3}{3} + 4800 \times 69.28 \right) = -\frac{221,702}{3,190,000} = -0.07 \ in = 0.07 \ in \downarrow$$

10.6 Statically Indeterminate Beams

One of the major advantages of determining deflection by the methods described in this chapter is that, it lends itself to the determination of reactions of a statically indeterminate beam. This approach is a very elegant method for the determination of reactions of single span statically indeterminate beams. Consider a propped cantilever beam, as shown in Figure 10.4. The beam has one fixed support and a roller support. This results in four unknown reactions, three at the fixed end and one at the roller end, and three equilibrium equations. Hence, the beam is statically indeterminate of degree one.

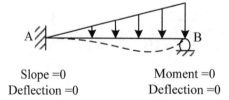

Slope =0   Moment =0
Deflection =0   Deflection =0

Figure 10.4: Propped cantilever beam and kinematic conditions

However, the deflected shape of the beam can be determined by using fourth order equations, since the distributed load function is known a-priori. The four constants of integration can be solved using four boundary conditions, as shown in Figure 10.4. Once the constants of integration are determined, the reactions are found by finding the boundary values of shear and moments from the third and second order equations. The following section illustrates the procedure described above in detail. Both, second and fourth order approaches can be used in the solution process.

10.7 Determination of Reactions of Statically Indeterminate Beams

The fourth order approach is illustrated in the determination of various kinetic and kinematic quantities. Consider a propped cantilever beam as shown in Figure 10.4 and subjected to a triangular load as shown.

Fourth Order Approach: The kinetic unknowns required are the reactions, both moment and force reactions at the fixed support A and the force reactions at the roller support B. The kinematic quantities determined are the slope at the pin support B and the location and value of maximum deflection.

Step 1: Determine the equation for the distributed load.

Since this is a triangular distributed load acting downwards this equation is $w(x) = -wx/L$ ($w=0$ at $x = 0$ and $w=-w$ at $x =L$)

Step 2: Integrate this equation four times and set up the constants of integration.

$$EI_{NA}\frac{d^4y}{dx^4} = -wx/L$$

$$EI_{NA}\frac{d^3y}{dx^3} = -\frac{wx^2}{2L} + C_1$$

$$EI_{NA}\frac{d^2y}{dx^2} = -\frac{wx^3}{6L} + C_1x + C_2$$

$$EI_{NA}\frac{dy}{dx} = -\frac{wx^4}{24L} + C_1\frac{x^2}{2} + C_2x + C_3$$

$$EI_{NA}y = -\frac{wx^5}{120L} + C_1\frac{x^3}{6} + C_2\frac{x^2}{2} + C_3x + C_4$$

Step 3: Determine and apply the boundary conditions.

As this is a propped cantilever beam, the deflection and the slope is zero at the fixed end while the deflection and the moment is zero at the pin end B as shown in Figure 10.4. Hence, the boundary conditions are

$$y_A = y(x = 0) = 0$$
$$y'_B = y'(x = 0) = 0$$
$$y_B = EIy_B(x = L) = 0$$
$$M_B = EIy''_B(x = L) = 0$$

To find the integration constant, apply these boundary conditions to the equations above.

$$y(x = 0) = 0$$

$$EI_{NA}y = -\frac{w0^4}{120L} + C_1\frac{0^3}{6} + C_2\frac{0^2}{2} + C_3 0 + C_4 = 0 \Rightarrow C_4 = 0$$

$$EIy'_A(x = 0) = 0$$

$$EI_{NA}\frac{dy}{dx} = -\frac{w0^3}{24L} + C_1 0 + C_2 0 + C_3 = 0 \Rightarrow C_3 = 0$$

$$EIy''_B(x = L) = 0$$

$$EI_{NA}\frac{d^2y}{dx^2} = -\frac{wL^3}{6L} + C_1L + C_2 = 0$$

$$EIy_B(x=L)=0$$

$$EI_{NA}y = -\frac{wL^5}{120L} + C_1\frac{L^3}{6} + C_2\frac{L^2}{2} = 0$$

gives two equations in C_1 and C_2 which, along with the solution, are shown below.

$$C_1 L + C_2 = \frac{wL^2}{6}$$

$$C_1\frac{L}{6} + C_2/2 = \frac{wL^2}{120}$$

gives

$$C_1 = \frac{9wL}{40}$$

$$C_2 = -\frac{7wL^2}{120}$$

The deflection equation or the elastic curve equation now reduces to

$$EI_{NA}y = -\frac{wx^5}{120L} + \frac{9wLx^3}{40} - \frac{7wL^2x^2}{120}$$

$$y = \frac{w}{120EI_{NA}L}\left[-x^5 + 27L^2x^3 - 7L^3x^2\right]$$

Reactions at A: The reactions are determined by finding the moment and shear values from the differential equation forms shown above. They are as follows

$$R_A = EI_{NA}\frac{d^3y}{dx^3}\bigg|_{x=0} = -\frac{w\times 0^2}{2L} + \frac{9wL}{40} = +\frac{9wL}{40}\uparrow$$

$$M_A = EI_{NA}\frac{d^2y}{dx^2}\bigg|_{x=0} = -\frac{w\times 0^3}{6L} + \frac{9w\times 0}{40} - \frac{7wL^2}{120} = -\frac{7wL^2}{120}\text{(Negative sign} - CCW)$$

Reaction at B: There is only a force reaction at B which is determined by using the expression for shear at $x=L$.

$$R_B = EI_{NA}\frac{d^3y}{dx^3}\bigg|_{x=L} = -\frac{wL^2}{2L} + \frac{9wL}{40} = -\frac{11wL}{40} = \frac{11wL}{40}\uparrow$$

Note: On the right hand side a negative sign for the force reaction indicates an upward force since shear is positive when acting downwards on the right hand side.

Maximum value of deflection: The maximum value of deflection occurs at points, within a span, where the slope is zero. In the above example, the slope is zero at

$$EI_{NA}\frac{dy}{dx} = -\frac{wx^4}{24L} + C_1\frac{x^2}{2} + C_2 x = 0$$

or

$$-\frac{wx^3}{24} + \frac{9wL}{40}\frac{x^2}{2} - \frac{7wL^2}{120}x = 0$$

This equation can be solved to find the x value at which the slope is zero. Substituting the value of x just derived in the deflection equation, the maximum deflection for a propped cantilever beam subjected to a uniformly distributed load can be found.

It has thus been shown that without using equations of static equilibrium the moment and shear reactions of indeterminate structures can be determined by the differential equation methods.

Example 10.6: Finding reactions for a statically indeterminate beam.

Problem Statement: A beam which is fixed at both the ends is subjected to triangular loading as shown in figure.

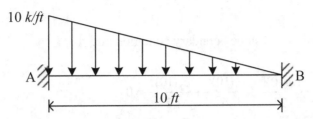

Required: Find reactions at A and B using 4th order method.

Solution:

Step 1: Find load function.

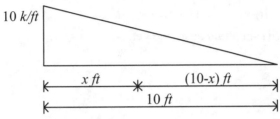

$\therefore W(x) = -(10-x)$

$\therefore W(x) = x-10$

Step 2: Setup 4th order equation and integrate.

$EIy'''' = x-10$

$$EIy''' = V = \frac{x^2}{2} - 10x + c_1 \qquad\qquad \text{Eqn(I)}$$

$$EIy'' = M = \frac{x^3}{6} - \frac{10x^2}{2} + c_1 x + c_2 \qquad\qquad \text{Eqn(II)}$$

$$\text{Slope: } EIy' = \frac{x^4}{24} - \frac{10x^3}{6} + \frac{c_1 x^2}{2} + c_2 x + c_3 \qquad\qquad \text{Eqn(III)}$$

$$\text{Deflection: } EIy = \frac{x^5}{120} - \frac{10x^4}{24} + \frac{c_1 x^3}{6} + \frac{c_2 x^2}{2} + c_3 x + c_4 \qquad \text{Eqn(IV)}$$

Step 3: Apply boundary conditions and solve for c_1, c_2, c_3 and c_4.

<table>
<tr><td>x=0</td><td>x=10</td></tr>
<tr><td>Deflection =0</td><td>Deflection =0</td></tr>
<tr><td>Slope =0</td><td>Slope =0</td></tr>
</table>

Substituting the deflection and slope boundary condition at $x=0$.

At $x = 0$, Deflection $= 0$

$$\therefore EIy(x=0) = \frac{0^5}{120} - \frac{10 \times 0^4}{24} + \frac{c_1 \times 0^3}{6} + \frac{c_2 \times 0^2}{2} + c_3 \times 0 + c_4 = 0$$

$$\therefore c_4 = 0$$

At $x = 0$, Slope $= 0$

$\therefore EIy'(x=0) = \dfrac{0^4}{24} - \dfrac{10 \times 0^3}{6} + \dfrac{c_1 \times 0^2}{2} + c_2 \times 0 + c_3 = 0$

$\therefore c_3 = 0$

Substituting the deflection and slope boundary condition at $x=10$.

At $x = 10$, Deflection $= 0$

$\therefore EIy(x=10) = \dfrac{(10)^5}{120} - \dfrac{10(10)^4}{24} + \dfrac{c_1(10)^3}{6} + \dfrac{c_2(10)^2}{2} = 0$

$\therefore 166.67c_1 + 50c_2 = 3333.33 \ldots\ldots\ldots(i)$

At $x = 10$, Slope $= 0$

$\therefore EIy'(x=10) = \dfrac{(10)^4}{24} - \dfrac{10(10)^3}{6} + \dfrac{c_1(10)^2}{2} + c_2(10) = 0$

$\therefore 50c_1 + 10c_2 = 1250 \ldots\ldots\ldots(ii)$

Solving equation (i) and (ii) simultaneously we get,

$c_1 = 35$

and

$c_2 = -50$

Step 4: Find reaction at A and B.

Substituting the value of integration constants in the shear and moment equation we have,

$V = \dfrac{x^2}{2} - 10x + 35$

$M = \dfrac{x^3}{6} - \dfrac{10x^2}{2} + 35x - 50$

To find reaction and moment at A substitute $x=0$ and $x=10$ to find reaction and moment at B.

$V_A = \dfrac{0^2}{2} - 10 \times 0 + 35$

$\therefore V_A = 35 \ k$

$M_A = \dfrac{0^3}{6} - \dfrac{10 \times 0^2}{2} + 35 \times 0 - 50$

$\therefore M_A = -50 \ k.ft$

$V_B = \dfrac{10^2}{2} - 10 \times 10 + 35$

$\therefore V_B = -15 \ k$

$M_B = \dfrac{10^3}{6} - \dfrac{10 \times 10^2}{2} + 35 \times 10 - 50$

$\therefore M_B = -33.33 \ k.ft$

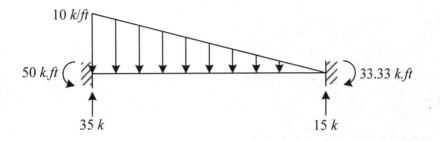

10.8 Method of Superposition

It can be seen that the computation of deflections and slope by the integration method can be fairly involved, mathematically, even for the simpler cases. In practice, it is often not feasible to go through the integration methods to try to estimate deflections involving more complex loading sets.

In order to calculate deflections and slopes, using some of the basic cases derived, the *principle of superposition* is used. The principle is based on the assumption that the beam behavior is in the elastic range due to applied loads. The elastic behavior assumption allows the treatment of multiple loads on a beam as separate and simpler entities. The deflections corresponding to each of the individual cases are then added to get the final deflection or slope.

In order to apply the principle of superposition, as table outlining the standard slopes and deflections is needed.

	θ_A	θ_B	Δ_{max}
	0	$\dfrac{wL^3}{24EI}$	$-\dfrac{5wL^4}{384EI}$
	0	$-\dfrac{wL^3}{6EI}$	$-\dfrac{wL^4}{8EI}$
	$-\dfrac{PL^3}{16EI}$	$\dfrac{PL^3}{16EI}$	$-\dfrac{PL^3}{48EI}$
	0	$-\dfrac{PL^2}{2EI}$	$-\dfrac{PL^3}{3EI}$

	0	$-\dfrac{ML}{2EI}$	$-\dfrac{ML^2}{2EI}$
	0	$-\dfrac{wL^3}{24EI}$	$-\dfrac{wL^4}{30EI}$

Example 10.7: Finding deflections and slopes using tables and geometric considerations

Problem Statement: A cantilever beam is partially loaded with a uniformly distributed load of 2 *k/ft.* as shown in the figure. Determine the slope and deflection at the free end using the tables. Assume that the beam is a wide flange steel section W8 x 15 with a moment of inertia of 48 in^4.

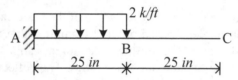

Required: Find slope and deflection at C

Solution:

Step 1: As the beam is partially loaded, up to point B, determine the slope and deflection at B using the tabulated values for point B, L=25 *in* & $EI = (29,000\,ksi)\times(48\,in^4) = 1,392,000\,k.in^2$

$$\theta_B = -\frac{wl^3}{6EI} = -\frac{\left(\frac{2}{12}\,k/in\right)(25\,in)^3}{6EI} = -\frac{2,604\,k.in^2}{6\times1,392,000\,k.in^2} = -0.0003\,rads = 0.0003\,rad\,CW$$

$$\Delta_B = -\frac{wl^4}{8EI} = -\frac{\left(\frac{2}{12}\,k/in\right)(25in)^4}{8EI} = -\frac{31,248\,k.in^3}{8\times1,392,000\,k.in^2} = -0.002\,in$$

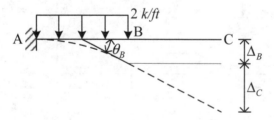

Step 2: The slope and deflection at C are found from geometry as follows
Slope at C = Slope at B (since the deflected shape is a straight line)
$\therefore \theta_c = 0.003\,rad\,CW$
$\Delta_C = \Delta_B + \theta_B \times L_{BC}$
$\Delta_C = -0.002\,in. - 0.003\times25\,in = -0.077\,in.$

10.9 Summary

This chapter has discussed the theory behind the deflection of beams. The relationship between the geometric relating deflection and curvature to moment equilibrium results in second and fourth order form of linear first order homogeneous differential equations. The highlights of each form are outlined below.

a. Second order form: The second derivative of the deflection equation is related to the bending moment equation. The solution of this form needs two kinematic boundary conditions.

$$EI_{NA}\frac{d^2y}{dx^2} = M(x)$$

b. Fourth order form: The fourth derivative of the deflection equation is related to the distributed loading function. The solution of this form needs two kinematic and two kinetic boundary conditions.

$$EI_{NA}\frac{d^4y}{dx^4} = w(x)$$

The keywords introduced in this chapter are as follows.

1. **Boundary conditions:** The type of support conditions that a beam is built with. The types of supports are a fixed type, pinned type, free etc.
2. **Design for Stiffness:** The criterion involved in the design for stiffness in a beam is that the maximum deflection should be less than some specified value.
3. **Flexural Rigidity:** The term EI_{NA} is called the *flexural rigidity* of the beam.

10.10 Problems:

10.1 Determine the maximum slope and deflection for the simply supported beam of length 6 *ft* subjected to a point load of 9 *kips* at a distance of 4 *ft* from end A.

10.2 Determine the maximum slope and deflection for a simply supported beam spanning 4 *m* subjected to a uniformly distributed load of 8 *kN/m*.

10.3 Determine the maximum slope and deflection in a simply supported beam subjected to a UDL and a point load as shown in figure below.

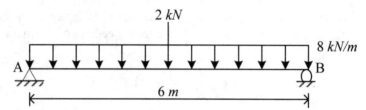

10.4 A simply supported beam is subjected to a triangular loading as shown in figures below. Find maximum slope and deflection for this beam.

a.

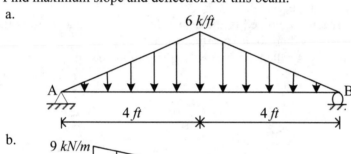

b.

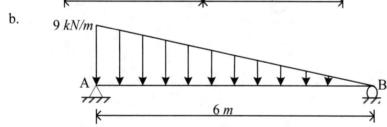

10.5 A simply supported beam of length 5 *ft*, is subjected to a UDL of 5 *k/ft* and an external moment of 10 *k.ft* at the end B. Find the maximum deflection that occurs in this beam.

10.6 A simply supported beam as shown in the problem 10.3 is subjected to an additional moment of 15 *kN.m* at end B. Find the maximum slope and deflection in the beam.

10.7 For the cantilever beam as shown below, find maximum slope and deflection.

a.

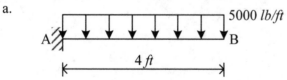

b.

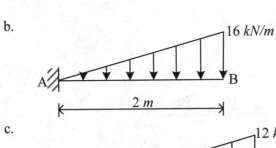

c.

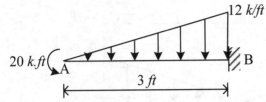

d.

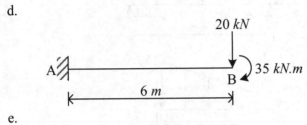

e.

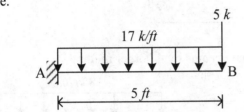

10.8 Determine the maximum slope and deflection in the beams shown below.

a.

b.

c.

d.

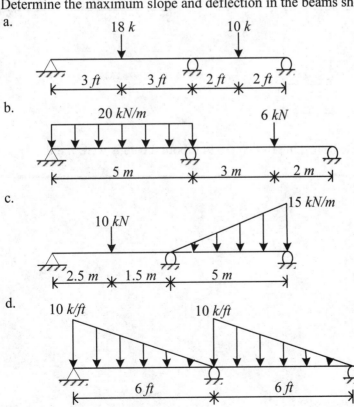

e.

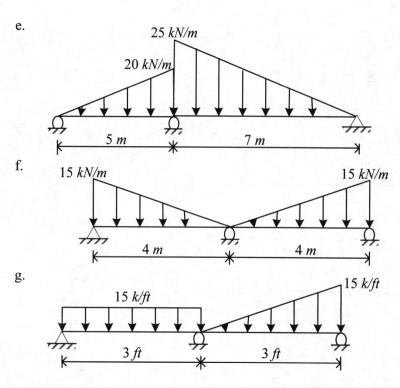

f.

g.

10.9 Determine the reactions for the indeterminate beams by 4th order method.

a.   b.

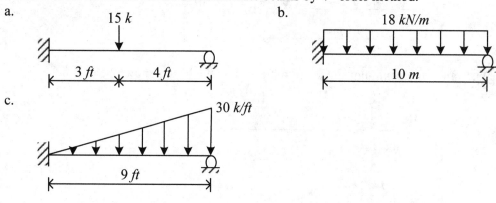

c.

10.10 Determine reactions of the beams in problem 10.9, if both the ends were fixed.

Chapter 11

Stability of Structures

Goal: The learning objectives of this chapter are as follows:

1. Introduce the concept of compression failure and buckling failure
2. Derive and apply the basic equations for buckling
3. Discuss the effect of slenderness ratio and effective length factor on buckling
4. Apply the concepts of buckling to some basic problems
5. Introduce the concept of eccentric loading in buckling problems

11 Stability of Structures

11.1 Introduction

The three criteria for designing any structure, namely the three *S*'s (*strength, stiffness* and *stability*), have been outlined in chapter 1. Two of these criteria, strength and stiffness, have been extensively discussed in the previous chapters. The strength criterion implies that the actual stresses remain below the allowable stress values while the stiffness criterion implies that the deflection or elongation in a structure remains less than some specified value.

The *stability* criterion is now considered and discussed in this chapter. Stability is a criterion that is usually associated with members in axial compression. The failure of compression members can occur in two ways:
1. Axial crushing or Compression failure
2. Buckling or Stability failure

Consider a bar made of a rectangular cross section, with an area A, as shown in Figure 11.1. The bar is subjected to an axial compression force. An axial compression force is defined as a force that passes through the line joining the centroid of the two end areas.

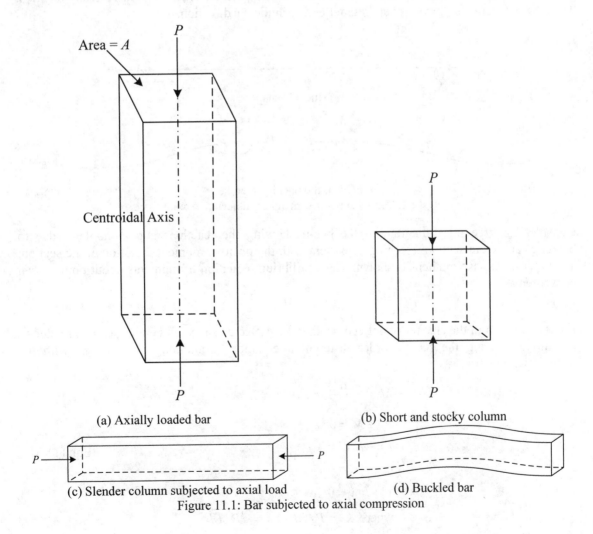

(a) Axially loaded bar

(b) Short and stocky column

(c) Slender column subjected to axial load

(d) Buckled bar

Figure 11.1: Bar subjected to axial compression

If the allowable stress in the material, in compression, is $\sigma_{all.} = 20\ ksi$ and the bar has a cross section area of $1\ in^2$, the load required to cause crushing or a compression failure is given as:

$$P = \sigma_{all.} A = (20\ ksi)(1\ in^2) = 20\ kips \qquad \text{Eqn (11.1)}$$

Such a failure would occur in a short and stocky column as shown in Figure 11.1(b). However, if the member is slender, as shown in Figure 11.1(c), the same structure will not be able resist the full force of 20 *kips* and will *buckle* or bend out of plane well before this load is reached as shown in Figure 11.1(d). Slenderness of a member is a combination of the cross section area (usually if the area is small) and the length of the member (usually if it is long). The phenomenon of buckling, occurring due to an internal instability, is a bending phenomenon.

Buckling or instability in general, is a rapid phenomenon. Failure due to this mode can be very catastrophic and hence must be carefully considered for all compression members. Buckling occurs in slender members when subjected to compression.

11.2 Euler Buckling Load and Buckling Stress

It has been seen that buckling of a compression member is a form of bending. Using this observation the load required to cause buckling is now derived. Figure 11.2 shows a member, which is simply supported and subjected to an axial compressive load P and has already buckled. The buckled shape is shown as bending/deflection in the $+y$ direction.

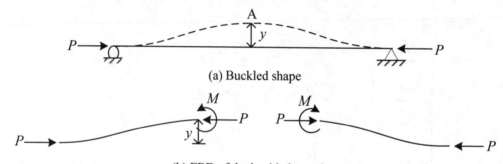

(a) Buckled shape

(b) FBD of the buckled member

Figure 11.2: Simply supported member subjected to axial force

Consider the free body diagram of the beam showing the reactions and a moment (due to bending) at the cut section. Keeping consistent with the positive moment direction at the section, a counter clockwise moment is shown. The equilibrium equation of moments about point A can be written as

$$Py + M = 0 \qquad \text{Eqn (11.2)}$$

It has been seen in the chapter of deflections that the deflected shape on bending can be related to the moment using the second order differential equation. Combining the concept with the differential equation

$$M = EI\frac{d^2 y}{dx^2} = EIy''$$

$$Py + M = 0$$

$$Py + EIy'' = 0 \qquad \text{Eqn (11.3)}$$

or

$$y'' + k^2 y = 0$$

where, $k^2 = P/EI$ or $k = \sqrt{P/EI}$

The equilibrium equation thus reduces to a differential equation form. Specifically, this differential equation is a simple harmonic equation and can be classified as a
1. linear (no powers of the derivative)
2. second order (order of the highest derivative)
3. homogeneous (right hand side of the equation is zero).

Important: The reader is alerted here to the concept that equilibrium equations can often be expressed as differential equations in many engineering problems. This is the first such example presented in this book. The student has usually seen equilibrium equations expressed as a combination of linear algebraic equations before.

The general solution to this second order differential equation, which might also be recognized as a form similar to the one encountered in simple harmonic problems in physics, can be written as follows

$$y = A\cos kx + B\sin kx \qquad\text{Eqn (11.4)}$$

where A and B are constants that must be determined using the boundary conditions of the problem.

Determination of Constants: The constants are determined from the deflection boundary conditions corresponding to the simply supported beam (the reader is reminded that in chapter of deflections only slope and deflection conditions are considered for second order differential equations).

$$y(x=0) = 0$$
$$y(x=l) = 0 \qquad\text{Eqn (11.5)}$$

Substituting these in the deflection equation

$$y(x=0) = A\cos(0) + B\sin(0) => A = 0$$
$$y(x=l) = B\sin(kl) \qquad\text{Eqn (11.6)}$$

The second boundary condition at ($x=l$) gives two possibilities
a) $B = 0$: This, of course, gives no solution but represents the physical condition of 'axial compression or crushing' failure, as it implies that the deflection is always zero or there is no bending.
b) $sin(kl) = 0$: This condition represents the solution of what is referred to as an eigen value problem and the solution represents a set of eigen values. There are infinite solutions to this equation and is represented as follows

$$\sin(kl) = \sin(n\pi) = 0$$
$$kl = n\pi \qquad\text{Eqn (11.7)}$$
$$k = \frac{n\pi}{l} \text{ for } n = 1,2,3,...,n$$

From the condition representing $k = n\pi/l$ the value of the axial load can be shown to be

$$k = \sqrt{\frac{P}{EI}} = \frac{n\pi}{l}$$
$$\qquad\text{Eqn (11.8)}$$
$$P = \frac{n^2\pi^2 EI}{l^2}$$

Physical Meaning of the Solution: The physical meaning of the 'n' solution values of P can be demonstrated by drawing the deflected shape corresponding to each value of 'n'. The axial load required to cause buckling for values of $n=1, 2, 3$ and the corresponding deflected shapes are shown in Figure 11.3 and also given below

$$P_1(n=1) = \frac{\pi^2 EI}{L^2}$$

$$P_2(n=2) = \frac{4\pi^2 EI}{L^2}$$ Eqn (11.9)

$$P_3(n=3) = \frac{9\pi^2 EI}{L^2}$$

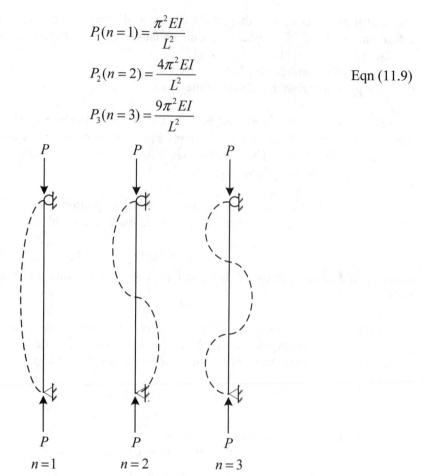

Figure 11.3: Deflected shapes for different n values of axial load

11.2.1   Euler Buckling Load and its Physical Significance

The deflected shape for $n=1$ shows one half sine wave, while that for $n=2$ and 3 show two and three half waves respectively. The axial loads required to cause the deflected shapes of modes two and three are four and nine times the axial load required corresponding to $n=1$. In practice, as the load on a compression member is gradually increased the member will buckle at the load

P_1. This load is called the *Euler Buckling Load* $\left(P_{Euler} = P_{critical} = P_{cr} = \dfrac{\pi^2 EI}{L^2} \right)$ and is named after

Leonhard Euler who derived this equation in 1744.

Generalized Form of Euler Buckling Load: The generalized form of the *Euler Buckling Load,* P_{cr} for any arbitrary cross section shape is given as

$$P_{cr} = \frac{\pi^2 EI_{min.}}{(L_{eff.})^2} = \frac{\pi^2 EI_{min.}}{(kL)^2}$$ Eqn (11.10)

where, E is the elastic (Young's) modulus of the material, $I_{min.}$ is the minimum principal moment of inertia of the cross section, $L_{eff.}$ is the effective length of the compression member and k is known as the effective length factor. The significance of each of the terms just described is given below.

Minimum Principal Moment of Inertia (I_{min}): The choice of I_{min} to represent the moment of inertia term physically represents the tendency of the member to buckle and bend about its *weakest bending axis*. As the member is free to buckle about any *centroidal axis*, it will bend first about its weakest centroidal axis whose moment of inertia value is represented by I_{min}. Figure 11.4 illustrates the reason behind this choice.

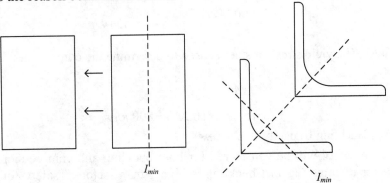

Figure 11.4: Physical justification for the choice of I_{min} based on displaced configuration

Effective Length ($L_{eff.}$): The effective length of the member, also defined as kL where k is the effective length factor and L the unsupported length, is the length to be used in the buckling load calculations. The effective length can be less or more than the actual length based on the type of supports at the ends of the members. For simply supported ends (pin at one end and a roller at the other end) the effective length is equal to the unsupported length. Examples for other support types are presented later in this chapter.

As a basic example, consider a compression member, simply supported at the two ends. It is required to find the axial load that the member can withstand in compression. The material is made of steel $\left(E = 29,000\ ksi, f_y = 50\ ksi \right)$. The cross section details are shown in Figure 11.5.

The axial load required to cause Euler buckling and axial compression is found and the least of the two values represents the axial load that the member can take.

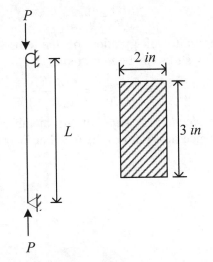

Figure 11.5: Compression member details

Buckling Load: The axial capacity required to cause buckling is given as follows

$$I_{min.} = \frac{hb^3}{12} = \frac{8(2)^3}{12} = 5.33 \ in^4$$

$$L_{eff.} = 60 \ in.$$

$$P_{cr} = \frac{\pi^2 (29,000 \ ksi)(5.33 \ in^4)}{(60 \ in)^2} = 424 \ kips$$

Compressive Load: The yield stress of steel is used to determine the compression load that the member can take.

$$P_{comp.} = f_y A$$

$$= (50 \ ksi)(16 \ in^2) = 800 \ kips$$

Buckling Governs: Buckling Capacity = 424 *kips*

In practice, factor of safety will be considered for both buckling and compression. It should be noted that the factor of safety against buckling is higher than factor of safety for compression. However, in this example it can be seen that the buckling load can be significantly lower than the compression capacity of the member. As the length of the member increases, the axial capacity of the member decreases. The axial capacity can never exceed the compression capacity of the member and hence in a good design the aim should be to achieve a capacity as close to the member compression capacity.

11.2.2 Critical Buckling Stress

The allowable or the maximum stress that a member subjected to axial compression can take is a variable quantity that depends on many factors. This limiting stress value is called the *Euler Critical Buckling Stress (f_{cr})* and is computed as shown below.

$$f_{cr} = \frac{P_{cr}}{A} = \frac{\pi^2 EI_{min.}}{(kL)^2} \frac{1}{A} \qquad \text{Eqn (11.11)}$$

From statics it is known that

$$r_{min.} = \sqrt{\frac{I_{min.}}{A}} \qquad \text{Eqn (11.12)}$$

where r_{min} is the minimum radius of gyration of the cross-section. Hence, the equation representing the critical buckling stress can be rewritten as

$$f_{cr} = \frac{\pi^2 E r_{min.}^2}{(kL)^2} = \frac{\pi^2 E}{(kL/r_{min.})^2} \qquad \text{Eqn (11.13)}$$

where *(kL/r_{min})* is called the *slenderness ratio* of the member. In theory this equation is a hyperbolic equation. As the slenderness ratio of the member increases the critical buckling stress decreases exponentially.

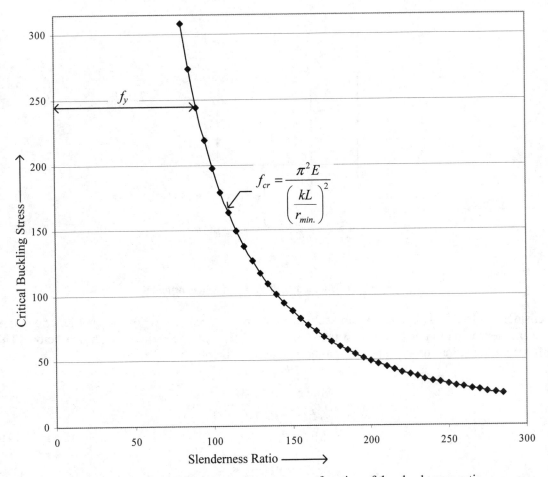

Figure 11.6: Allowable compressive stress as a function of the slenderness ratio

Figure 11.6 shows a plot of the critical buckling stress as a function of the slenderness ratio. It should be kept in mind that the maximum allowable stress in a material that is in the elastic range is the yield stress, which can never be exceeded. This criterion is shown in Figure 11.6 as the flat horizontal cut off line. From Figure 11.6 it can be seen that at low slenderness ratio values the yield stress governs while the buckling stress governs as the slenderness ratio increases.

11.3 Boundary Conditions

The derivations shown so far involved only pin and roller ended boundary conditions. There are numerous other boundary types, which affect the effective length in the Euler buckling load and stress calculations. The theoretical effective length can be mathematically computed in some cases. One such example is given below.

Fixed-Free Boundary Condition: Consider a cantilever with one fixed end and the other free end, as shown in Figure 11.7 subjected to an axial load *P*. The effective length of a cantilever column subjected to an axial load is derived below. It has been seen in chapter 10 that the fixed end restrains both the deflection and the slope while the free end has non zero values for both deflection and slope.

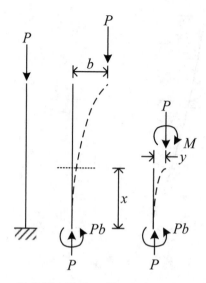

Figure 11.7: Buckled configuration of a cantilever

Consider the free body of the bottom section, as shown in Figure 11.7, of the cantilever column. The moment equation at the section taken at a distance x can be written as shown below. The differential equation for the cantilever column is derived below.

$$M - Pb + Py = 0$$

Since, $EIy'' = M$

$$\therefore EIy'' - Pb + Py = 0$$

$$EIy'' + Py = Pb \qquad \text{Eqn (11.14)}$$

$$y'' + \frac{P}{EI}y = \frac{P}{EI}b$$

$$y'' + k^2 y = k^2 b$$

where $k^2 = \sqrt{\dfrac{P}{EI}}$. The differential equation is classified as a second order, linear and non-homogeneous differential equation. The solution to this equation has a homogeneous and a particular form as shown below

$$y = y_h + y_p$$

$$y_h = A\cos(kx) + B\sin(kx)$$

$$y_p = b \qquad \text{Eqn (11.15)}$$

$$\therefore y = A\cos(kx) + B\sin(kx) + b$$

Applying the boundary condition for a fixed end

$$y(x=0) = 0 \Rightarrow 0 = A\cos(0) + B\sin(0) + b \Rightarrow A = -b$$

$$y'(x=0) = 0 \Rightarrow 0 = B$$

The solution of the differential equation is now rewritten and the deflection condition of $(x = l, y = b)$ is applied as shown below to get

$$y = -b\cos kx + b$$
$$(x = l, y = b) \text{ gives}$$
$$b = -b\cos kl + b$$
$$\therefore 0 = -b\cos(kl)$$

Eqn (11.16)

$$\cos(kl) = 0 \quad \text{when} \quad kl = \frac{n\pi}{2} \quad \text{for } n = 1, 2, 3, \dots.$$

Consider the basic case for $n = 1$. The condition results in

$$kL = \pi/2$$

$$\sqrt{\frac{P}{EI}} = \pi/2$$

Eqn (11.17)

$$P = \frac{\pi^2 EI}{4L^2} = \frac{\pi^2 EI}{(2L)^2} = \frac{\pi^2 EI}{(kL)^2}$$

The last equation in the denominator indicates that the effective length $L_{eff} = 2L$.

Physical meaning of the effective length: Consider the two cases for which the effective lengths have been derived so far. Figure 11.8 shows the deflected shapes of the two end types.

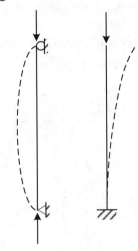

Figure 11.8: Pin-Pin and Fixed-Free Boundary condition

For the pin-pin end condition the effective length equals to L, which is also the nearest distance between points of zero moments in the column. Hence, the effective length can be determined from the deflected shape of a column with other kinds of boundaries by determining the distance between two adjacent zero moment locations. For the cantilever case (Figure 11.8) if a mirror image of the deflected shape is considered it can be seen that the points of zero moments are $2L$ apart. Figure 11.9 shows the effective length of column with different types of boundary conditions.

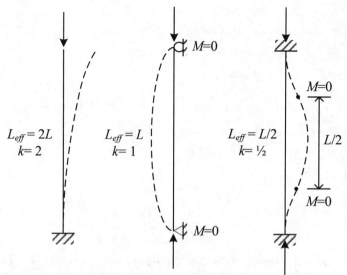

Figure 11.9: Different boundary conditions

Minimum Principal Moment of Inertia: The minimum principal moment of inertia is used for the computations of the Euler buckling load and buckling stress calculations. This concept has been discussed in detail in statics and some of the salient points are briefly summarized here.

In general, any area as shown in Figure 11.10 has a moment of inertia I_x and I_y about any specified axes. It has also another inertia terms called the Product of Inertia I_{xy}. The principal axes are those axes (x', y') about which the product of inertia $I_{x'y'}=0$. The minimum and maximum moment of inertia are determined as

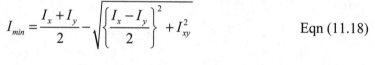

$$I_{min} = \frac{I_x + I_y}{2} - \sqrt{\left\{\frac{I_x - I_y}{2}\right\}^2 + I_{xy}^2}$$

Eqn (11.18)

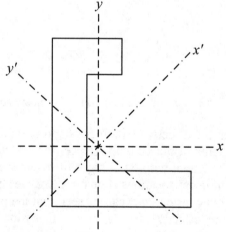

Figure 11.10: Different axis of symmetry

Axes of Symmetry: If the area is symmetric about either one or both axes then the product of inertia about those axes is zero. Consequently, the axes are the principal axes and the axis with a lower value of the moment of inertia represents I_{min}. The calculation of I_{min} is illustrated in the following examples.

Example 11.1: Basic Buckling Problem

Problem Statement: Find the shortest length for which the column with section properties shown in the figure will begin to buckle.

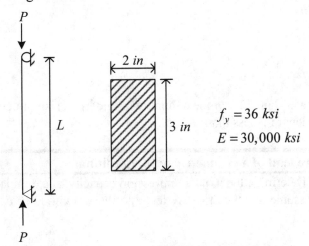

$f_y = 36\ ksi$

$E = 30,000\ ksi$

Required: To find shortest length.

Solution:

Strategy: As the length of the column increases the tendency to buckle increases. The shortest length of the column at which buckling starts is when the Euler critical buckling stress equals the allowable stress in yielding. In this problem the factor of safety against either buckling or yielding is not considered. Generally, the two factors of safety are different.

Step 1: Determine the cross section properties I_{min} and r_{min}

$$I_x = \frac{1}{12} 2 \times 3^3 = 4.5\ in^4$$

$$I_y = \frac{1}{12} 3 \times 2^3 = 2\ in^4$$

$$\therefore I_{min} = I_y = 2\ in^4$$

$$A = 2 \times 3 = 6\ in^2$$

$$r_{min} = \sqrt{I_{min}/A} = \sqrt{2/6} = \sqrt{1/3}\ in$$

Here since the section is symmetric, I_x and I_y represent the centroidal and principal moments of inertia.

Step 2: Determine the Euler buckling stress using the elastic buckling stress equation and equate it to the yield stress in order to determine the length at which the buckling will begin. As the column is pin ended $L_{eff}=L$.

$$f_y = f_{cr} = \frac{\pi^2 E}{\left(L_{eff.}/r_{min.}\right)^2}$$

$$36\ ksi = \frac{\pi^2 (30,000\ ksi)}{\left(L/1/\sqrt{3}\right)^2}$$

or

$L = 52.3\ in.$

Or, if the length is greater than 52.3 *in* the column will undergo elastic buckling. The column will fail by crushing if the length is less than 52.3 *in*.

Example 11.2: Failure load of a symmetric built up column

Problem Statement: Determine the axial compression capacity of a double angle column as shown in the figure. Assume that the effective length of the column is 10 *ft*.

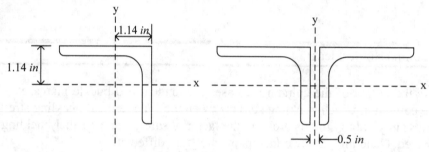

$f_y = 36\ ksi;\ E = 29,000\ ksi;\ A = 2.86\ in^2;\ I_x = I_y = 4.36\ in^4;\ r_x = r_y = 1.23\ in$

Required: To find axial compression capacity of a double angle column

Solution:

Step 1: Determine the minimum principal centroidal moment of inertia of the double angle section.

a) Locate the centroid of the cross section
   - Due to symmetry the y-centroidal axis is at the middle of the two angles as shown
   - The x-centroidal axis of the double angle corresponds to the x-centroidal axis of each column as shown

b) As the double angle has one centroidal axis of symmetry (y-axis), the product of inertia $I_{xy}=0$. Hence, the minimum of the centroidal moments of inertia represents $I_{min.}$

$I_x = 2I_{xx} = 2 \times 4.36 = 8.72\ in^4$

$I_y = \overline{I}_{yy} + Ad^2$

$d = 1.14 + 0.25 = 1.39\ in$

$A = 2.86\ in^2$

$\overline{I}_{yy} = 4.36\ in^4$

$I_y = 2\left[4.36 + 2.86 \times 1.39^2\right] = 19.77\ in^2$

Hence $I_y = I_{max} = 19.77\ in^4$ and $I_x = I_{min} = 8.72\ in^4$

$r_{min} = \sqrt{I_{min}/A} = \sqrt{8.72/(2 \times 2.86)} = 1.23\ in$

Step 2: Determine the Euler buckling stress using the elastic buckling stress equation.

$$f_{cr} = \frac{\pi^2 E}{\left(L_{eff.}/r_{min.}\right)^2}$$

$$= \frac{\pi^2 (29,000 \ ksi)}{\left(120 \ in/1.23 \ in\right)^2}$$

$$f_{cr} = 30 \ ksi$$

Step 3: Assuming that the factors of safety against buckling and yielding are 1.5 and 2.25 respectively (in general the factor of safety against buckling will be higher than that in yielding), determine the failure capacity

Allowable compression capacity in compression and buckling are

$$P_{comp} = \frac{f_y A}{1.5} = \frac{36 \ ksi \times 2 \times 2.86 \ in^2}{1.5} = 137.3 \ kips$$

$$P_{cr} = \frac{f_{cr} A}{2.25} = \frac{30 \ ksi \times 2 \times 2.86 \ in^2}{2.25} = 76.3 \ kips$$

As the buckling load is lower than the compression load, buckling governs. $P_{all} = 76.3 \ kips$.

Example 11.3: Failure load of a unsymmetric built up column

Problem Statement: Determine the axial compression capacity of the single angle column as shown in the figure. Assume that the effective length of the column is 10 ft.

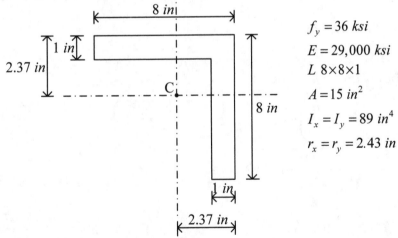

$$f_y = 36 \ ksi$$
$$E = 29,000 \ ksi$$
$$L \ 8 \times 8 \times 1$$
$$A = 15 \ in^2$$
$$I_x = I_y = 89 \ in^4$$
$$r_x = r_y = 2.43 \ in$$

Required: To find axial compression capacity

Solution:

Step 1: Determine the minimum principal centroidal moment of inertia of the single angle section.

The centroidal axis of the column is at 2.37 in. from each edge as shown in the figure as the single angle is not symmetric about the centroidal axis, the product of inertia $I_{xy} \neq 0$. Hence, the product of inertia and the centroidal principal moments of inertia must be found. In order to do this the angle shape is broken down into two rectangles as shown

$$I_{xy} = \overline{I}_{x'y'} + A\overline{x}\,\overline{y}$$

for a rectangle $\overline{I}_{x'y'} = 0$

$$I_{xy} = \sum A\overline{x}\,\overline{y}$$

where, $\overline{x}$ and $\overline{y}$ are centroidal coordinates of the two rectangles with respect to the origin C

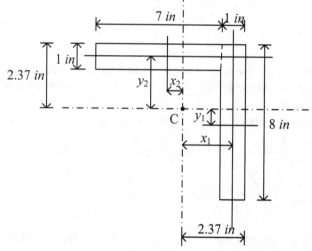

$\overline{x}_1 = -(2.37 - 0.5) = -1.87\ in$

$\overline{y}_1 = 4 - 2.37 = 1.63\ in$

$A_1 = 8 \times 1 = 8\ in^2$

$\overline{x}_2 = 1 + 3.5 - 2.37 = 2.13\ in$

$\overline{y}_2 = -(2.37 - 0.5) = -1.87\ in$

$A_2 = 7 \times 1 = 7\ in^2$

$\sum \overline{xy}A = (-1.87) \times 1.63 \times 8 + 2.13 \times (-1.87) \times 7 = -52.27\ in^4$

$$I_{max,min} = \frac{I_x + I_y}{2} \pm \sqrt{\left(\frac{I_x - I_y}{2}\right) + I_{xy}^2}$$

$$I_{max,min} = \frac{89 + 89}{2} \pm \sqrt{\left(\frac{89 - 89}{2}\right) + (52.27)^2}$$

$I_{max,min} = 89 \pm 52.27$

$I_{max} = 141.27\ in^4;\ I_{min} = 36.73\ in^4$

$r_{min} = \sqrt{I_{min}/A} = \sqrt{36.73/15} = 1.565\ in$

The orientation of the principal axes are as shown

$$\tan(2\theta_p) = -\frac{2I_{xy}}{I_x - I_y} = -\frac{2(-52.27)}{89 - 89} = \infty$$

$2\theta_p = 90$ or $\theta_p = 45^o$

Step 2: Determine the Euler buckling stress using the elastic buckling stress equation.

$$f_{cr} = \frac{\pi^2 E}{\left(L_{eff.}/r_{min.}\right)^2}$$

$$= \frac{\pi^2 (29{,}000 \; ksi)}{\left(120 \; in/1.565 \; in\right)^2}$$

$$f_{cr} = 48.68 \; ksi$$

Step 3: Since the allowable stress in buckling is greater than the yield stress, it is clear that the member will failure due to crushing. Hence, the allowable compression capacity in compression can be determined as follows

$$P_{comp} = \frac{f_y A}{1.5} = \frac{\left(36 \; ksi\right)\left(15 \; in^2\right)}{1.5} = 360 \; kips$$

As the buckling load is lower than the compression load, buckling governs. $P_{all} = 360 \; kips$.

Example 11.4 Stress analysis of a compression member of a truss

Problem Statement: Determine the allowable compressive stress in member DF and EF, if the yield stress in compression is 36 *ksi*. Assume a factor of safety against yielding of 1.5 and 1.92 with respect to buckling for the two members respectively. Using the data from example 11.2, assume that the members have an area of $A = 2 \times 2.86 = 5.72 \; in^2$ and $I_{min.} = 8.72 \; in^4$. Are the member adequate for the given forces?

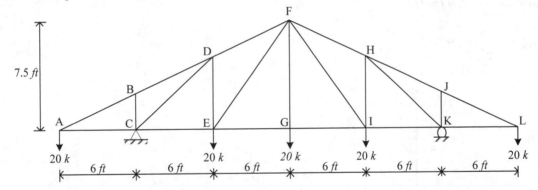

Required: a) Allowable compressive stress in DF and EF.
b) Are the members DF and EF safe for the applied forces?

Solution:
Step 1: Determine the reactions of the truss and the force in member DF.

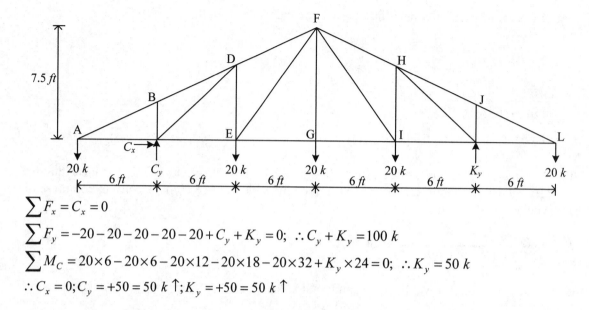

$$\sum F_x = C_x = 0$$

$$\sum F_y = -20 - 20 - 20 - 20 - 20 + C_y + K_y = 0; \quad \therefore C_y + K_y = 100\ k$$

$$\sum M_C = 20 \times 6 - 20 \times 6 - 20 \times 12 - 20 \times 18 - 20 \times 32 + K_y \times 24 = 0; \quad \therefore K_y = 50\ k$$

$$\therefore C_x = 0; C_y = +50 = 50\ k \uparrow; K_y = +50 = 50\ k \uparrow$$

Step 2: Analyze forces in DF and EF by method of sections. To determine T_{DF} we have to eliminate the other two forces. This can be done by considering a moment equation through a point through with these two forces pass, which is point E.

Similarly, the force in member EF is determined by taking the moments through the point through which members DF and EG pass, which is A. The calculations and the free body diagram are shown below

$$\tan \theta_A = \frac{7.5}{18} \quad \therefore \theta_A = 23°$$

$$\tan \theta_E = \frac{7.5}{6} \quad \therefore \theta_E = 52°$$

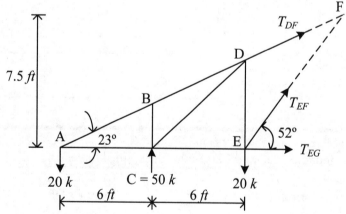

$$\sum M_E = 0$$

$$20 \times 12 - 50 \times 6 - (T_{DF} \cos 22.62) \times 5 = 0$$

$$T_{DF} = -13\ k(C)$$

$$\sum M_A = 0$$

$$50 \times 6 - 20 \times 12 + (T_{EF} \sin 52) \times 12 = 0$$

$$T_{EF} = -6.34\ k(C)$$

Note: Here the negative sign implies that it is a compression member.

Step 3: Determine the Euler compression stress using the elastic compression stress equation. For a truss all the ends are assumed to be pin ended, hence the actual length is also equal to the effective length.

<table>
<tr><td align="center">Member DF</td><td align="center">Member EF</td></tr>
</table>

$$L_{eff.} = 6/\cos(22.62) = 6.5\, ft = 78\, in. \qquad L_{eff.} = \sqrt{6^2 + 7.5^2} = 9.6\, ft = 115.2\, in.$$

$$r_{min.} = \sqrt{\frac{I_{min}}{A}} = \sqrt{\frac{8.72\, in^4}{5.72\, in^2}} = 1.23\, in \qquad r_{min.} = \sqrt{\frac{I_{min}}{A}} = \sqrt{\frac{8.72\, in^4}{5.72\, in^2}} = 1.23\, in$$

$$\frac{L_{eff}}{r_{min}} = \frac{78\, in.}{1.23\, in} = 63.4 \qquad \frac{L_{eff}}{r_{min}} = \frac{115.2\, in.}{1.23\, in} = 93.7$$

$$f_{cr} = \frac{\pi^2 E}{\left(L_{eff.}/r_{min.}\right)^2} \qquad f_{cr} = \frac{\pi^2 E}{\left(L_{eff.}/r_{min.}\right)^2}$$

$$= \frac{\pi^2(29,000\, ksi)}{63.4^2} \qquad = \frac{\pi^2(29,000\, ksi)}{93.7^2}$$

$$f_{cr} = 71.2\, ksi \qquad f_{cr} = 32.6\, ksi$$

Compression governs: $f_y = 36\, ksi$ Buckling governs: $f_{cr} = 32.6\, ksi$

Step 4: Determine the allowable stresses in buckling and yielding using the respective factors of safety. Allowable compression capacity in compression and buckling are

<table>
<tr><td align="center">Member DF</td><td align="center">Member EF</td></tr>
</table>

$$f_{comp,all.} = \frac{f_y}{1.5} = \frac{36\, ksi}{1.5} = 24\, ksi \qquad f_{cr,all.} = \frac{f_{cr}}{1.92} = \frac{31.6\, ksi}{1.92} = 16.46\, ksi$$

$$f_{actual} = \frac{T_{DF}}{A} = \frac{-13\, k}{5.72\, in^2} = -2.27\, ksi \qquad f_{actual} = \frac{T_{DF}}{A} = \frac{-6.34\, k}{5.72\, in^2} = -1.11\, ksi$$

As the allowable stress is less than the actual stress the members are safe. Since the actual stresses are much lower than the allowable stresses the sections sizes for both the members can be considerably reduced.

11.4 Eccentric Loading

In practice it is often very difficult to achieve perfectly axial loading. Incidental eccentricity always exists, which is defined as the offset from the centroid of the area, at which the axial load acts. In this section a general derivation of eccentric loads is presented in order to describe this phenomenon.

Figure 11.10: Eccentric loading on a column

Consider a simply supported column subjected to an eccentric axial load P. The eccentricity is considered along only one direction, such that when the force is moved to the centroid of the cross-section it results in an additional moment $M = Pe$ caused due to this eccentricity, as seen in Figure 11.11.

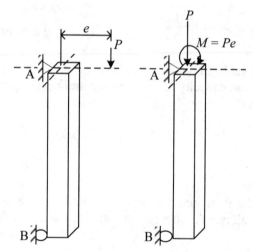

Figure 11.11: Simple supported column subjected to eccentric load.

The combination of the axial force P and the moment Pe causes the column to have a greater tendency to buckle. Figure 11.12 shows a free body diagram of the column at a distance y from one of the supports. The equilibrium equation can be written as

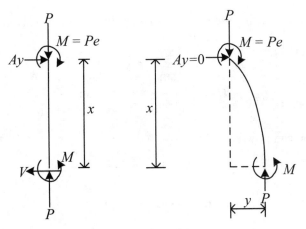

Figure 11.12: Free body diagram of the column

$$Py - Pe + M = 0$$
$$M = -Py + Pe$$

Eqn (11.19)

From the relation expressing the moment as a function of deflection, as seen in chapter 10

$$M = EIy'' = -Py + Pe$$
$$EIy'' + Py = +Pe$$

Eqn (11.20)

$$y'' + \frac{P}{EI}y = +\frac{Pe}{EI}$$

The resulting expression is a second order non-homogeneous linear differential equation. The solution to such an equation has both a homogeneous and a particular part of the solution. The homogeneous part can be written as

$$y + k^2 y = 0$$
$$y_h = A\cos kx + B\sin kx$$

Eqn (11.21)

The particular part can be written as

$$y'' + k^2 y = +k^2 e$$

Eqn (11.22)

Let $y_p = +e$. Substituting this in the differential equation and differentiating it twice the second derivative part vanishes

$$0 + k^2 e = +k^2 e$$

hence, $y_p = +e$ is a valid particular solution. The total solution can thus be written as

$$y = y_p + y_h = A\cos kx + B\sin kx + e$$

Eqn (11.23)

The next step is the determination of the constants using the boundary conditions. For this case a pin and a roller form the two boundaries. Applying these conditions

$$y = 0, x = 0$$
$$0 = A\cos 0 + B\sin 0 + e \implies A = -e$$
$$y = 0, x = L$$
$$0 = A\cos kL + B\sin kL + e$$

Eqn (11.24)

$$0 = -e \cos kl + B\sin kL + e$$
$$0 = -e(\cos kL - 1) + B\sin kL$$
$$B = \frac{e(1 - \cos kL)}{\sin kL}$$

From trigonometry, $\sin kL = 2\sin\dfrac{kL}{2}\cos\dfrac{kL}{2}$ and $1 - \cos kL = 2\sin^2\dfrac{kL}{2}$. Hence the constant B can be rewritten as

$$B = e\frac{2\sin^2\dfrac{kL}{2}}{2\sin\dfrac{kl}{2}\cos\dfrac{kL}{2}} = e\tan\dfrac{kL}{2} \qquad\text{Eqn (11.25)}$$

The deflection equation can now be written as

$$y = e\cos kx + e\tan\dfrac{kL}{2}\sin kx - e$$

$$= e(\tan\dfrac{kL}{2}\sin kx + \cos kx - 1) \qquad\text{Eqn (11.28)}$$

$$= e(\frac{\sin\dfrac{kL}{2}}{\cos\dfrac{kL}{2}}\sin kx + \cos kx - 1)$$

11.4.1 Maximum load and deflection for a given eccentricity

It can be seen that this is not an *Eigen* value problem. The maximum value of the deflection occurs at $x = L/2$. Substituting this in the equation of deflection

$$y_{max.} = e\left(\frac{\sin^2\dfrac{kL}{2}}{\cos\dfrac{kL}{2}} + \cos\dfrac{kL}{2} - 1\right)$$

$$= e\left(\frac{\sin^2\dfrac{kL}{2} + \cos^2\dfrac{kL}{2}}{\cos\dfrac{kL}{2}} - 1\right) \qquad\text{Eqn (11.27)}$$

$$y_{max} = e\left(\sec\dfrac{kL}{2} - 1\right)$$

The conditions of buckling occurs when the maximum deflection tends to infinity or when

$$\sec kL/2 \to \infty = \sec\frac{n\pi}{2}$$

$$\frac{kL}{2} = \frac{n\pi}{2} \qquad\text{Eqn (11.28)}$$

Substituting for $k = \sqrt{\dfrac{P}{EI}}$ the expression for the critical buckling can be derived

$$\sqrt{\frac{P}{EI}}\frac{L}{2} = \frac{n\pi}{2}$$

$$P_{cr} = \frac{\pi^2 EI}{L^2}\quad\text{for } n = 1 \qquad\text{Eqn (11.29)}$$

This expression is the same as the one derived for a column subjected to a concentric load. The expression for y_{max} in the deflection equation can now be written as

$$y_{max} = e\left(\sec\frac{\pi}{2}\sqrt{\frac{P}{P_{cr}}} - 1\right)$$
Eqn (11.30)

The above expression for y_{max} allows one to determine the maximum load P that can be applied for a given eccentricity e if y_{max} is to be limited (Stiffness criterion).

Maximum stress: An increase in eccentricity results in an increased value of the applied end moments (Pe) and hence causes an increase in the maximum normal stress value

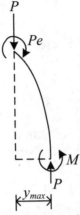

Figure 11.13: Section of eccentrically loaded column

At the location where the deflection has a maximum value the normal stress is also expected to have a maximum value. The value of the maximum stress is determined as follows

$$M_{max} = Pe + Py_{max}$$

$$\sigma_{max} = \frac{P}{A} + \frac{M_{max}}{I}c$$

$$\sigma_{max} = \frac{P}{A} + \frac{Pe + Py_{max}}{I}c$$

$$\sigma_{max} = \frac{P}{A} + \frac{P(e + y_{max})}{I/A}\frac{c}{A}$$

$$\sigma_{max} = \frac{P}{A} + \frac{P(e + y_{max})}{r^2}\frac{c}{A}$$

$$\therefore \sigma_{max} = \frac{P}{A}\left[1 + \frac{ec}{r^2} + \frac{cy_{max}}{r^2}\right]$$
Eqn (11.31)

Substituting for y_{max} from equation (11.30) the expression for the normal stress can be rewritten as follows

$$\sigma_{max} = \frac{P}{A}\left[1 + \frac{ec}{r^2} + \frac{ec}{r^2}\left(\sec\frac{\pi}{2}\sqrt{\frac{P}{P_{cr}}} - 1\right)\right]$$

$$\sigma_{max} = \frac{P}{A}\left[1 + \frac{ec}{r^2}\left(\sec\frac{\pi}{2}\sqrt{\frac{P}{P_{cr}}}\right)\right]$$

$$\sigma_{max} = \frac{P}{A}\left[1 + \frac{ec}{r^2}\left(\sec\frac{\pi}{2}\sqrt{\frac{PL^2}{\pi^2 EI}}\right)\right] \qquad \text{Eqn (11.32)}$$

$$\sigma_{max} = \frac{P}{A}\left[1 + \frac{ec}{r^2}\left(\sec\frac{\pi}{2}\sqrt{\frac{PL^2}{\pi^2 EAr^2}}\right)\right]$$

$$\sigma_{max} = \frac{P}{A}\left[1 + \frac{ec}{r^2}\left(\sec\frac{L}{2r}\sqrt{\frac{P}{EA}}\right)\right]$$

The above expression is commonly known as the *secant formula* for eccentric columns. It can be readily seen that the expression for the maximum stress varies non-linearly with the *eccentricity ratio ec/r^2* and the slenderness ratio *(L/r)*.

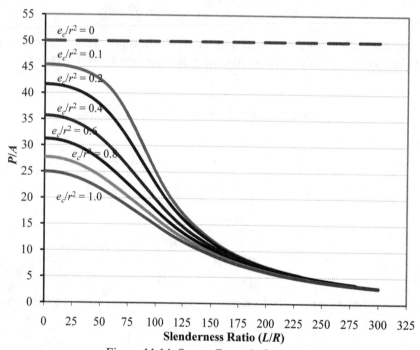

Figure 11.14: Secant Formula for eccentric bukling

Maximum allowable stress for eccentrically loaded columns: In order to study the variation of the maximum stress with eccentricity a numerical example is used as follows. Consider a simply supported column of symmetric cross section made of steel (*E*=29,000 *ksi*) and has a yield stress of (*f$_y$*=50 *ksi*). Assume that the length of the column is 6 *ft*. The expression for the maximum stress can now be written as

$$50 = \frac{P}{A}\left[1 + \frac{ec}{r^2}\left(\sec\frac{L}{2r}\sqrt{\frac{P}{A\,29{,}000}}\right)\right] \qquad \text{Eqn (11.33)}$$

By substituting different values of ec/r^2 (0,0.1,0.2,0.4,0.6,0.8,1.0 etc.) the expression can be solved for different values of P/A for different values of L/r. The resulting solution can be expressed graphically as shown in Figure 11.14.

It can be seen that for an eccentricity equal to zero σ_{max} reduces to the yield stress and the Euler buckling equation starts governing. As the eccentricity e increases the column maximum allowable stress decreases as shown in the figure. It is also observed that for a particular eccentricity, column maximum allowable stress decreases as the slenderness ratio increases.

Example 11.5 Stress analysis of an eccentric column

Problem Statement: The column shown in the figure is subjected to compressive loads with an eccentricity e as shown. The material is made of steel with an elastic modulus of 29,000 *ksi*. Determine the maximum load that can be applied if f_y =50 *ksi* and a factor of safety of 2.0 is used. Also determine the maximum deflection under the load.

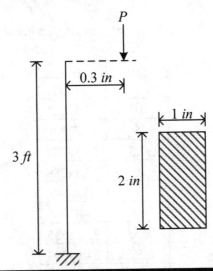

Required: a) Allowable compressive force in the member?

b) Maximum deflection under the load?

Solution:

Step 1: Determine the geometric properties

$A = 2 \times 1 = 2\ in^2$

$I_y = \dfrac{1}{12} 1 \times 2^3 = 0.66\ in^4$

$r_y = \sqrt{\dfrac{I_y}{A}} = \sqrt{\dfrac{0.66\ in^4}{2\ in^2}} = 0.574\ in.$

Eccentricity ratio:

$\dfrac{ec}{r_y^2} = \dfrac{0.3\ in \times 1\ in}{0.574^2} = 0.91$

Slenderness ratio:

$\dfrac{L}{r} = \dfrac{36\ in}{0.574\ in} = 62.72$

Step 2: Determine the P/A value be either using graphs or solving the transcendental equation as shown below. The equation for the determining the maximum stress due to an eccentric compressive loading is given as

$$\sigma_{max.} = \frac{P}{A}\left[1 + \frac{ec}{r_y^2}\sec\left(\frac{L}{r}\sqrt{\frac{P}{EA}}\right)\right]$$

where $\sigma_{max.} = \dfrac{\sigma_y}{FOS} = \dfrac{50\ ksi}{2} = 25\ ksi$

$$25\ ksi = \frac{P}{A}\left[1 + (0.91)\sec\left(62.72\sqrt{\frac{P}{(29000\ ksi)A}}\right)\right]$$

$$25\ ksi = \frac{P}{A}\left[1 + (0.91)\sec\left(0.37\sqrt{\frac{P}{A}}\right)\right]$$

The nonlinear equation can be solved by either checking an appropriate graph or a trial and error process as shown below.

P/A	σ_{max}
1	1.976052
10	33.32661
5	11.72249
7.5	20.39988
8	22.54289
9	27.4185
8.5	24.87205
8.55	25.11635
8.525	24.99393
8.526	24.99881
8.52625	25.00003

Hence, the P/A solution value is equal to 8.526, giving $P = 8.526 \times 2\ in^2 = 17.05\ kips$

Step 3: Determine the maximum deflection for the given load value.

$$k = \sqrt{\frac{P}{EI}} = \sqrt{\frac{17.05\ kips}{(29,000\ ksi)(0.66\ in^4)}} = 0.03$$

$$y_{max.} = e\left(\sec\frac{kL}{2} - 1\right)$$

$$y_{max.} = (0.3\ in)\left(\sec\frac{(0.03)(36\ in.)}{2} - 1\right)$$

$$y_{max.} = 0.0000133\ in$$

11.5 Summary

This chapter has discussed some of most critical aspects of the structural behavior of axially loaded members subjected to compression. The most important aspect of the behavior is to bring out the difference between

a. Crushing behavior – where the member acts like a strut and fails by compression/crushing. Short and stock members experience this type of failure.

b. Buckling behavior – the member bends out of plane while in compression. Long and slender members typically experience this type of behavior.

The keywords introduced in this chapter are as follows.

1. **Actual compressive stress:** The actual compressive stress is the compressive force acting on the member divided by the cross sectional area. $f_{actual} = P/A$

2. **Allowable stress:** The allowable stress is the lower of the yield stress f_y and the critical buckling stress f_{cr}, divided by a factor or safety. $f_{all} = \dfrac{f_y}{F.O.S} \, or \, \dfrac{f_{cr}}{F.O.S}$

3. **Axially loaded member:** A member which is loaded along the axial direction. A column is considered as an axially loaded member.

4. **Buckling:** The process of an axially loaded compression member failing suddenly by a bending process.

5. **Boundary conditions:** The type of support conditions that a column is built with. The types of supports are a fixed type, pinned type, free etc.

6. **Effective length:** The length $L_{eff}=kL$ that is used for determining the slenderness ratio. Physically it can be visualized as the distance between two adjacent zero moment locations.

7. **Effective length factor:** The factor k that is used for representing the effective length. The effective length factor depends on the boundary conditions of the column.

8. **Euler buckling load:** The axial load at which the column fails in buckling is called as the Euler buckling load. It is given in equation form as

$$P_{cr} = \frac{\pi^2 E I_{min.}}{(L_{eff.})^2} = \frac{\pi^2 E I_{min.}}{(kL)^2}$$

9. **Euler buckling stress:** The Euler buckling stress is the stress at which the member buckles. It is given as $f_{cr} = \dfrac{\pi^2 E r_{min.}^2}{(kL)^2} = \dfrac{\pi^2 E}{(kL/r_{min.})^2}$

10. **Factor of safety:** The factor with which either the buckling stress or the yield stress is divided in arriving at the allowable stress in compression. They have different vales in crushing and buckling cases.

11. **Principal minimum moment of Inertia:** The least value of the resistance $I_{min.}$ bending that a section has. The magnitude of this resistance is the principal minimum moment of inertia. In buckling bending occurs about this axis.

12. **Radius of gyration:** A term from Statics that is used to determine the slenderness ratio.

$$r_{min.} = \sqrt{\frac{I_{min.}}{A}}$$

13. **Slenderness ratio:** It is a measure of the slenderness of the member and is given as $\dfrac{L_{eff.}}{r_{min.}}$

14. **Unsupported length:** This is the actual length of the column between two adjacent end or support points.

15. **Yield stress:** The material parameter which determines the crushing strength of the member.

11.6 Problems

11.1   What is the difference between compression and buckling failure?

11.2   How does the slenderness ratio affect the axial compressive capacity of a column?

11.3   A column is made of a 6 *in.* x 6 *in.* wood cross section and is 10 *ft* long. If the allowable stress in compression for wood is 1100 *psi*, determine the axial load capacity of the wooden post. Assume that the column in simply supported. (Note: Wooden cross sections are typically ½ *in* lesser in each dimension).

11.4   Determine the axial carrying capacity of the wooden column in problem 1, for the following end conditions:
   a. Fixed at both ends
   b. Fixed at one end and free at the other
   c. Fixed at one end and pinned at the other

11.5   For the two member structure loaded as shown by a 10 *kip* force, assume that the members are made of wood (E_{wood}= 2000 *ksi*) and have a cross section of 2 *in* by 4 *in*.

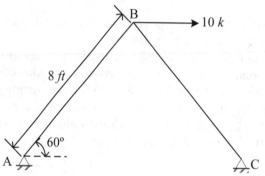

If the allowable stress in wood is 1300 *psi* and the factors of safety against compression is 1.5 and buckling is 2.0, determine
   a. The force in each of the members. Are they in compression or tension?
   b. For members in compression, determine whether the member will buckle, crush or is safe against both forms of failure.

11.6   If the structure in problem 11.5 is loaded by an unknown force *P* instead of the 10 *kip* force, determine the maximum force *P* that the structure can carry.

For problems 11.7 to 11.12, use the following data for the material. E_{steel}=29,000 *ksi*, f_y=50 *ksi*, *factor of safety* in compression = 1.5 and *factor of safety* in buckling = 1.92.

11.7   The cross section of a steel column is shown in the Figure. If the column is fixed at the base and hinged at the top, determine the axial compressive capacity of the column.

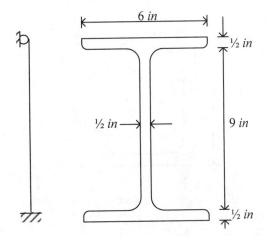

11.8 Determine the axial compression capacity of a doubly symmetric hollow steel section with an outer dimension of 6 *in* x 4 *in*. and a wall thickness of ½ *in* as shown in the figure. Assume that ends of the column are pinned-pinned and the unsupported length is 12 *ft*.

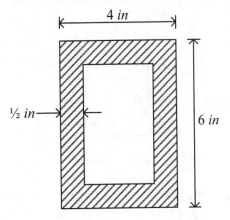

11.9 Determine the axial compression capacity of a solid circular steel section with a diameter of 3 *in*. Assume the ends of the column are fixed and free and the unsupported length is 8 *ft*.

11.10 Determine the compression capacity of a hollow circular steel section with an outer radius of 6 *in*. and a wall thickness of ¼ *in*. Assume that the column is simply supported with an unsupported length of 10 *ft*.

11.11 For a singly symmetric channel section as shown in the figure below determine the axial compression capacity. Assume that the column has an unsupported length of 9 *ft*. and is simply supported at the ends.

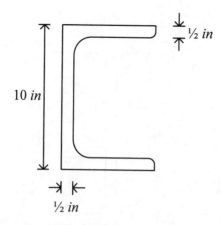

11.12 For the angle section shown that has no axis of symmetry, determine the axial compressive capacity. Assume that the angle is part of a truss system and has a length of 7.5 *ft.*

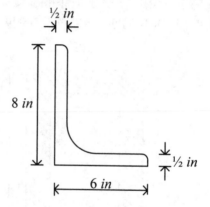

11.13 The frame shown in the figure is loaded by a force *P.* The member AB is made of a hollow structural steel section of diameter 50 *mm* and a thickness of 8 *mm*. Determine the maximum load *P* that can be applied for the member AB to not fail either in compression or buckling. (E_{steel}=200 *GPa*, f_y=415 *MPa*).

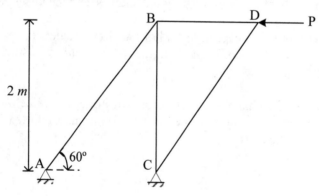

Index

Notes:

Notes:

Notes:

Notes:

Notes:

Notes:

Notes: